Named and Miscellaneous Reactions in Practical Organic Chemistry

Named and Miscellaneous Reactions in Practical Organic Chemistry

R. J. W. CREMLYN

B.SC., PH.D. (WALES), PH.D. (CANTAB), F.R.I.C.

Principal Lecturer in Organic Chemistry,
Hatfield College of Technology

R. H. STILL

DIP. TECH., PH.D. (LOND.), A.R.I.C.

Lecturer in Organic Chemistry, Hatfield College of Technology

JOHN WILEY & SONS, INC.

NEW YORK

Printed and bound in Great Britain

Preface

Practical work in organic chemistry can degenerate into boring exercises in following given recipes once the basic practical techniques have been mastered. The object of the present book is to try to combat this, by including with each practical example, a fairly detailed modern treatment of the mechanism and scope of the basic reaction involved. We have found this approach is particularly valuable, because the student can then be questioned about the theory of a given reaction when the practical note book is submitted for appraisal. Thus theory and practice are brought closer together, enabling simple electronic theory to be impressed from the practical viewpoint on the students mind.

The book will be of value to students in universities and colleges who are preparing for Special and General Degrees; Grad.R.I.C. (Parts I and II); and the Ordinary and Higher National Certificate Examinations. Some of the reactions will also be suitable for the sixth forms of schools.

The authors wish to thank Mrs C. A. Still for typing the manuscript and for assistance with proof reading. They also wish to thank Mr H. MacGibbon of Heinemann Educational Books for his help during the passage of the book through the press.

R. J. CREMLYN
R. H. STILL

v

Abbreviations

The following abbreviations are used throughout this book:

b.p.	boiling point	decomp.	decomposition
f.p.	freezing point	$\equiv$	equivalent to
m.p.	melting point	$>$	greater than
d.	density	$<$	less than
g	grammes	$\simeq$	approximately equal to
N	normal		

All temperatures in this book are in degrees Centigrade

Contents

NAMED REACTIONS

Balz-Schiemann Reaction

This is the pyrolytic decomposition of an aromatic diazonium fluoroborate yielding an aryl fluoride. It provides a useful method of converting aromatic amines into fluorides:

$$Ar·NH_2 \xrightarrow[0°]{NaNO_2/HCl} Ar·\overset{+}{N_2}\overset{-}{Cl} \xrightarrow{\substack{HBF_4 \text{ or} \\ NaBF_4}}$$

$$Ar·\overset{+}{N_2}\overset{-}{BF_4} \xrightarrow{Heat} Ar·F + BF_3 + N_2$$

Fluoroboric acid or a fluoroborate is added to the diazonium salt solution from which is precipitated the sparingly soluble diazonium fluoroborate. The dry salt is gently heated to the decomposition point yielding the aryl fluoride. The method depends on the remarkable stability of the dry diazonium fluoroborates, which do not explode when heated but undergo smooth decomposition. The reaction is of wide application and overall yields of 70% are often obtained; and fluorine has been introduced, for example, into benzene, naphthalene, anthracene, pyridine, and quinoline by this procedure. Two fluorine atoms may also be simultaneously introduced, though the yields of such reactions are poor unless the two diazonium groups are attached to different rings, as in preparative example 1.

The mechanism of the decomposition of diazonium fluoroborates is not definitely known, nor is the reason for their exceptional stability fully understood. Three possible mechanisms have been suggested:

(*a*) *Free radical*

1. $$Ar\overset{+}{N_2}\overset{-}{BF_4} \xrightarrow{Slow} Ar· + F· + BF_3 + N_2$$

2. $$Ar· + F· \xrightarrow{Fast} ArF$$

(*b*) *Ionic, involving a carbonium ion*

1. $$Ar\overset{+}{N_2}\overset{-}{BF_4} \rightarrow Ar^+ + [BF_4]^- + N_2$$

2. $$Ar^+ + [BF_4]^- \rightarrow ArF + BF_3$$

3

(c) Rearrangement

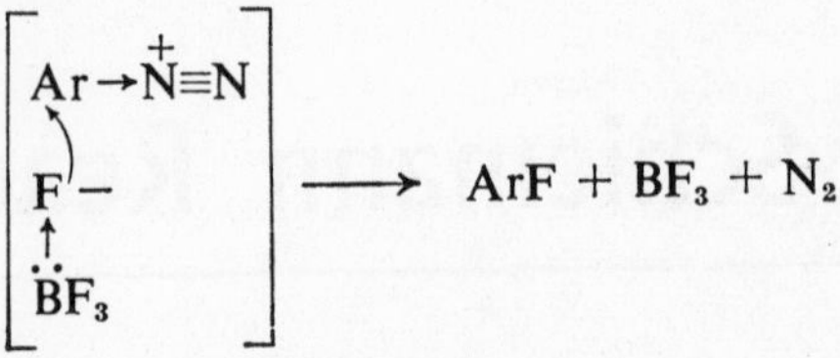

$$\left[\begin{array}{c} Ar \rightarrow \overset{+}{N} \equiv N \\ \diagdown \\ F'^{-} \\ \uparrow \\ \ddot{B}F_3 \end{array} \right] \longrightarrow ArF + BF_3 + N_2$$

Relatively little work has been reported on the decomposition of fluoroborates, as compared with the decomposition of diazonium salts in general. However, it has been shown that the following reaction occurs with almost complete racemization:

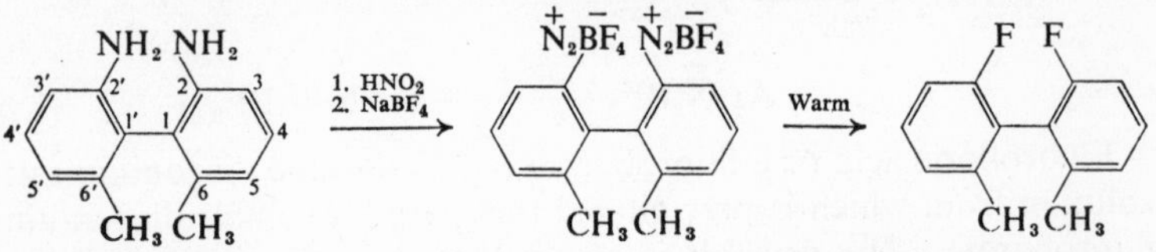

2,2'-Diamino-6,6'-
dimethylbiphenyl
(*laevo*-form)

2,2'-Difluoro-6,6'-dimethyl-
biphenyl (practically no
optical activity)

Thus mechanism 1 or 2 is favoured as compared with 3, since the latter would be less likely to cause racemization.

Example 1. Preparation of 4,4'-Difluoro-biphenyl

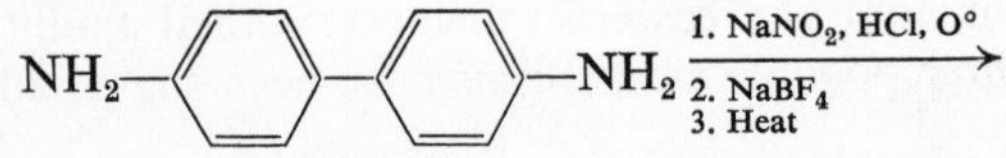

Benzidine

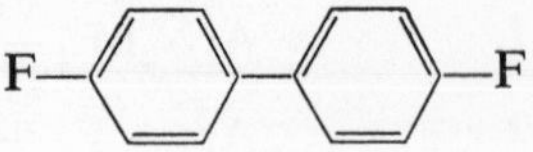

4,4'-Difluorobiphenyl

Dissolve benzidine (6·2 g.) in 5N hydrochloric acid [concentrated acid (20 ml.) and water (20 ml.)] in a 250 ml. beaker, then cool in ice. Diazotize by dropwise addition of a solution of sodium nitrite

(4·8 g.) in water (8 ml.), keeping the temperature $<5°$ during the addition of the nitrite solution. If necessary, filter the diazotized solution, and slowly add it with stirring to a filtered solution of sodium fluoroborate (borofluorate) (12 g.) in water (20 ml.). Stir for 10 minutes, and collect the precipitated bis-diazonium fluoroborate on a small Buchner funnel, wash it with ice-cold water (2 ml.), and dry at 90–100° for 20 minutes. Place the dry salt in a 150 ml. bolt-head flask fitted with a reflux air-condenser, immerse the flask in an oil-bath and gradually increase the temperature of the bath to 150°. (This operation MUST be performed in a fume-cupboard.) When decomposition of the salt is complete, steam distil the mixture, collecting the 4,4'-difluorobiphenyl which passes over and recrystallize it from ethanol. The yield is 2·6 g; m.p. 92–93° (40% of theory based on benzidine).

Example 2. Preparation of Fluorobenzene

$$C_6H_5NH_2 \xrightarrow{\text{NaNO}_2/\text{HCl}} C_6H_5\overset{+}{N_2}\overset{-}{Cl} \xrightarrow{\text{NaBF}_4}$$

Aniline

$$C_6H_5\overset{+}{N_2}\overset{-}{BF_4} \xrightarrow{\text{Heat}} C_6H_5F + BF_3 + N_2$$

Fluorobenzene

Dissolve aniline (6·7 ml.) in 5N-hydrochloric acid (40 ml.) (20 ml. of concentrated acid and 20 ml. of water), cool the solution to 5° and diazotize by gradually adding a solution of sodium nitrite (5·5 g.) in water (10 ml.), keeping the temperature between 5 and 10°.

Now add to the cold diazonium salt solution, a cold solution of sodium fluoroborate (8 g.) in water (20 ml.), stirring well during the addition. Allow to stand for 10 minutes with occasional stirring keeping the temperature $<10°$. Filter with suction; wash the precipitate successively with ice-water (4 ml.), cold ethanol (3 ml.), and ether (5 ml.), dry first by suction and finally in a desiccator.

Now set up the apparatus as indicated in Figure 1. Gently heat the dry benzene diazonium fluoroborate with a small flame near the surface of the crystals, until decomposition begins, then remove the flame and let the reaction proceed spontaneously, further gentle heating being applied whenever the reaction gets too sluggish. Finally, heat the flask more powerfully to make certain that all the fluorobenzene is distilled over into the receiver. A small amount of solid generally remains in the distillation flask.

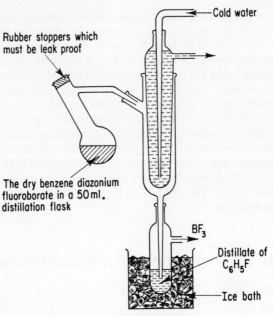

Figure 1

Now wash the distillate in a small separatory funnel with a 10%
aqueous sodium hydroxide solution (6 ml.) (to remove any phenol
present), and with water (6 ml.). Then dry the distillate over anhydrous sodium sulphate ($\simeq 0.5$ g.) and filter into a 20 ml. pear-
shaped distillation flask. Distil, slowly, collecting the fraction boiling
at 83–87°. The yield of fluorobenzene as a colourless liquid is 2·0 ml.
(30% of theory based on aniline).

Bart Reaction

This is the conversion of an aromatic diazonium salt into the corresponding arylarsonic acid, by treatment with sodium arsenite in the presence of a copper catalyst:

$$Ar\cdot\overset{+}{N_2}\overset{-}{X} + Na_3AsO_3 \xrightarrow{Cu} Ar\cdot AsO_3Na_2 + NaX + N_2$$
$$\downarrow H^+$$
$$Ar\cdot AsO_3H_2$$

There have been several modifications of the Bart reaction; one of the most valuable involves the use of diazonium fluoroborates (cf. Balz–Schiemann reaction). In this way a high yield of certain arsonic acids, e.g. p-nitrobenzenearsonic acid, can be obtained:

$$p\text{-}O_2N\cdot C_6H_4\cdot\overset{+}{N_2}\overset{-}{Cl} \xrightarrow{NaBF_4} p\text{-}O_2N\cdot C_6H_4\cdot\overset{+}{N_2}\cdot\overset{-}{BF_4}$$
$$\downarrow \overset{Na_3AsO_3}{\text{(CuCl catalyst)}}$$
$$o\text{-}O_2N\cdot C_6H_4\cdot AsO_3H_2$$
$$\text{(after acidification)}$$

The process has also been extended to include the preparation of arylstibonic acids as follows: the diazonium salt is treated with a solution of antimony oxide in hydrochloric acid, and the product then reacted with sodium hydroxide:

$$Ar\cdot\overset{+}{N_2}\overset{-}{X} \xrightarrow{SbCl_3/NaOH} Ar\cdot SbO_3H_2$$

The activating influence of copper catalysts in the Bart reaction suggests that it is a free-radical process (like the Sandmeyer reaction), since it is known that copper facilitates the formation of aryl radicals from diazonium salts. So the reaction may proceed as follows:

1. $\quad Ar\cdot\overset{+}{N_2}\cdot\overset{-}{X} + Cu \rightarrow Ar\cdot + CuX + N_2$

2. $\quad Ar\cdot + As(ONa)_3 \rightarrow Ar\cdot OAs(ONa)_2 + Na\cdot$

3. $\quad Na\cdot + Ar\overset{+}{N_2}\overset{-}{X} \rightarrow Ar\cdot + NaX + N_2$

The aryl radical can then continue the process.

7

Example. Preparation of Phenylarsonic Acid

$$C_6H_5NH_2 \xrightarrow[5°]{\text{NaNO}_2/\text{HCl}} C_6H_5\overset{+}{N}_2\overset{-}{Cl} \xrightarrow[\text{(CuSO}_4)]{\text{As(ONa)}_3}$$

Aniline   Benzenediazonium chloride

$$C_6H_5 \cdot AsO_3Na_2 \xrightarrow{\text{H}^+} C_6H_5 \cdot AsO_3H_2$$

Phenylarsonic acid

Place aniline (4·5 ml.), water (25 ml.), concentrated hydrochloric acid (10 ml.), and sufficient crushed ice to make a total volume of $\simeq$ 80 ml. in a 150 ml. beaker. Stir the mixture and add dropwise a solution of sodium nitrite (3·6 g.) in water (12 ml.), taking care that the temperature does not exceed 5°. Prepare a sodium arsenite suspension as follows:

Place water (25 ml.) in a 250 ml. round-bottomed flask, and heat to boiling and add anhydrous sodium carbonate (12·5 g.). When this has dissolved add pure arsenious oxide (6·3 g) and crystalline copper sulphate (0·4 g) with stirring. When complete solution has been attained, cool in cold water to 15°. Continue stirring and cool the suspension of sodium arsenite in an ice-salt bath to 0°. Extract the cold diazonium salt solution with a pipette and add it dropwise to the cold sodium arsenite suspension keeping the temperature, if possible, less than 5°; but not higher than 10°. Control any frothing during this process by adding a little benzene, continue stirring for half an hour after the addition has been completed. Filter the mixture, and wash the solid precipitate with cold water (12 ml.) and concentrate the combined filtrate and washing, over a free flame to a volume of $\simeq$ 40 ml. Add concentrated hydrochloric acid ($\simeq$ 2·5 ml.) to the dark brown solution until no further tarry material separates and then filter using fluted filter paper. Add some more hydrochloric acid to the filtrate, until after filtration a pale yellow solution is obtained.

Precipitate the phenylarsonic acid by further addition of concentrated hydrochloric acid ($\simeq$ 6·5 ml.) but avoid a large excess of acid because of the solubility of the product. Cool and filter off the product with suction, and wash it with cold water (5 ml.). Recrystallize the pale yellow crystals from boiling water (12 ml.) in the presence of activated charcoal (0·5 g.), yielding phenylarsonic acid as white crystals 4·5 g.; m.p. 155–158° decomp. after drying in an oven at 100° (48% of theory).

Beckmann Rearrangement (B.R.)

This is the conversion of ketoximes into *N*-substituted acid amides by treatment with certain acidic reagents, e.g. phosphorus pentachloride, thionyl chloride, sulphuric acid, or polyphosphoric acid. The latter reagent will also often cause aldoximes to undergo the rearrangement.

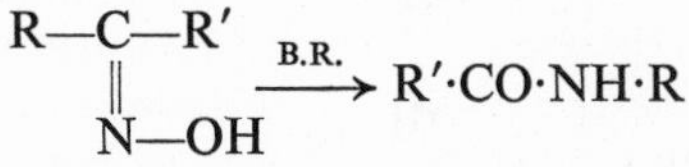

$$\begin{array}{c} R-C-R' \\ \parallel \\ N-OH \end{array} \xrightarrow{\text{B.R.}} R'\cdot CO\cdot NH\cdot R$$

Similarly, acetyl chloride or benzenesulphonyl chloride may be employed to effect the reaction. The first step of the reaction is ester formation with the acidic reagent HX and the probable mechanism involves an ion-pair intermediate as follows:

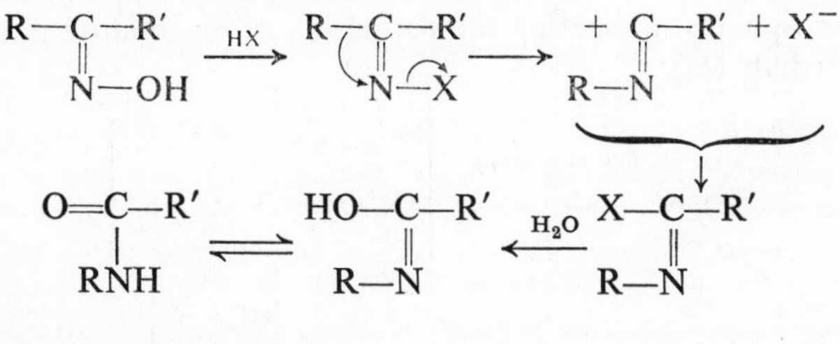

$$\begin{array}{ccc} R-C-R' & R-C-R' & +C-R' + X^- \\ \parallel & \parallel & \\ N-OH & N-X & R-N \end{array}$$

$$\begin{array}{ccc} O=C-R' & HO-C-R' & X-C-R' \\ \mid & \parallel & \parallel \\ RNH & R-N & R-N \end{array}$$

Examination of the product has shown that it is always the hydrocarbon radical *trans* to the hydroxyl group that migrates; hence the Beckmann rearrangement may be used to distinguish between the *syn* and *anti* forms of ketoximes. Furthermore, this migration must be *intra*molecular (i.e. R never becomes completely free from the rest of the molecule as R+), because when the migrating carbon atom

9

is asymmetric there is no loss of optical activity during the rearrangement. Thus:

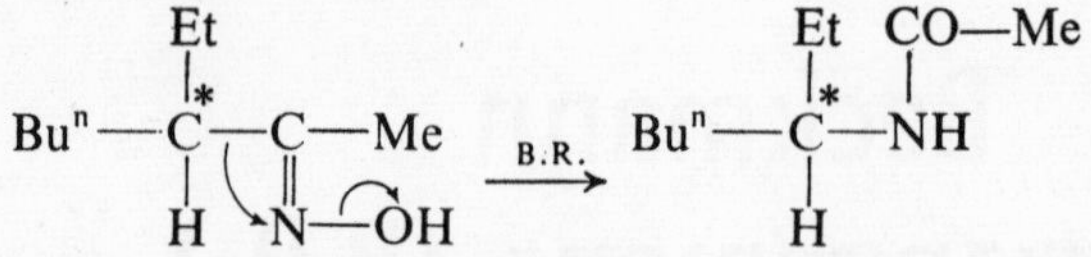

$$\text{Bu}^n\text{—}\overset{\overset{\displaystyle \text{Et}}{|}}{\underset{\underset{\displaystyle \text{H}}{|}}{\text{C}}}\text{—}\overset{*}{\text{C}}\text{—Me} \xrightarrow{\text{B.R.}} \text{Bu}^n\text{—}\overset{\overset{\displaystyle \text{Et}}{|}}{\underset{\underset{\displaystyle \text{H}}{|}}{\overset{*}{\text{C}}}}\text{—}\overset{\overset{\displaystyle \text{CO—Me}}{|}}{\text{NH}}$$

(retention of optical activity)

(* = an asymmetric carbon atom)

The rate of the rearrangement is dependent on the strength of the anion X⁻, and also on the ion-solvating power of the medium. Evidence has been obtained for the imidoyl ester intermediate (I) in the rearrangement of a 17-keto-16-oxime steroid:

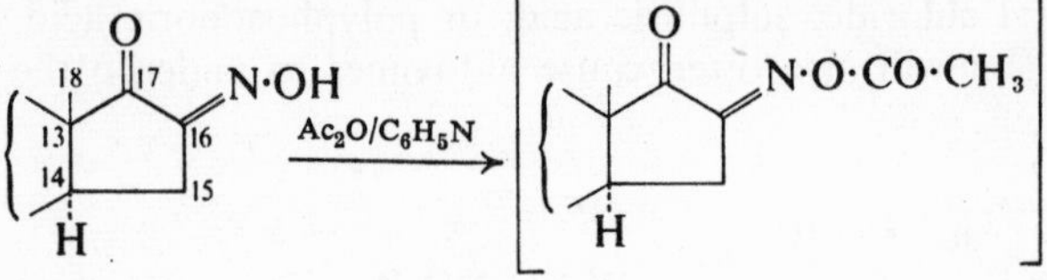

(I)

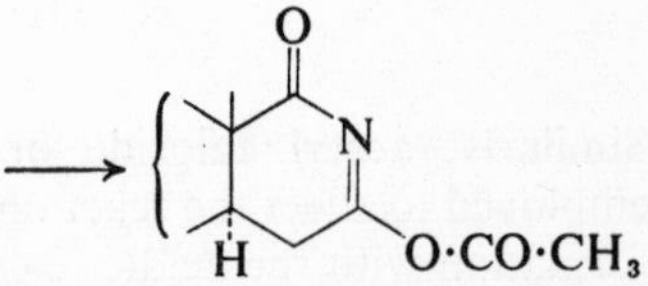

{ = Remainder of the steroid nucleus.

Further evidence may be found in the spontaneous B.R. of ketoxime arylsulphonates in the presence of phosphates which yields pyrophosphates, indicating the formation of an imidoyl phosphate intermediate (II):

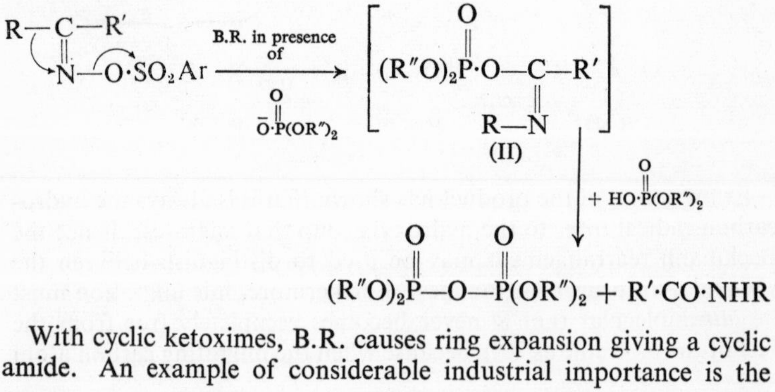

(II)

$$+ \text{HO·}\overset{\overset{\displaystyle \text{O}}{\|}}{\text{P}}(\text{OR}'')_2$$

$$(\text{R}''\text{O})_2\overset{\overset{\displaystyle \text{O}}{\|}}{\text{P}}\text{—O—}\overset{\overset{\displaystyle \text{O}}{\|}}{\text{P}}(\text{OR}'')_2 + \text{R}'\text{·CO·NHR}$$

With cyclic ketoximes, B.R. causes ring expansion giving a cyclic amide. An example of considerable industrial importance is the preparation of caprolactam from cyclohexanone oxime:

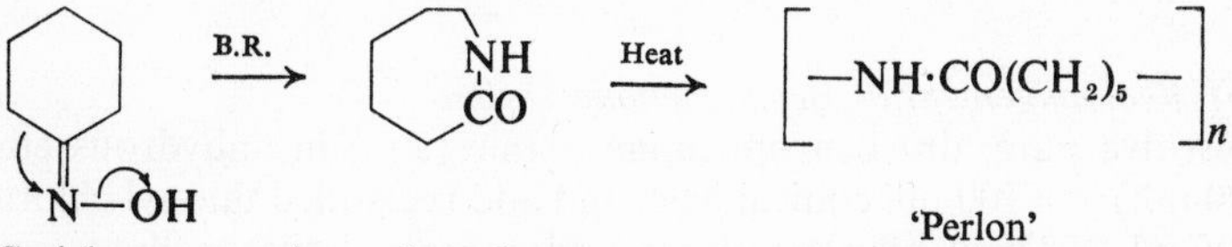

Cyclohexanone oxime   Caprolactam

'Perlon'
(an important polyamide fibre)

similarly:

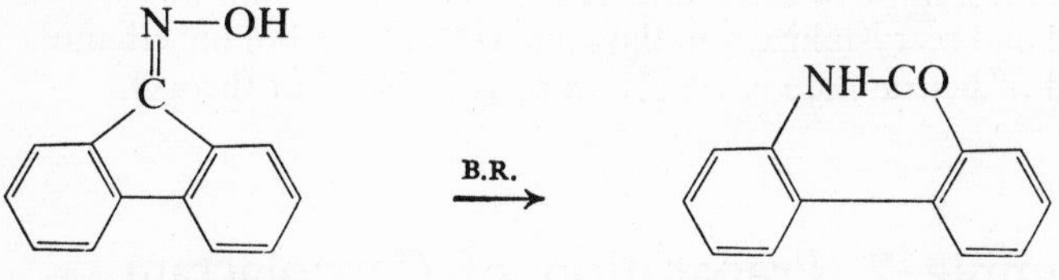

Fluorenone oxime   2,2′-Amidobiphenyl

It is therefore obvious that the Beckmann rearrangement has considerable synthetic as well as mechanistic interest.

Example 1. Preparation of Benzanilide

This is prepared by the rearrangement of benzophenone oxime.

$$C_6H_5 \cdot C—C_6H_5 \xrightarrow[\text{2. H}_2\text{O}]{\text{1. SOCl}_2} C_6H_5 \cdot CO \cdot NHC_6H_5$$
$$\| \atop N \cdot OH$$

Benzophenone oxime   Benzanilide

(a) Preparation of Benzophenone Oxime

Place benzophenone (2·5 g.) (m.p. 47–48°), hydroxylamine hydro-chloride (1·5 g.), ethanol (5 ml.) and water (1 ml.) in a 50 ml. round-bottomed flask. Add sodium hydroxide pellets (2·8 g.) portion-wise with cooling and shaking. After addition, attach a reflux condenser and boil under reflux for five minutes. Cool the reaction flask and pour the contents into a mixture of water (50 ml.), and concentrated hydrochloric acid (7·5 ml.), contained in a 250 ml. beaker. Filter off the precipitated solid at the pump, wash well with cold water and finally dry by suction. Recrystallize the product from methanol ($\simeq$ 10 ml.). The yield of benzophenone oxime is 2·5 g.; m.p. 142°. If possible the product should be submitted to the B.R. as soon as it is prepared; if this is not possible store in a vacuum desiccator filled with dry carbon dioxide.

(b) Rearrangement of Benzophenone Oxime

Dissolve pure, dry benzophenone oxime (2 g.) in anhydrous ether (20 ml.) in a 100 ml. conical flask and add redistilled thionyl chloride (3·0 ml.). Distil off the solvent and other volatile products on a water-bath. (*Caution: ether*) and add water (25 ml.). Boil the mixture for several minutes, breaking up any lumps which may be present. Allow to stand and decant the supernatant liquid from the solid and recrystallize it in the same vessel from boiling ethanol. The yield of benzanilide is 1·6 g.; m.p. 163° (80% of theory).

Example 2. Preparation of Caprolactam (2-Ketohexamethyleneimine)

This is prepared by the rearrangement of cyclohexanone oxime.

(a) Cyclohexanone Oxime

Dissolve hydroxylamine hydrochloride (10 g.) and crystalline sodium acetate (16 g.) in water (40 ml.) in a 100 ml. conical flask. Warm the solution to about 40° and add cyclohexanone (10 g.). Close the flask with a cork and shake vigorously for a few minutes; the oxime soon separates as a crystalline solid. Cool the flask in ice, and filter off the crystals at the pump using a Buchner funnel, washing the resultant solid with a little cold water. Recrystallize from petroleum ether (b.p. 60–80°). (*Care: very inflammable solvent*). Then air-dry the crystals on filter paper. The yield of cyclohexanone oxime is 10 g.; m.p. 90°.

(b) Caprolactam (2-Ketohexamethyleneimine)

Place cyclohexanone oxime (10 g.) in a 1 litre beaker and add 85% sulphuric acid (20 ml.) [made by mixing concentrated acid (5 volumes with water (1 volume)]. Hold the beaker in the hand, warming with a low flame, and gently swirling the contents until bubbles appear. Then remove the beaker from the flame and allow the violent reaction to subside. Cool the mixture to 0° (using an ice-salt bath) and then slowly add, while stirring, 24% aqueous potassium hydroxide solution until the solution is faintly alkaline to litmus. (Approximately 130 ml. of solution will be required.) The temperature must not be allowed to rise above 10° during this addition. Potassium sulphate will be precipitated at this stage, and is removed by filtration, the residue being washed with a little chloroform.

Extract the aqueous alkaline solution with chloroform (50 ml.; 3 times) and wash the combined chloroform extract with water to remove any potassium hydroxide. Remove the chloroform by distillation, and fractionally distil the residue under reduced pressure. The yield is 6 g., b.p. 127–133°/7 mm. m.p. 65–68° (60% of theory).

Blanc Chloromethylation Reaction

This is the direct replacement of an aromatic nuclear hydrogen atom by a chloromethyl group—CH_2Cl.

The aromatic compound is heated with formaldehyde or paraformaldehyde, hydrogen chloride, and anhydrous zinc chloride, e.g.

$$Ar \cdot H + CH_2O + HCl \xrightarrow{ZnCl_2} Ar \cdot CH_2 \cdot Cl + [H_2O]$$

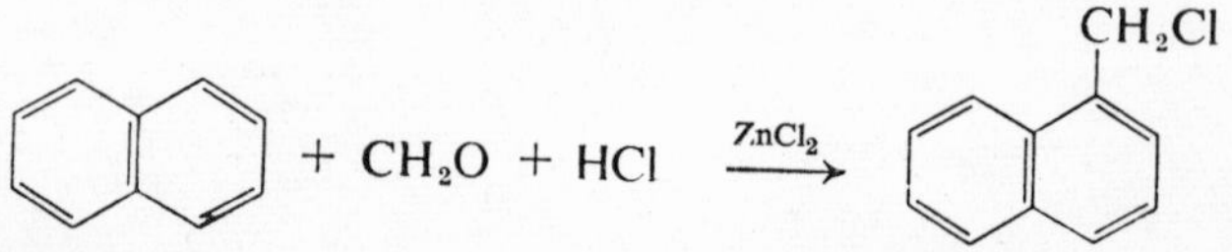

Naphthalene　　　　　　　　　　　α-Chloromethylnaphthalene

Chloromethylation is valuable in organic synthesis, because the —CH_2Cl group can be easily converted into other groups, e.g. —CH_2CN, —CH_2CO_2H, —$CH_2 \cdot OH$, —CHO. The reaction is generally successful with aromatic hydrocarbons; using monoalkylbenzenes the main product is the *p*-chloromethyl derivative, and a second chloromethyl group can often be introduced. The basic reaction has been modified in various ways, e.g. stannic chloride, sulphuric acid, or syrupy phosphoric acid may also be used as catalysts. The presence of halogeno, keto, nitro, or carboxyl groups tend to inhibit the process.

The directing influence of substituents and kinetic studies indicate that chloromethylation as an electrophilic substitution reaction, in which the rate-determining step is attack by $^+CH_2Cl$:

1.

$$CH_2{=}\overset{\frown}{O} + \overset{+}{H}{-}\overset{-}{Cl} \rightleftharpoons Cl \cdot CH_2 \cdot OH \xrightarrow{H^+} Cl \cdot CH_2 \overset{+}{O}H_2$$

$$\downarrow {\scriptstyle (-H_2O)}$$

$$Cl \cdot \overset{+}{C}H_2$$

2.

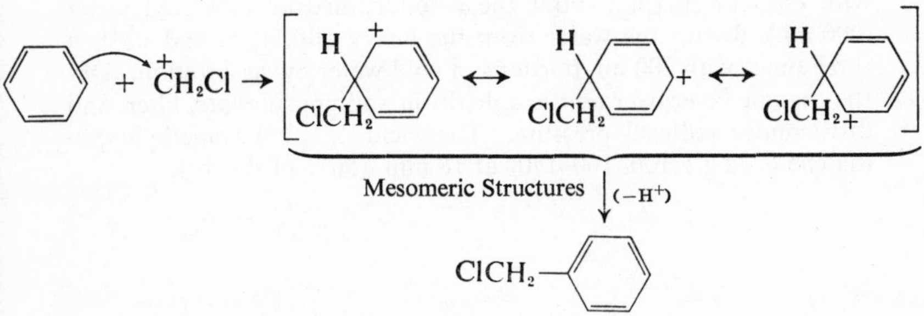

$$ClCH_2 - \langle \rangle$$

Example 1. Preparation of Benzyl Chloride

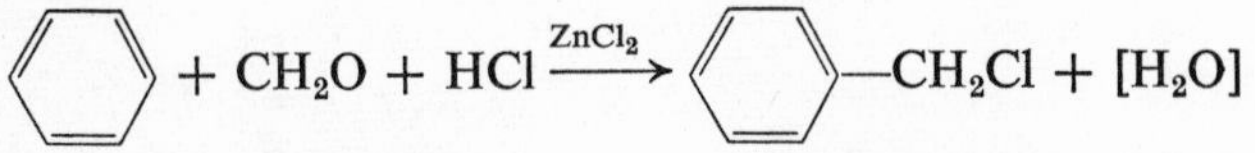

$$\langle \rangle + CH_2O + HCl \xrightarrow{ZnCl_2} \langle \rangle - CH_2Cl + [H_2O]$$

Benzene   Formaldehyde   Benzyl chloride

In a 250 ml. round-bottomed three-necked flask, fitted with a mechanical stirrer, place dry benzene (60 g.), paraformaldehyde (6 g.), and pulverized anhydrous zinc chloride (6 g.). Immerse the flask in a water-bath maintained at 60° and pass a steady stream of dry hydrogen chloride into the stirred mixture, until no more gas is absorbed (about 10 minutes) and then allow the mixture to cool. Transfer the mixture to a separatory funnel and wash it with two 10 ml. portions of water, two 10 ml. portions of dilute aqueous sodium bicarbonate, and finally with 10 ml. of water.

Dry the upper benzene layer over anhydrous calcium chloride, and fractionally distil under reduced pressure. After the excess benzene has been removed, benzyl chloride distils at 70°/15 mm. The yield is 20 g. (79% of theory). From the residue approximately 1 g. of *p*-xylylene chloride (*p*-chloromethylbenzyl chloride); m.p. 100°, can be obtained.

Example 2. Preparation of α-Chloromethyl-naphthalene (α-Naphthylmethyl Chloride)

A mixture of naphthalene (25 g.), paraformaldehyde (9 g.), glacial acetic acid (25 g.), concentrated hydrochloric acid (30 ml.), and syrupy phosphoric acid (14 ml.) is heated at 98–100° for $4\frac{1}{2}$ hours with efficient stirring. Pour the reaction mixture into cold water (200 ml.), decant the water from the heavy oily layer, and wash it three times with 200 ml. portions of cold water by decantation. Dry the organic layer over a little anhydrous sodium sulphate, filter, and distil under reduced pressure. The yield of α-chloromethylnaphthalene is 22 g.; b.p. 160–170° at 18 mm. (56% of theory).

Bouveault-Blanc Reduction

This is the reduction of aldehydes, ketones, esters, nitriles, or oximes by boiling with an excess of sodium in ethanol or a higher alcohol. A modification, sometimes resulting in improved yields, is to use only theoretical amounts of sodium and ethanol in the presence of an inert solvent, e.g. toluene or xylene:

$$R{\cdot}CO{\cdot}R' \xrightarrow{\text{Na/EtOH}} R{\cdot}CHOH{\cdot}R' \quad (R \text{ or } R' \text{ may be H})$$

$$R{\cdot}CO_2Et \xrightarrow{\text{Na/EtOH}} R{\cdot}CH_2OH + EtOH$$

$$R{\cdot}C{\equiv}N \xrightarrow{\text{Na/EtOH}} R{\cdot}CH_2{\cdot}NH_2$$

$$RR'C{=}N{\cdot}OH \xrightarrow{\text{Na/EtOH}} RR'CH{-}NH_2$$

$$R{\cdot}CH{=}CH{\cdot}CO_2Et \xrightarrow{\text{Na/EtOH}} R{\cdot}CH_2{\cdot}CH_2{\cdot}CH_2OH$$

Carbon–carbon double bonds are not affected, unless they are in conjugation with, for instance, a carbonyl group, as in the last example above. A possible mechanism for the Bouveault–Blanc reduction of an ester is as follows:

$$2Na + 2EtOH \longrightarrow 2NaOEt + 2[H]$$

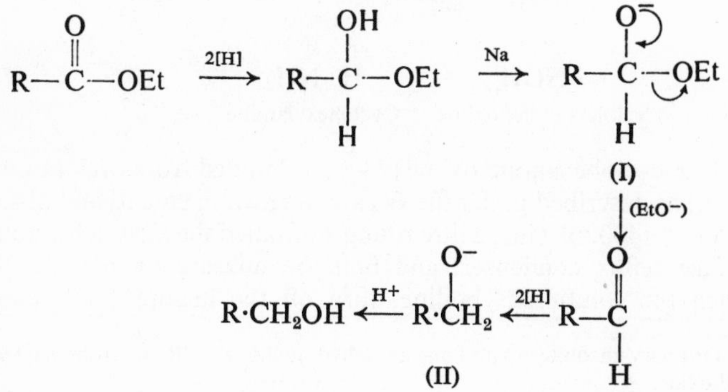

The reaction between the sodium and ethanol produces nascent hydrogen, which then reduces the carbonyl group of the ester yielding the enolate (I). This expels an ethoxide ion giving the aldehyde, subsequently reduced to the enolate (II); the latter on acidification gives the primary alcohol.

Example 1. Preparation of 2-Heptanol

$$CH_3 \cdot CO \cdot (CH_2)_4 \cdot CH_3 \xrightarrow{\text{Na/EtOH}} CH_3 \cdot CH(OH)(CH_2)_4 \cdot CH_3$$

n-Amyl methyl ketone   2-Heptanol
(2-Heptanone)

Dissolve n-amyl-methyl ketone (23 g.) in a mixture of ethanol (60 ml.) and water (20 ml.) in a 400 ml. round-bottomed flask. Attach an efficient reflux condenser, and gradually add sodium wire (13 g.) through the top of the condenser. Cool the flask, during the addition, by swirling in ice-cold water to prevent the reaction becoming violent. When all the sodium has dissolved, slowly add water (200 ml.), cool the mixture to 15°, and separate off the upper oily layer; wash it with 1:1-aqueous hydrochloric acid (5 ml.), then with water (5 ml.); dry over anhydrous sodium sulphate, and filter. Distil using a short fractionating column, collecting pure 2-heptanol 15 g.; b.p. 154–158° (65% of theory).

Example 2. Preparation of Cyclohexylamine

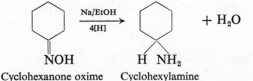

NOH   H NH₂
Cyclohexanone oxime   Cyclohexylamine

Place cyclohexanone oxime (23 g.), [obtained from cyclohexanone (25 g.) as described under the Beckman rearrangement] and absolute ethanol† (400 ml.) in a 2 litre round-bottomed flask, attach a double-surface reflux condenser, and boil the mixture on a water-bath. When the solution is boiling, turn off the heating and maintain

† Ordinary absolute ethanol may be dehydrated by distillation from magnesium methoxide.

boiling by rapid addition of small slices of sodium (50·8 g. through the top of the condenser (*care*) with shaking; carry out this operation, as fast as possible, without causing loss of ethanol.

When all the sodium has dissolved, cool the mixture, and add water (500 ml.). Now arrange the flask for distillation, so that the distillate is carried below the surface of 5N-hydrochloric acid (concentrated acid (30 ml.) and water (30 ml.)) contained in a 1 litre flask. Distil the mixture until no further basic material passes over; towards the end of the distillation add more water (300 ml.) to the distillation flask (to cut down frothing). The total volume of the distillate is approximately 800 ml. and now evaporate it under reduced pressure (to remove the excess of ethanol, water and unreduced oxime), until the amine hydrochloride crystallizes out in the distillation flask. Cool the flask, add 40% aqueous potassium hydroxide solution (100 ml.) with swirling, and transfer it to a separatory funnel. Remove the lower alkaline layer, and add potassium hydroxide to the amine in the funnel until no further separation of an aqueous alkaline solution occurs. Allow the mixture to stand overnight to dry the amine, and then decant it into a 25 ml. pear-shaped distillation flask, and distil it under reduced pressure. Collect cyclohexylamine 11 g.; at 131–137° (60% of theory).

Cannizzaro Reaction

This is the disproportionation of two molecules of an aromatic aldehyde (or an aliphatic aldehyde without any α-hydrogen atoms) in the presence of alkali, to give an equimolar mixture of the corresponding acid and alcohol:

$$2R \cdot CHO \xrightarrow{\text{NaOH}} RCO_2Na + R \cdot CH_2OH$$

Similar reactions involving two different aldehydes are termed 'crossed Cannizzaro reactions'.

$$R \cdot CHO + CH_2{=}O \xrightarrow{\text{NaOH}} R \cdot CH_2OH + HCO_2Na$$

The Cannizzaro reaction involves a hydride ion transfer as is shown when benzaldehyde undergoes this reaction in deuterated water. The alcohol formed contains no carbon–deuterium bonds, showing that the hydrogen which reduces one of the aldehyde molecules to the alcohol must arise directly from the second aldehyde molecule and not from the solvent. The reaction may exhibit either third or fourth order kinetics or a mixture of both, depending on the experimental conditions and the aldehyde used. On the basis of the above evidence the mechanism of the Cannizzaro reaction may be written as follows:

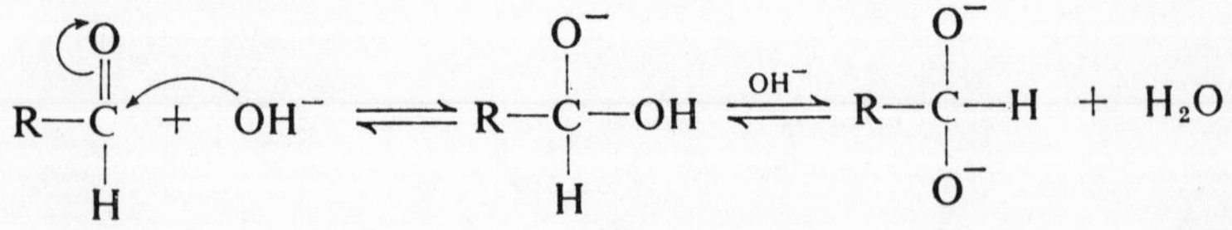

Either (I) or (II) can function as the hydride ion donor and this is presumably the rate-determining step.

In the third order Cannizzaro reaction, this step is:

$$R-\overset{\overset{\displaystyle O^-}{|}}{\underset{\underset{\displaystyle OH}{|}}{C}}-H \quad \overset{\overset{\displaystyle R}{|}}{\underset{\underset{\displaystyle H}{|}}{C}}=O \rightarrow R-\overset{\overset{\displaystyle O}{\|}}{\underset{\underset{\displaystyle OH}{|}}{C}} \quad + \quad H-\overset{\overset{\displaystyle R}{|}}{\underset{\underset{\displaystyle H}{|}}{C}}-O^- \rightarrow RCO_2^- + RCH_2OH$$

(I)

Whereas in those cases where the Cannizzaro reaction obeys fourth-order kinetics it is the more reactive species (II) which functions as the hydride ion donor:

$$R-\overset{\overset{\displaystyle O^-}{|}}{\underset{\underset{\displaystyle O^-}{|}}{C}}-H \ + \ \overset{\overset{\displaystyle O^-}{\|}}{\underset{\underset{\displaystyle H}{|}}{C}}-R \longrightarrow R-\overset{\overset{\displaystyle O}{\|}}{\underset{\underset{\displaystyle O^-}{|}}{C}} \ + \ H-\overset{\overset{\displaystyle O^-}{|}}{\underset{\underset{\displaystyle H}{|}}{C}}-R \ \overset{H_2O}{\rightleftharpoons} \ R \cdot CH_2OH + OH^-$$

(II)

In further agreement with this general mechanism, it has been shown that electron-withdrawing substituents increase the reactivity of aldehydes in the reaction. The Cannizzaro reaction is useful, in some cases, in synthetic work: for instance α-naphthylcarbinol and 5-methylfurfurylcarbinol have been obtained from the corresponding aldehydes by 'crossed Cannizzaro reactions' in better yields than by other methods.

Example 1. Preparation of Benzyl Alcohol and Benzoic Acid

$$2C_6H_5CHO \xrightarrow{KOH} C_6H_5 \cdot CH_2OH + C_6H_5CO_2K$$

Benzaldehyde   Benzyl alcohol   Potassium benzoate

(a) Benzyl alcohol
Dissolve potassium hydroxide pellets (12·5 g.) in water (60 ml.) in a 200 ml. round-bottomed flask and to this add freshly distilled benzaldehyde (21 g.≡20 ml.). Fit a Liebig condenser to the flask and boil under reflux for one hour. Cool the mixture and, if necessary, add sufficient water to dissolve any precipitated potassium benzoate. Pour the mixture into a separatory funnel, rinsing out the flask with ether (20 ml.) and add this to the solution in the separatory funnel. Shake the funnel to ensure efficient extraction of the benzyl alcohol by the ether. Separate the lower aqueous layer and extract it with ether (20 ml.) and combine the ethereal extracts. *Keep the aqueous solution for isolation of benzoic acid.*

Treat the combined ethereal extract in the following manner; wash it with water (5 ml.), dry with anhydrous sodium sulphate (2 g.), and filter. Remove the ether by distillation from a water-bath (*care*). Then distil the residue using an air-condenser; collect benzyl alcohol at 204–207°. The yield is 5·9 g. (pure benzyl alcohol has b.p. 205·5°) (54% of theory).

(b) Benzoic acid
Pour the aqueous solution (remaining after the ether extraction) with stirring into a mixture of concentrated hydrochloric acid (30 ml.) and crushed ice ($\simeq$ 50 g.). Filter off the precipitated benzoic acid at the pump, wash it with a little cold water, dry by suction and recrystallize from boiling water (150–200 ml.). The yield is 8.8 g.; m.p. 121° (80% of theory).

Aldehydes containing two α-hydrogen atoms in the presence of formaldehyde react as follows:

$$RCH_2CHO + 2CH_2O \xrightarrow{OH^-} RC(CH_2OH)_2 \cdot CHO$$

with an excess of formaldehyde, further condensation occurs yielding a trimethylolalkane:

$$RC(CH_2OH)_2 \cdot CHO + CH_2O \xrightarrow{OH^-} RC(CH_2OH)_3 + HCO_2^-$$

A special example of this 'crossed Cannizzaro reaction' is afforded by Example 2 below.

Example 2. Preparation of Pentaerythritol (Tetramethylolmethane)

$$2CH_3CHO + 8CH_2O + Ca(OH)_2 \rightarrow 2C(CH_2OH)_4 + (HCOO)_2Ca$$

Acetaldehyde   Formaldehyde   Pentaerythritol Calcium formate

In a 250 ml. round-bottomed flask place a mixture of calcium hydroxide (3·7 g.) and formaldehyde (15 g.) in water (100 ml.) Now slowly add acetaldehyde (4·5 g.) with swirling, maintaining the temperature of the reaction mixture at 15° during the addition of the aldehyde. When addition is complete gradually raise the temperature of the mixture to 45° with occasional shaking. Allow the mixture to cool, then precipitate the calcium by addition of oxalic acid, and filter off the calcium oxalate. Evaporate the filtrate to dryness under reduced pressure, and dissolve the residual solid in hot ethanol (40 ml.). Cool the solution, yielding pentaerythritol 10 g; m.p. 257–258° (73% of theory).

Chichibabin Reaction

This is the amination of pyridine and similar π-deficient heterocycles by treatment with sodamide: E.g.,

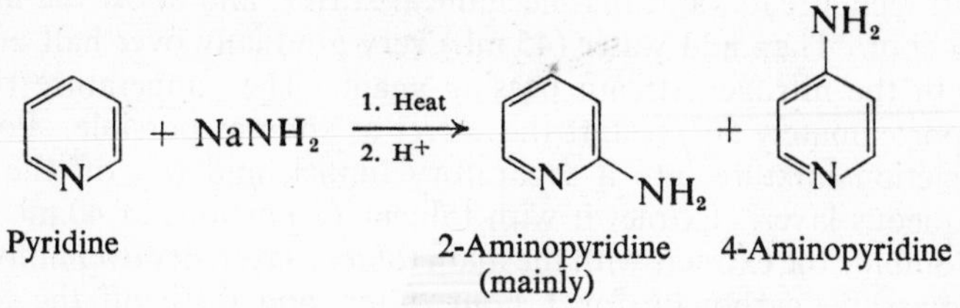

Pyridine ⟶ 2-Aminopyridine (mainly)   4-Aminopyridine

The probable mechanism involves the nucleophilic displacement of hydrogen as a hydride ion:

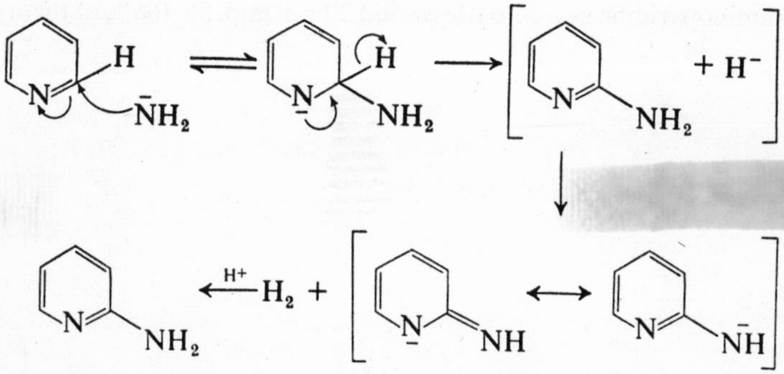

As it is a nucleophilic substitution reaction, attack occurs at the points of *minimum* electron density.

Example. Preparation of 2-Aminopyridine

Equip a 250 ml. three-necked round-bottomed flask with a mercury-sealed mechanical stirrer, (see Figure 4, p. 124), reflux condenser, and an inlet tube for nitrogen. Add freshly prepared, fine granular, sodamide (19 g.) and dry toluene (75 ml.) and pass a steady stream of dry nitrogen through the toluene. Heat the flask in an oil-bath with vigorous stirring until the temperature of the *reaction mixture* reaches 110°. Add dropwise pure, dry pyridine (25 g.) through the top of the condenser (during about 1 hour), stir and continue the stream of nitrogen. After approximately 1 hour the mixture becomes very dark, and after 3 hours viscous, and bubbling occurs due to the evolution of hydrogen. Heat for a further 2 hours at 110°; at the end of this period stirring often becomes difficult owing to the separation of solid material. Stop the nitrogen stream, and the mechanical stirrer, and allow the mixture to cool. Then add water (45 ml.) very gradually over half an hour with the nitrogen stream passing again. The temperature rises to approximately 50°, restart the stirrer as soon as possible. Pour the reaction mixture into a separatory funnel, and run off the lower aqueous layer. Extract it with toluene (2 portions of 40 ml. each). Combine the extracts with the main toluene layer, dry over anhydrous potassium carbonate for 1 hour, filter, and distil off the toluene (*Care: highly inflammable*). Finally distil the syrupy residue from an oil-bath (at 120–130°) under reduced pressure; Collect the fraction coming over at 95°/10 mm., which solidifies on cooling, giving 2-aminopyridine as a colourless solid 20 g.; m.p. 55° (66% of theory).

Claisen Condensation

This is the condensation of a carboxylic ester with a compound containing an activated α-hydrogen atom, e.g. an ester, ketone, or nitrile, under the influence of a basic catalyst, e.g. sodium alkoxide, sodamide, or sodium hydride. The reaction is essentially the acylation of an active methylene compound:

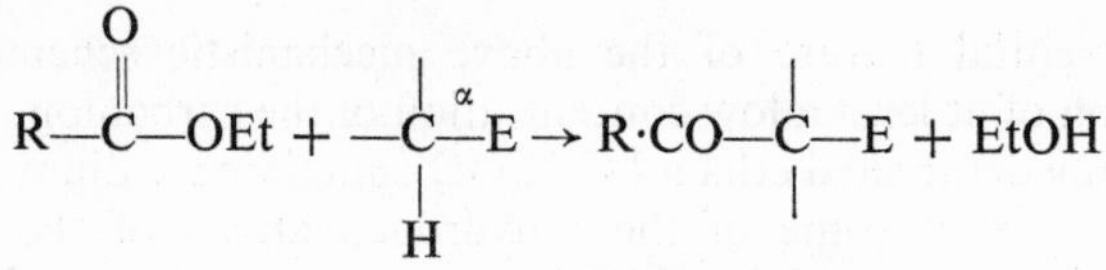

$$R-\overset{\overset{\displaystyle O}{\|}}{C}-OEt + -\overset{|}{\underset{|}{\underset{\displaystyle H}{C}}}\overset{\alpha}{-}E \rightarrow R\cdot CO-\overset{|}{\underset{|}{C}}-E + EtOH$$

(where E = an electrophilic group, i.e., $-CO_2Et$, $-\overset{\overset{\displaystyle O}{\|}}{C}-$, $-CN$) e.g.,

$$CH_3\cdot CO_2Et + C_6H_5\cdot CH_2\cdot CN \xrightarrow{\ NaOEt\ }$$
$$C_6H_5CH(CN)CO\cdot CH_3 + EtOH$$

The classic example is the preparation of acetoacetic ester (ethylacetoacetate) by the self condensation of ethyl acetate. The mechanism of the Claisen condensation resembles that of the aldol condensation, and involves the formation of a carbanion by reaction of the basic catalyst with one molecule of the ester (or other compound containing a reactive hydrogen atom) (step 1 below); subsequently the carbanion adds to the carbonyl group of the ester molecule with displacement of an alkoxide ion (step 2). Thus considering the formation of acetoacetic ester:

1.

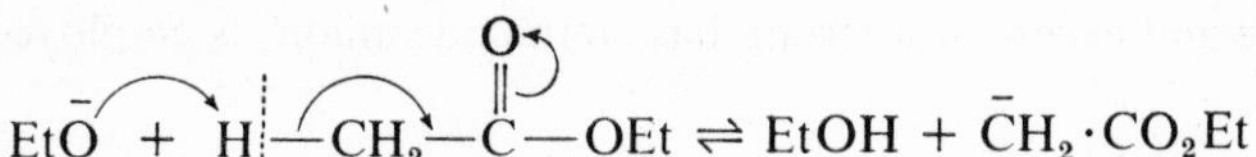

$$EtO^- + H-CH_2-\overset{\overset{\displaystyle O}{\|}}{C}-OEt \rightleftharpoons EtOH + \bar{C}H_2\cdot CO_2Et$$

2.

$$CH_3-\underset{\underset{OEt}{|}}{\overset{\overset{O}{||}}{C}}\,\bar{C}H_2CO_2Et \rightleftharpoons CH_3-\underset{\underset{OEt}{|}}{\overset{\overset{O^-}{|}}{C}}-CH_2CO_2Et \rightleftharpoons CH_3.\overset{\overset{O}{||}}{C}-CH_2CO_2Et$$

$$+$$
$$EtO^-$$

3.

$$CH_3CO \cdot CH_2CO_2Et + \bar{O}Et \rightleftharpoons CH_3\overset{\overset{O}{||}}{C}-\bar{C}H \cdot CO_2Et + EtOH$$

$$O^- \updownarrow$$

$$CH_3 \cdot C{=}CH \cdot CO_2Et$$

The essential feature of the above mechanistic scheme is the production of at least a low concentration of the carbanion. Experiments using deuterated ethanol C_2H_5OD containing sodium ethoxide have shown that some of the α-hydrogen atoms of the reactive compound (ester) are replaced by deuterium, suggesting the following equilibria:

$$H-\underset{\alpha}{\overset{|}{C}}-COOR + EtO^- \rightleftharpoons -\overset{|}{C}-COOR + EtOH$$

$$-\overset{|}{C}-COOR + EtOD \rightleftharpoons D-\overset{|}{C}-COOR + EtO^-$$

Similarly, optical active esters of the type RR'^*CHCO_2Et are racemized in the presence of ethoxide ion, indicating the formation of a planar carbanion which could be subjected to protonation from two different sides yielding the racemic modification.

In step 3 the acetoacetic ester is converted into its anion, and this is of great importance for the practical success of the reaction, because it is in this way that the keto-ester is converted into an unreactive form (i.e. it is stabilized by conversion to the anion). This ought to be almost complete because the keto-ester is definitely acidic and excess of a strong base (ethoxide anion) is employed.

* Asymmetric carbon atom.

Example 1. Preparation of Acetoacetic Ester

Place, in a 250 ml. round-bottomed flask fitted with a double-surface reflux condenser and a calcium chloride tube, dry ethyl acetate. (138 ml.)† and clean sodium wire (12·5 g.). Warm the flask on a water-bath to start the reaction, which may proceed so vigorously as to require external cooling to moderate it. After the initial reaction has subsided, boil the mixture under reflux until all the sodium has dissolved (about one and a half hours). Cool the mixture, and make it slightly acid to litmus paper by the addition of 50% aqueous acetic acid ($\simeq$ 70 ml.). Saturate the liquid with salt, and separate the upper layer of ester and dry it over anhydrous calcium chloride. Remove the drying agent by filtration, and distil the filtrate under reduced pressure. Collect the acetoacetic ester at 69–73°/12 mm. (unchanged ethyl acetate distils first). The yield is 38 g. (40% of theory).

Example 2. Preparation of Oxalacetic Ester

$$\begin{array}{c} \text{COOEt} \\ | \\ \text{COOEt} \end{array} + \text{CH}_3\text{COOEt} \xrightarrow[\text{2. H}^+]{\text{1. NaOEt}} \begin{array}{c} \text{CO·CH}_2\text{·COOEt} \\ | \\ \text{COOEt} \end{array} + \text{EtOH}$$

Ethyl oxalate   Ethyl acetate   Oxalacetic ester

Place sodium wire (2·3 g.) in a 250 ml. round-bottomed flask containing anhydrous ether (60 ml.). Add pure ethyl oxalate (14·6 g.) and then gradually introduce pure ethyl acetate (8·8 g.) with shaking. Gently warm the mixture on a water-bath under reflux until all the sodium dissolves, but take care to avoid overheating. Set the solution aside at room temperature; after several hours it solidifies to a yellow crystalline mass which is the sodio-derivative of oxalacetic ester. Decompose this material with dilute sulphuric acid, keeping the flask well cooled during addition of the acid, the ester then separates as an oil. Extract the product with ether; then wash the ethereal layer with dilute aqueous sodium hydroxide solution, and water; and dry it over anhydrous sodium sulphate. Filter, and distil off the ether from the water-bath (*care*); finally fractionally distil the residual liquid under reduced pressure. Collect oxalacetic ester at 130–132° at 24 mm. the yield is 14 g. (75% of theory).

† The ethyl acetate used must contain 2–3% of ethanol (3 ml.) and this will have to be added if ethanol-free ethyl acetate is used.

Claisen-Schmidt Reaction

This is the synthesis of $\alpha\beta$-unsaturated keto-compounds by the condensation of an aromatic aldehyde with an aliphatic aldehyde, ketone, or nitro compound containing an active α-methylene group, in the presence of dilute aqueous alkali at room temperature:

$$\overset{R}{\underset{|}{Ar\ CH}}\!\!=\!\!O + H_2\overset{R}{\underset{|}{C}}\!\!-\!\!CO\!\!-\!\!R' \xrightarrow{NaOH} Ar\cdot CH\!\!=\!\!\overset{R}{\underset{|}{C}}\!\!-\!\!CO\!\!-\!\!R' + H_2O$$

e.g.,

$$\underset{\text{Benzaldehyde}}{C_6H_5CHO} + \underset{\text{Acetophenone}}{CH_3CO\cdot C_6H_5} \longrightarrow \underset{\substack{\text{Benzalacetophenone}\\\text{or chalcone}}}{C_6H_5CH\!\!=\!\!CH\cdot COC_6H_5} + H_2O$$

$$\underset{\text{Benzaldehyde}}{C_6H_5CHO} + \underset{\text{Nitromethane}}{CH_3NO_2} \longrightarrow \underset{\beta\text{-Nitrostyrene}}{C_6H_5\overset{\alpha}{C}H\!\!=\!\!\overset{\beta}{C}H\cdot NO_2} + H_2O$$

The mechanism of the base-catalysed reaction is closely similar to the Claisen Condensation, involving initial formation of a carbanion and its subsequent nucleophilic addition to the carbonyl group of the aromatic aldehyde; thus considering the formation of chalcone:

1 $\quad H\bar{O} + H\!\!-\!\!CH_2\!\!-\!\!\overset{\overset{\displaystyle O}{\|}}{C}\!\!-\!\!C_6H_5 \rightleftharpoons \bar{C}H_2.CO.C_6H_5 + H_2O$

2 $\quad C_6H_5\!\!-\!\!\overset{\overset{\displaystyle O}{\|}}{\underset{\underset{\displaystyle H}{|}}{C}}\ \bar{C}H_2COC_6H_5 \rightleftharpoons C_6H_5\!\!-\!\!\overset{\overset{\displaystyle O^-}{|}}{\underset{\underset{\displaystyle H}{|}}{C}}\!\!-\!\!CH_2COC_6H_5$

$$\Big\updownarrow H_2O$$

$$C_6H_5\cdot CH\!\!=\!\!CH\cdot COC_6H_5 \underset{(-H_2O)}{\longleftarrow} C_6H_5\!\!-\!\!\overset{\overset{\displaystyle OH}{|}}{\underset{\underset{\displaystyle H}{|}}{C}}\!\!-\!\!CH_2COC_6H_5$$

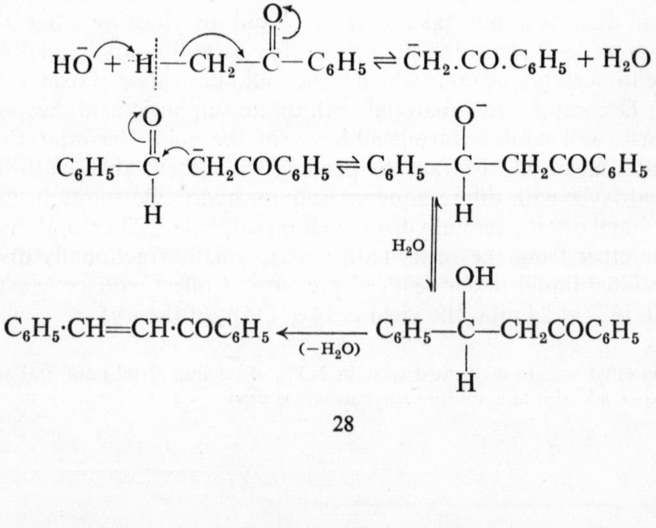

It appears likely that an aldol-type intermediate is formed, but this must be unstable since it is not isolated.

Example 1. Preparation of Benzalacetone (Benzylideneacetone)

$$Ph \cdot CHO + CH_3 \cdot CO \cdot CH_3 \xrightarrow{\text{NaOH}} Ph \cdot CH = CH \cdot CO \cdot CH_3 + H_2O$$

Benzaldehyde   Acetone   Benzalacetone

Place pure *freshly distilled* benzaldehyde (8·4 g. ≡ 8·0 ml.), A.R. acetone (12·7 g. ≡ 16 ml.), and 10% aqueous sodium hydroxide solution (2·0 ml.) in a 100 ml. conical flask. Warm the mixture to 25–30° on a water-bath for one and half hours with frequent shaking. Make the solution just acid to litmus paper by the addition of dilute hydrochloric acid. Transfer the mixture to a 50 ml. separatory funnel and remove the upper organic layer. Extract the lower aqueous layer with benzene (5 ml.) and add this to the upper yellow layer. Wash the latter with water (5 ml.) and dry over anhydrous sodium sulphate. Remove the benzene by distillation from a steam-bath, and then distil the residue from a Claisen flask under reduced pressure. Collect the product at 133–143°/16 mm. (or at 100–108°/ 2 mm.). Benzalacetone solidifies on standing giving colourless crystals, m.p. 38–39°, which may be recrystallized from petroleum ether (40–60°) (*Care: highly inflammable solvent*). The yield is 8·1 g.; m.p. 40–42° (69% of theory).

Example 2. Preparation of Dibenzalacetone (Dibenzylideneacetone)

$$2Ph \cdot CHO + CH_3 \cdot CO \cdot CH_3 \xrightarrow[(-2H_2O)]{\text{NaOH}} Ph \cdot CH = CHCOCH = CH \cdot Ph$$

Benzaldehyde   Acetone   Dibenzalacetone

Prepare a cold solution of sodium hydroxide pellets (2.5 g.) in water (25 ml.) and ethanol† (20 ml.) and place it in a 100 ml. conical flask. Swirl the contents of the flask and add a mixture of pure redistilled benzaldehyde (2·6 g. ≡ 2·5 ml.) and A.R. acetone

---

† Sufficient ethanol is added to dissolve the benzaldehyde, and to keep the initially formed benzalacetone in solution, until it has time to react with the second molecule of benzaldehyde.

(0·75 g. ≡ 0·9 ml.). Shake frequently and keep the temperature at 20–25° for 15 minutes by immersing the flask in a bath of cold water. Filter off the precipitated dibenzalacetone at the pump, and wash with cold water to remove alkali. Dry the product at room temperature on filter paper; the weight of crude product should be 2·6 g.; m.p. 105–107°. Recrystallize from hot ethyl acetate (2·5 ml./g.) giving pure dibenzalacetone 2·2 g.; m.p. 112° (72% of theory).

Clemmensen Reduction

This is the conversion of a carbonyl group in an aldehyde or ketone into a methylene group, by treatment with amalgamated zinc and concentrated hydrochloric acid:

$$R \cdot CO \cdot R' \xrightarrow[\text{[4H]}]{\text{Zn(Hg)}_x/\text{HCl}} R \cdot CH_2 \cdot R' + H_2O$$

The reduction is applicable to a wide range of ketones, but with aldehydes it is generally less successful. High molecular weight compounds tend to react sluggishly and the reaction rate may be assisted by addition of an organic solvent, e.g. ethanol, dioxan, or toluene. The Clemmenson reduction cannot proceed through the corresponding carbinol, since these are not reduced under the reaction conditions. The mechanism is now considered to be a chemisorption process which makes use of the high over-potential of hydrogen on mercury. The rate-determining step is possibly the co-ordination of the carbonyl carbon atom with the metal surface. The reaction requires strongly acidic conditions, so it is probably the oxonium salt that is adsorbed onto the metal surface; the following mechanism satisfies the known facts about this reduction:

$$\begin{array}{ccc} O & & H{-}O^+ \\ \| & & \| \\ R{-}C & + H_3O^+ \rightleftharpoons & R{-}C & + H_2O \\ | & & | \\ R' & & R' \end{array}$$

Zn	$^+$O—H $\overset{\|}{:} + \overset{+}{C}RR'$	$\overset{+}{Zn}$	O—H $\underset{|}{:}$:CRR'	$\overset{+}{Zn}$	H $\underset{|}{\overset{+}{O}{-}H}$ CRR'	Zn^{++}		$+ H_2O$
Zn	:	Zn	: $\underset{\text{with}}{\overset{\text{Subsequent}}{\text{reaction}}}$ Zn	:	Zn	:		
Zn	: $\longrightarrow$	Zn	: $\overset{\text{another}}{\text{H}^+}$ Zn	:	$\longrightarrow$	Zn	:CRR'	
Zn	:	Zn	: Zn	:	Zn	:		
					Zn	:		

31

Now the adsorbed :CRR′ radical may react successively with two adsorbed hydrogen atoms, or abstract protons from the strongly acid solution, giving the final products of hydrocarbon and zinc cations:

$$
\begin{array}{c|c}
\text{Zn} & : \quad\quad\quad \text{Zn}^{++}
\end{array}
$$

$$
\left.\begin{array}{c|c}
\text{Zn} & : \\[4pt]
 & :\text{CRR}'
\end{array}\right\} \xrightarrow{2\text{H}^+}
\left.\begin{array}{c|c}
\text{Zn} & :\text{H} \\[4pt]
\text{Zn} & :\text{CRR}' \\[4pt]
\text{Zn} & :\text{H}
\end{array}\right\} \longrightarrow
\begin{array}{c|c}
\text{Zn} & : \quad \text{R} \\
 & \quad\quad | \\
 & +\,\text{CH}_2 \\
 & \quad\quad | \\
\text{Zn} & : \quad \text{R}'
\end{array}
$$

or

$$
\left.\begin{array}{c|c}
\text{Zn} & : \\[4pt]
 & :\text{CRR}'
\end{array}\right\} \xrightarrow{\text{H}^+}
\left.\begin{array}{c|c}
\text{Zn}^+ & :\!\!\overset{..}{\underset{..}{\text{H}}}\!\!\text{CRR}' \\[4pt]
\text{Zn} & :
\end{array}\right\} \xrightarrow{\text{H}^+}
\begin{array}{c|c}
 & \text{Zn}^{++} \\[4pt]
\text{Zn} & : \quad \text{R} \\
 & \quad\quad | \\
\text{Zn} & : +\,\text{CH}_2 \\
 & \quad\quad | \\
\text{Zn} & : \quad \text{R}'
\end{array}
$$

Example 1. Preparation of Ethylbenzene

$$
\underset{\text{Acetophenone}}{C_6H_5COCH_3} \xrightarrow[\substack{4[H]}]{Zn(Hg)_\alpha/HCl} \underset{\text{Ethylbenzene}}{C_6H_5 \cdot CH_2 \cdot CH_3} + H_2O
$$

Place zinc wool (20 g.) in a 150 ml. round-bottomed flask, add mercuric chloride (1·5 g.) (*poisonous*), concentrated hydrochloric acid (1 ml.), and water (25 ml.), and then shake or stir for 5 minutes. Decant the aqueous solution and cover the *zinc amalgam* with water (25 ml.) and concentrated hydrochloric acid (25 ml.). Equip the flask with a reflux condenser and then add redistilled acetophenone (10 g.) and boil gently under reflux for 5 hours. During this time add concentrated hydrochloric acid (20 ml.) (in 5 ml. portions) down the condenser. After 5 hours the reaction is almost complete, but allow the reaction mixture to stand for at least 12 hours. Separate the upper hydrocarbon layer, extract the aqueous layer with ether

(2 × 10 ml.), and combine these extracts with the hydrocarbon layer. Wash this mixture with 5% aqueous sodium hydroxide solution (10 ml.); and next with water (10 ml.), and finally dry over anhydrous sodium sulphate. Remove the desiccant, by filtration through a fluted filter paper, and distil off the ether from a water-bath taking the normal precautions; finally distil the residue from an air-bath collecting ethylbenzene at 134–137°. The yield is 4·0 g. (45% of theory).

Example 2. Preparation of Bibenzyl

$$C_6H_5\cdot CO\cdot CO\cdot C_6H_5 \xrightarrow[8[H]]{Zn(Hg)_x/HCl} C_6H_5\cdot CH_2CH_2\cdot C_6H_5 + 2H_2O$$

Benzil   Bibenzyl

Boil benzil (7 g.), zinc amalgam† (30 g.) and 1:1 aqueous hydrochloric acid (1 volume conc. hydrochloric acid:1 volume of water) (100 ml.) under reflux for 5 hours. At the end of each hour further concentrated hydrochloric acid (4 ml.) is added. When the reaction is complete, decant the liquid from the zinc and cool it. The product solidifies and is filtered off at the pump and well washed with water The product b.p. 280° is then distilled from a small flask, and is finally recrystallized from ethanol giving pure bibenzyl 4 g.; m.p. 50–52° (65% of theory).

† *Preparation of the Zinc Amalgam*

Granulated zinc in thin pieces or preferably zinc foil cut in small strips, is allowed to stand for 1 hour in contact with an equal weight of 5% aqueous mercuric chloride solution with frequent shaking. The solution is then poured off and the metal washed once with distilled water.

Dieckmann Reaction

This is the intramolecular cyclisation of δ or ε—dicarboxylic esters, having an activated hydrogen atom attached to the δ or ε carbon atom, in the presence of a basic catalyst, e.g. sodium alkoxide, or sodium hydride. The Dieckmann reaction is essentially an intramolecular Claisen condensation:

$$-\overset{|}{\underset{|}{C}}{}^{-}\quad \underset{\underset{O}{\|}}{C}-O\dot{R} \;\rightarrow\; -\overset{|}{\underset{|}{C}}-\!-\!-\underset{\underset{O}{\|}}{C} \;+\; OR^{-}$$

The mechanism is similar to that of the ordinary Claisen condensation, and requires that carbanions are formed at least in low concentration. Considering the conversion of ethyl adipate (adipic ester) into 2-carbethoxycyclopentanone:

$$\text{EtO}^{-} + H\!-\!\underset{\underset{\text{CO}_2\text{Et}}{|}}{\overset{\overset{\text{CH}_2-\text{CH}_2}{|}}{\text{CH}}}\quad \text{CH}_2\!\cdot\!\text{CO}_2\text{Et} \;\rightleftharpoons\; \text{EtOH} + {}^{-}\underset{\text{COOEt}}{\overset{\overset{\text{CH}_2-\text{CH}_2}{|}}{\text{CH}}}\quad \text{CH}_2\!\cdot\!\text{COOEt}$$

Ethyl adipate

$$\underset{\underset{\underset{O}{\diagdown}\;\diagup{OEt}}{C}}{\overset{\overset{\text{CH}_2-\text{CH}_2}{|\quad\;\;|}}{\underset{\text{EtO}_2\text{C}}{\text{CH}}\;\;\text{CH}_2}} \rightleftharpoons \underset{\underset{\underset{{}^{-}O}{\diagdown}\;\diagup{OEt}}{C}}{\text{EtO}_2\text{C}\!\cdot\!\overset{\overset{\text{CH}_2-\text{CH}_2}{|\quad\;\;|}}{\text{CH}\;\;\text{CH}_2}} \rightleftharpoons \underset{\underset{\underset{O}{\|}}{C}}{\overset{\overset{\text{CH}_2-\text{CH}_2}{|\quad\;\;|}}{\underset{\text{EtO}_2\text{C}}{\text{CH}}\;\;\text{CH}_2}} + \text{EtO}^{-}$$

2-Carbethoxycyclopentanone

The initially formed carbanion then undergoes intramolecular cyclization by the operation of the electron shifts indicated, leading to the formation of the α-keto-ester.

34

The yields in the Dieckmann reaction are only good for δ or ε dicarboxylic esters, $\alpha\omega$-dicarboxylic esters may also undergo the acyloin condensation which requires four equivalents of sodium in boiling xylene:

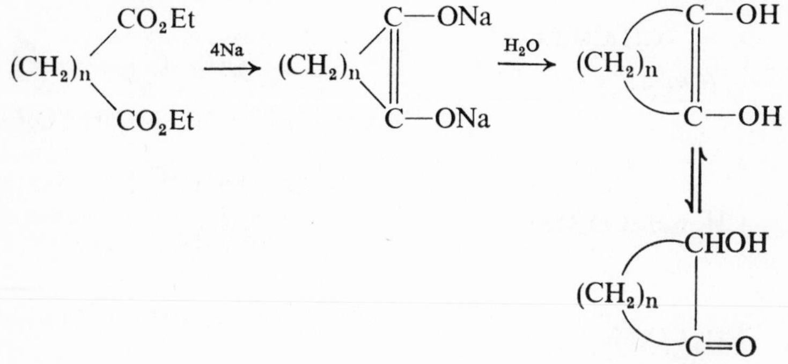

$$(CH_2)_n \begin{array}{c} CO_2Et \\ \\ CO_2Et \end{array} \xrightarrow{4Na} (CH_2)_n \begin{array}{c} C-ONa \\ \| \\ C-ONa \end{array} \xrightarrow{H_2O} (CH_2)_n \begin{array}{c} C-OH \\ \| \\ C-OH \end{array}$$

$$\Updownarrow$$

$$(CH_2)_n \begin{array}{c} CHOH \\ | \\ C=O \end{array}$$

The acyloin

Thus with 1 equivalent of sodium, ethyl adipate undergoes the Dieckmann reaction giving the α-keto-ester in 78% yield; but with 4 equivalents of sodium in xylene the acyloin is obtained in 55% yield. The Dieckmann reaction may be used for the synthesis of five- and six-membered alicyclic ketones:

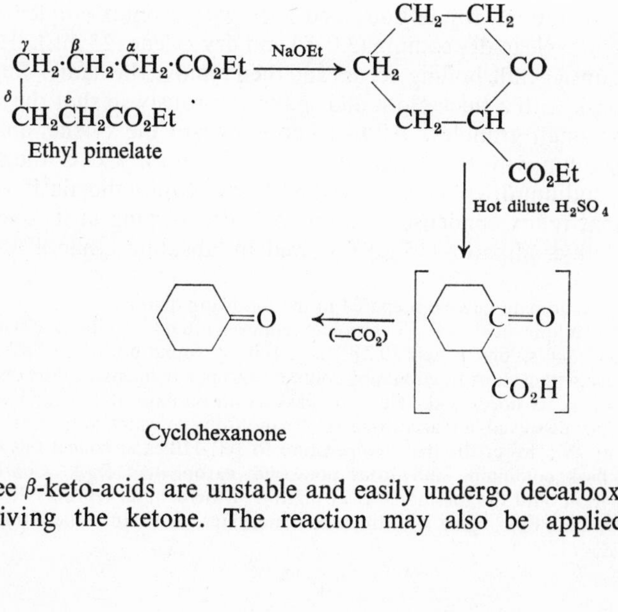

$$\begin{array}{c} \overset{\gamma}{C}H_2 \cdot \overset{\beta}{C}H_2 \cdot \overset{\alpha}{C}H_2 \cdot CO_2Et \\ \overset{\delta}{|} \quad \overset{\varepsilon}{} \\ CH_2CH_2CO_2Et \end{array} \xrightarrow{NaOEt} \begin{array}{c} CH_2-CH_2 \\ CH_2 \qquad CO \\ CH_2-CH \\ \qquad CO_2Et \end{array}$$

Ethyl pimelate

Hot dilute H_2SO_4

$$\begin{array}{c} \\ \end{array} \xleftarrow[(-CO_2)]{} \left[\begin{array}{c} C=O \\ CO_2H \end{array} \right]$$

Cyclohexanone

The free β-keto-acids are unstable and easily undergo decarboxylation giving the ketone. The reaction may also be applied to heterocyclic compounds:

$$\overset{\delta}{CH_3}\ N \overset{\overset{\gamma}{CH_2}\cdot\overset{\beta}{CH_2}\cdot\overset{\alpha}{CH_2}\cdot CO_2Et}{\underset{\overset{\epsilon}{CH_2}CO_2Et}{}} \xrightarrow{\text{NaOEt}}$$

$$CH_3-N \overset{CH_2-CH_2}{\underset{CH_2-CO}{}} CH\cdot CO_2Et$$

$$S \overset{CH_2\cdot CH_2\cdot CO_2Me}{\underset{CH_2\cdot CO_2Me}{}} \longrightarrow MeO_2C \underset{S}{\overset{O}{\diagup}} + \underset{S}{\overset{O}{\diagdown}}CO_2Me$$

In contrast, the acyloin reaction may be applied to the synthesis of large ring alicyclic compounds (see p. 35).

Example. Preparation of 2-Carbethoxycyclopentanone

Equip a 150 ml. round-bottomed flask with a reflux condenser, and place in it clean dry sodium (3·0 g.) and dry xylene (25 ml.). Heat the flask until gentle boiling occurs and then remove the flame. Surround the flask with a thick cloth and shake vigorously so that the sodium forms small granules. Allow to cool, decant the xylene, and wash the sodium with two portions of ether (10 ml.). Cover the sodium with sodium-dried benzene (60 ml.) and equip the flask with an efficient reflux condenser, with a cotton wool plug at its open end. Add ethyl adipate† (15 g.) followed by absolute ethanol (0·2 ml.).

---

† Ethyl adipate may be prepared in the following manner.

Place adipic acid (15 g.), absolute ethanol (36 ml.), toluene (20 ml.) and concentrated sulphuric acid (0.2 g.) in a 100 ml. round-bottomed flask. Equip the flask with a short fractionating column bearing a condenser in the distillation position at its upper end. Heat the flask in an oil-bath at 115° and when the acid has dissolved an azeotrope of ethanol/toluene/water will start to distil over at 75°; lower the bath temperature to 100–110° and collect this distillate in a flask containing anhydrous potassium carbonate (15 g.). Continue the distillation until the thermometer at the top of the column registers 78°. Shake the distillate thoroughly with the carbonate, filter, and return the filtrate to the

Warm the flask on a water-bath for a few minutes, until a vigorous reaction sets in and a cake of the sodio-derivative begins to separate. Shake the flask by hand during the initial reaction, and when this reaction has subsided, boil for 12 hours on a water-bath, and then cool in ice water. Decompose the product with a mixture of ice and 1:1-hydrochloric acid [1 volume of conc. acid:1 volume of water] adding the acid until the solution turns Congo red indicator blue. Place the solution in a separatory funnel and separate the benzene layer. Extract the aqueous layer with benzene (20 ml.). Combine the benzene layers and wash the combined extract with 5% aqueous sodium carbonate solution (20 ml.), followed by water (20 ml.). Dry the benzene solution over anhydrous sodium sulphate, filter off the desiccant and remove the benzene by distillation from a water-bath (*care*). Fractionally distil the residue under reduced pressure. The yield of 2-carbethoxycylcopentanone is 9·5 g.; b.p. 108–111°/15 mm. or 102°/11 mm. (82% of theory).

---

distillation flask and distil again until the temperature indicated by the thermometer is 78°. Transfer the residue to a Claisen flask and distil under reduced pressure. Ethanol and toluene distil first and then the temperature will rise sharply and ethyl adipate will distil. The yield of ethyl adipate is 19 g.; b.p. 138°/20 mm. (The b.p. may rise several degrees towards the end of the distillation due to superheating.)

Diels–Alder Reaction (or Diene Synthesis)

This is the addition of a multiple-bonded compound (the dienophile) across the 1,4-positions of a conjugated diene (the diene) with the formation of a six-membered ring compound (the adduct):

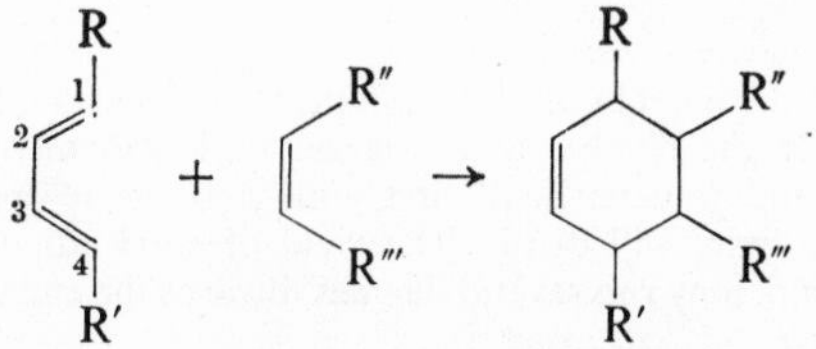

(Diene)   (Dienophile)   (Adduct)

The process involves a reorganization of electron density during which two single bonds are created, two double bonds are converted into single bonds, and one single bond is converted into a double bond. The mechanism of the addition may be either heterolytic (ionic) or homolytic (free radical), and it is possible that the reaction can go by either mechanism. Thus the process is not accelerated by free-radical producing agents, e.g. peroxides; also the rate of reaction is more sensitive to the polarity of the solvent than are the majority of free radical reactions. On the other hand, the rate is less responsive to polarity than are most ionic reactions. The Diels–Alder reaction is a *cis* addition with respect to both the diene and the dienophile (i.e. groups *cis* to each other in the dienophile will also be *cis* in the adduct). This suggests that if the reaction is heterolytic then the interval between the formation of the first and second of the new carbon–carbon bonds must be very short indeed, and some workers consider the Zwitterion intermediate does not intervene at all and that the bonds are formed simultaneously (i.e. a four-centre type reaction). The process is generally a simple second-order

38

reaction, and it is found that electron donor groups on the diene, and electron-attracting groups on the dienophile generally facilitate the addition. The heterolytic mechanism may be illustrated by the reaction between butadiene and acraldehyde (acrolein):

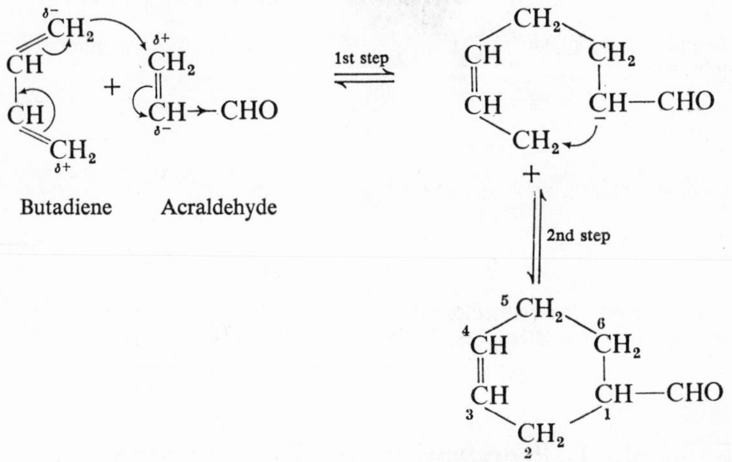

Butadiene   Acraldehyde

1st step

2nd step

1,2,5,6-Tetrahydrobenzaldehyde

Additions generally proceed without a catalyst, and as little heat as possible is used, because the reaction is reversible and excessive heating decomposes the adduct into the reactants. The reaction is capable of wide variation and is especially valuable for the synthesis of compounds containing *endo*-bonds.

A large number of compounds will serve as dienophiles, the more reactive ones contain electron-withdrawing groups X adjacent to the multiple bond, i.e. $-\overset{|}{C}=\overset{|}{C}-CX-$ (where X = CO—, —CN, —NO_2, —SO_2, etc.). Common examples are, $\alpha\beta$-unsaturated carbonyl compounds, and quinones. Some additions, illustrating the wide scope of the diene synthesis, are shown below:

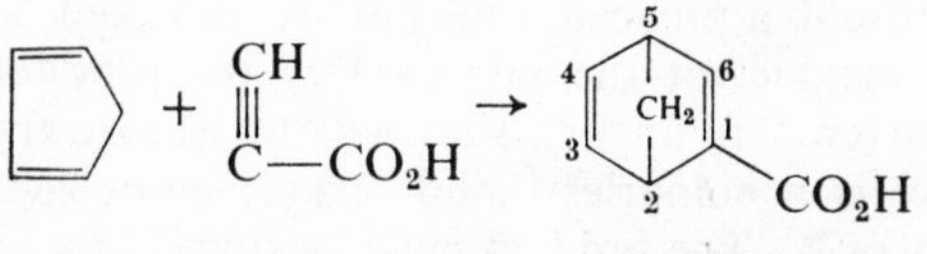

Cyclopentadiene   Acetylenecarboxylic   2,5-*endo*Methylene-2,5-
acid   dihydrobenzoic acid

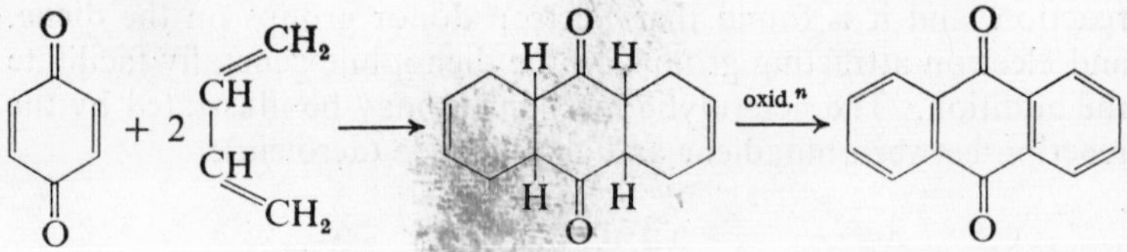

p-Benzo-   Butadiene   Anthraquinone
quinone

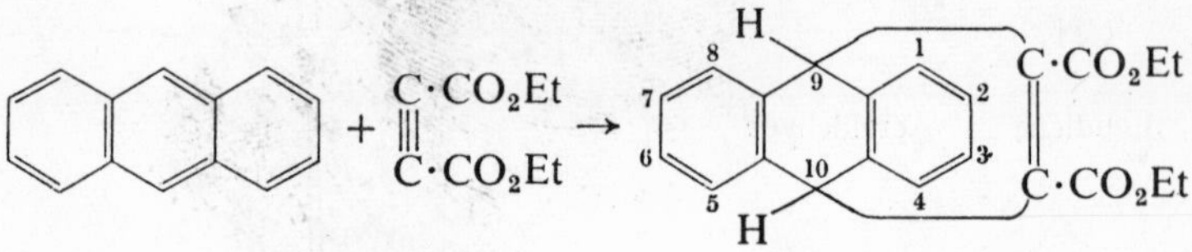

Anthracene   Acetylenedicarboxylic   9,10-Dihydroanthracene-9,10-
(Diene)   ester (Dienophile)   endo-αβ-diethylmaleate

Example 1. Preparation of 9,10-Dihydro-anthracene-9,10-endo-αβ-Succinic Anhydride

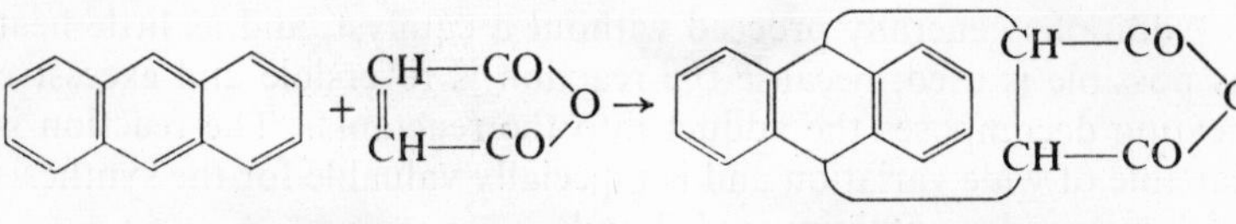

Anthracene   Maleic anhydride   9,10-Dihydroanthracene-9,10-
                                     endo-αβ-succinic anhydride

Place pure anthracene (2·0 g.), maleic anhydride (1 g.), and pure xylene (25 ml.) in a 50 ml. round-bottomed flask fitted with a reflux condenser. Boil the mixture under reflux, with frequent shaking, for 20 minutes. Allow to cool slightly and then add decolourizing charcoal (0·5 g.) and boil for a further 5 minutes. Filter the hot solution through a preheated Buchner funnel, cool, and filter off the crystalline product at the pump. Dry the product in a vacuum desiccator over paraffin wax shavings (to remove traces of xylene). The adduct is a colourless solid, 2·3 g.; m.p. 262–263° decomp. (77% of theory). The product must be stored in a well-sealed tube, since it is subject to hydrolysis by moisture.

Example 2. Preparation of 3,6-*endoxo*-1,2:3,6-Tetrahydrophthalic Anhydride

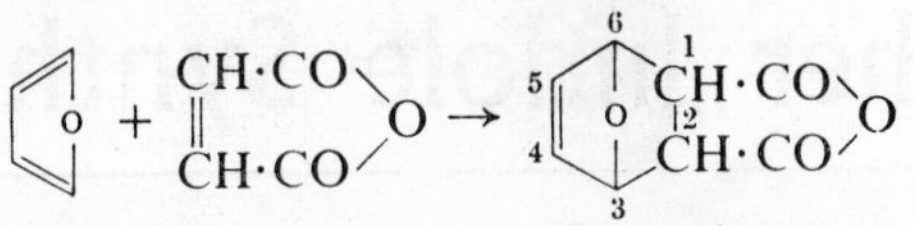

Furan   Maleic   3,6-*endoxo*-1,2,3,6-Tetra-
         anhydride   hydrophthalic anhydride

Add furan (furfuran) (1·5 g.) to a suspension of maleic anhydride (2 g.) in ether (10 ml.) with shaking. An exothermic reaction begins and the mixture becomes warm; set it aside overnight at room temperature. Then cool in ice-water and filter off the solid product at the pump. The yield of 3,6-*endoxo*-1,2,3,6-tetrahydrophthalic anhydride is 2·5 g.; m.p. 120° decomp. (70% of theory). A further crop of crystals is obtainable by evaporation of the ethereal mother liquor.

Fischer Indole Synthesis

This is the formation of indoles (benzopyrroles) by heating an aldehyde or ketone phenylhydrazone having a free *o*-position with an acidic catalyst, e.g. anhydrous zinc chloride. It is the most important method for the preparation of indoles, although it fails for indole itself; and is an intramolecular condensation with elimination of ammonia:

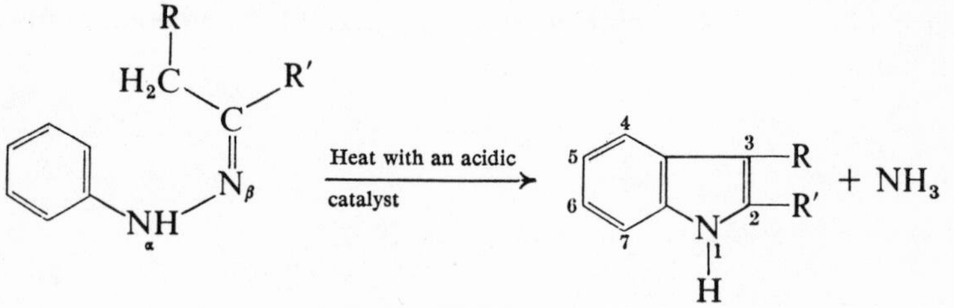

e.g.,

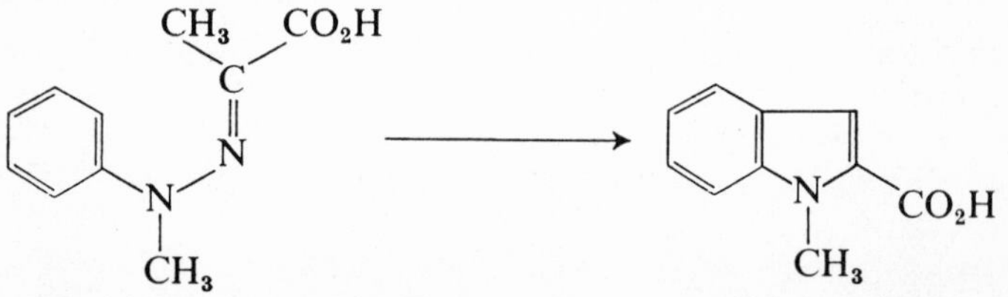

Pyruvic acid *N*-methylphenylhydrazone   1-Methylindole-2-carboxylic acid

A large number of catalysts may be employed, for example concentrated sulphuric acid, cuprous chloride, zinc chloride, boron trifluoride or polyphosphoric acid, and the yields of the substituted indoles are often high. Studies using N^{15} as a tracer have revealed that it is the nitrogen furthest from the benzene ring (i.e. N_β) that is lost as ammonia, and the generally accepted mechanism (supported by kinetic studies) involves an intramolecular rearrangement similar

42

to an *o*-benzidine rearrangement:

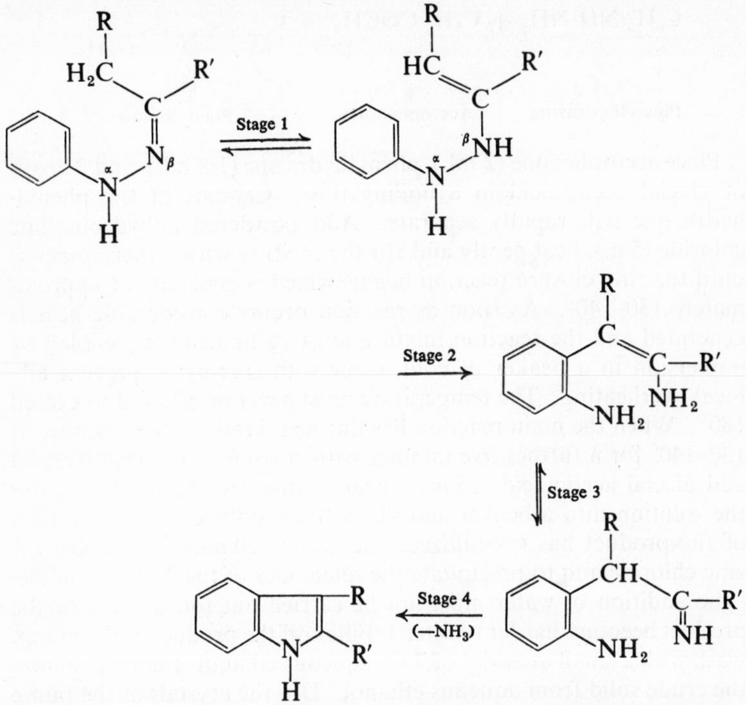

In the first stage the double bond migrates one position further away from the benzene ring, and the latter is then attacked by the doubly bonded carbon giving the diamino-compound (stage 2) which subsequently rearranges (stage 3) and cyclizes with loss of ammonia (stage 4). The ease of the reaction varies considerably; it is particularly facile with cyclohexanone phenylhydrazone which gives tetrahydrocarbazole (example 2) after a few minutes boiling in glacial acetic acid. Indeed, in several cases, good yields of substituted indoles have been obtained by boiling the required phenylhydrazone in a solvent like ethylene glycol or tetralin without any acidic catalyst being present.

Example 1. Preparation of 2-Phenylindole

Phenylhydrazine is used in this preparation and since it is poisonous and can cause severe skin burns it should be handled with caution.

$$C_6H_5 \cdot NH \cdot NH_2 + C_6H_5 \cdot COCH_3 \rightarrow$$

Phenylhydrazine   Acetophenone   2-Phenylindole

Place acetophenone (2 ml.), phenylhydrazine (1·8 ml.), and 2 drops of glacial acetic acid in a boiling tube. Crystals of the phenyl-hydrazone will rapidly separate. Add powdered anhydrous zinc chloride (5 g.), heat gently and stir the mixture with a thermometer, until the ring closure reaction begins which is generally at approxi-mately 130–140°. As soon as reaction occurs considerable heat is generated and the reaction mixture must be immediately cooled by immersion in a beaker of cold water with stirring to prevent any local overheating. The temperature must never be allowed to exceed 180°. When the main reaction has finished, keep the temperature at 130–140° for a further five minutes with stirring. Cool slightly, and add glacial acetic acid (15 ml.), heat to dissolve the product, pour the solution into a beaker and allow to crystallize. After the bulk of the product has crystallized, add water (20 ml.) to dissolve the zinc chloride and to precipitate the remainder of the 2-phenylindole. (The addition of water must not be carried out too quickly or the product becomes harder to filter.) Filter off the product at the pump, wash with a small quantity of 75% aqueous ethanol, and recrystallize the crude solid from aqueous ethanol. Dry the crystals at the pump and finally dry in an air-oven at 60°.

The yield of 2-phenylindole is 2 g.; m.p. 189° (60% of theory based on acetophenone).

Example 2. Preparation of 1,2,3,4-Tetra-hydrocarbazole

The Fischer indolization reaction may be carried out without isola-tion of the intermediate hydrazone in certain cases, notably where the reaction involves an alicyclic ketone. Equip a 50 ml. round-bottomed flask with a reflux condenser, and place in it a mixture of cyclohexanone (2·8 g.) and glacial acetic acid (9·0 g. ≡ 8·6 ml.), and heat the solution to boiling. When the solution is gently boiling, add redistilled phenylhydrazine (2·7 g. ≡ 2·5 ml.) dropwise down the condenser, shaking the flask frequently during the addition.

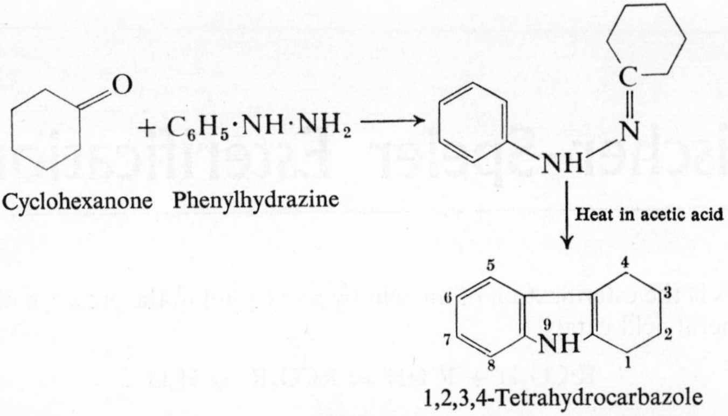

Cyclohexanone   Phenylhydrazine

Heat in acetic acid

1,2,3,4-Tetrahydrocarbazole

Gently boil the mixture under reflux for 30 minutes after completion of the addition, and then pour into a 150 ml. beaker cooled in ice. Vigorously stir until the liquid solidifies, and when the temperature reaches 5°, filter off the crude product at the pump. Cool the filtrate to 0° and refilter. Wash the product with water (3 ml.) and then with 75% aqueous ethanol (3 ml.). Recrystallize by boiling under reflux with methanol† (17 ml.) with the addition of a little activated charcoal; filter through a preheated Buchner funnel. Pure 1,2,3,4-tetrahydrocarbazole crystallizes in the filtrate on cooling. Filter off the crystals at the pump, dry by suction, and finally dry in a desiccator over paraffin wax. The yield is 3·2 g.; m.p. 116–117° (75% of theory based on phenylhydrazine).

† The recrystallization may also be made from a solution of equal volumes of glacial acetic acid and water.

Fischer–Speier Esterification

This is the esterification of an acid by an alcohol in the presence of a mineral acid catalyst:

$$R \cdot CO_2H + R'OH \rightleftharpoons RCO_2R' + H_2O$$

$$\text{Acid + Alcohol} \underset{\substack{\text{Saponification} \\ \text{(Hydrolysis)}}}{\overset{\text{Esterification}}{\rightleftarrows}} \text{Ester + Water}$$

Esterification and hydrolysis are part of the same equilibrium and information about both can, therefore, be derived from the study of one. The majority of work has been done on ester hydrolysis; and there is considerable evidence indicating that most of these reactions probably involve acyl-oxygen fission rather than alkyl-oxygen fission: e.g. (*a*) Hydrolysis of optically active acetoxysuccinic acid occurs with retention of configuration at the asymmetric atom (marked *):

$$HO_2C-CH_2-\overset{*}{C}H-CO_2H \xrightarrow{H_2O/H^+ \text{ or } OH^-} HO_2C-CH_2 \cdot \overset{*}{C}H-CO_2H$$
$$\underset{O \cdot CO \cdot CH_3}{|} \qquad\qquad\qquad \underset{OH}{|}$$

(*dextro* or *laevo*)-Acetoxysuccinic acid

(*dextro* or *laevo*)- Malic acid

(*b*) A number of experiments using isotopic labelling; thus when benzoic acid is esterified with methanol containing an excess of the O^{18} isotope no unusual quantity of the O^{18} isotope was discovered in the water formed, supporting the scheme below:

$$\overset{\displaystyle O}{\underset{\displaystyle \|}{C_6H_5 \cdot C}} \!\!-\!\! OH + CH_3O^{18}H \rightarrow \overset{\displaystyle O}{\underset{\displaystyle \|}{C_6H_5 \cdot C}} \!\!-\!\! O^{18}CH_3 + H_2O$$

Benzoic acid	Methanol (labelled)	Methyl benzoate

Also kinetic measurements show that the alkaline saponification of most esters is a second-order reaction (first order in ester and first order in hydroxide ion); so the mechanism may be written as follows:

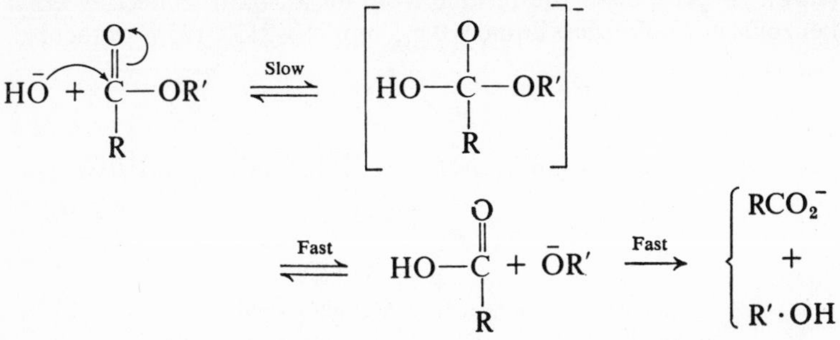

During partial alkaline hydrolysis of alkyl benzoates, labelled at the benzoyl-oxygen atom the radioactivity of the unreacted ester decreased, indicating that the intermediate anion (I) lasts for sufficient time for some isomerization to (II) to occur. This subsequently loses labelled oxygen as $O^{18}H^-$:

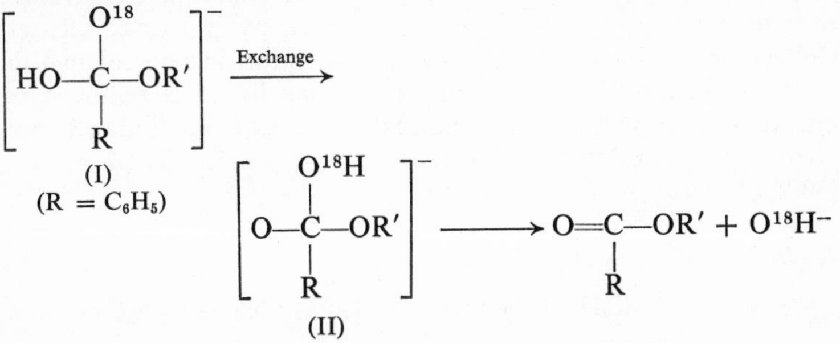

Example 1. Preparation of Ethyl Benzoate

$$C_6H_5 \cdot CO_2H + C_2H_5OH \xrightarrow{H^+} C_2H_5CO_2C_6H_5 + H_2O$$

Benzoic Acid   Ethanol   Ethyl benzoate

Place benzoic acid (10 g.), absolute ethanol (35 ml.), and concentrated sulphuric acid (1 ml.) in a 250 ml. round-bottomed flask. Add a few boiling chips, and boil the mixture gently under reflux for 2 hours. Remove the excess of ethanol by distillation from a water-bath, and pour the residue into cold water (100 ml.). Neutralize by addition of solid sodium carbonate and extract the oil with ether (100 ml.). Separate the ethereal layer, wash it with a little water, dry with anhydrous sodium sulphate, filter, and distil off the ether (*care*). Finally distil the residue from an air-bath, collecting ethyl benzoate as a colourless liquid 9·0 g.; b.p. 210–213°. (75% of theory).

Example 2. Preparation of Methyl Oxalate†

$$\begin{array}{ccc} CO_2H \\ | & + 2CH_3OH \rightarrow & | & + 2H_2O \\ CO_2H & & CO_2CH_3 \end{array}$$

$$\begin{array}{ccc} & & CO_2CH_3 \\ & & | \\ & & CO_2CH_3 \end{array}$$

Oxalic acid   Methanol   Methyl oxalate

Dehydrate oxalic acid crystals (10 g.) by heating in an air-oven at 110–120° for approximately 1 hour (test when dehydration is complete by determination of the loss in weight). Place the anhydrous acid and absolute methanol (10 ml.) in a 100 ml. round-bottomed flask fitted with a reflux condenser, and boil the mixture for 2 hours. Rearrange the apparatus for distillation, and when the temperature reaches 120° replace the water condenser by an air-condenser. Collect the fraction boiling above this temperature in a porcelain dish. On cooling, it solidifies and any remaining liquid is removed by filtration at the pump. Recrystallize the product from dilute ethanol, giving methyl oxalate as colourless plates, 4 g.; m.p. 54°, b.p. 163°, (40% of theory).

Hydrolysis of an ester (e.g. ethyl acetate)

$$CH_3 \cdot COOC_2H_5 + NaOH \rightarrow CH_3 \cdot COONa + C_2H_5OH$$

Ethyl acetate   Sodium acetate   Ethanol

Place ethyl acetate (20 g.) and 20% aqueous sodium hydroxide (80 ml.) in a 250 ml. round-bottomed flask. Boil the mixture under reflux, until the upper ester layer has dissolved and the odour of the ester has disappeared (this requires about 1 hour). Distil the solution until the distillation temperature reaches 100°, saturate the distillate with anhydrous potassium carbonate when the ethanol separates as the upper layer. Remove the upper layer, dry it over anhydrous potassium carbonate, filter, and fractionally distil. Carefully neutralize the alkaline residue in the flask with dilute sulphuric acid, and evaporate to dryness on the steam-bath. Powder the solid residue

---

† Here the oxalic acid is a sufficiently strong acid that addition of a mineral acid is not necessary.

in a mortar and transfer it to a distillation flask, add excess of concentrated sulphuric acid (25 ml.), and distil collecting the fraction boiling at 115–125°. By redistillation of the lower boiling fractions some further acetic acid may be obtained. Purify the crude acetic acid by cooling in ice, until it freezes and draining off remaining liquid, yielding crystals of pure acetic acid 12 g.; m.p. 16·7°, b.p. 119° (90% of theory).

Friedel–Crafts Reaction

In its simplest form the reaction consists in the alkylation or acylation of an aromatic hydrocarbon by treatment with an alkyl or acyl halide respectively, in the presence of an acidic catalyst, e.g. aluminium chloride:

$$Ar \cdot H + RX \xrightarrow{AlCl_3} Ar \cdot R + HX$$

$$Ar \cdot H + R \cdot CO \cdot X \xrightarrow{AlCl_3} Ar \cdot CO \cdot R + HX$$

The process is capable of wide variation and is of great synthetic importance; for instance the halides may be replaced by olefins, alcohols, anhydrides, or alicyclic compounds. Also many different catalysts may be employed, e.g. $FeCl_3$, $SnCl_4$, H_3PO_4, BF_3, H_2SO_4, $ZnCl_2$, HF. Some of these modifications are illustrated by the following equations:

$$C_6H_6 + C_6H_5 \cdot SO_2Cl \xrightarrow{AlCl_3} C_6H_5 \cdot SO_2 \cdot C_6H_5 + HCl$$

$$C_6H_6 + C_2H_5OH \xrightarrow{BF_3} C_6H_5 \cdot C_2H_5 + H_2O$$

$$C_6H_6 + CH_3 \cdot CH{=}CH_2 \xrightarrow{H_3PO_4} C_6H_5 \cdot CH(CH_3)_2$$

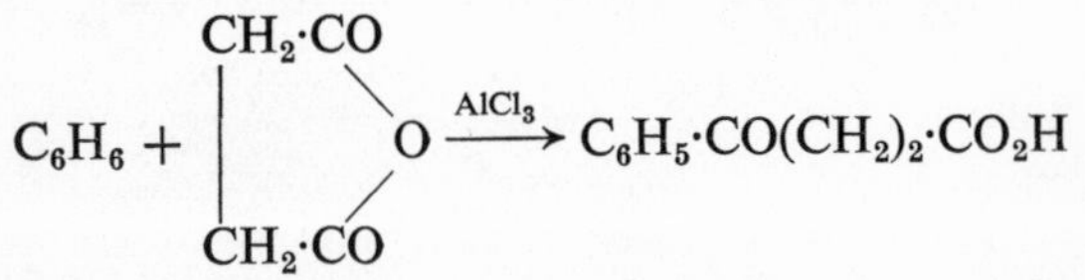

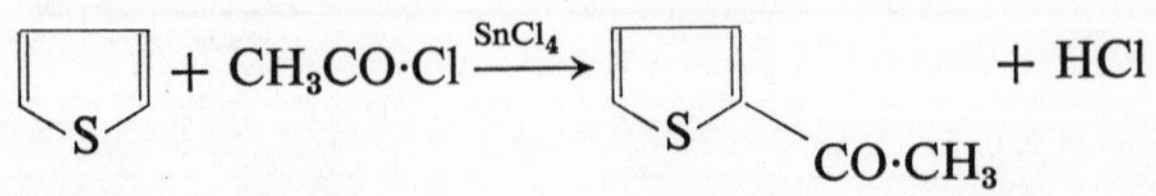

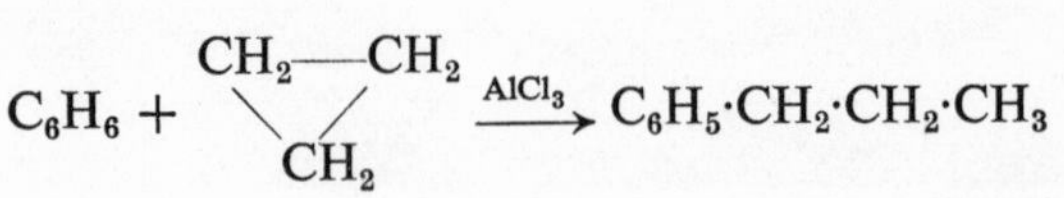

$$C_6H_6 + \begin{matrix} CH_2 \cdot CO \\ | \quad\quad\;\; O \\ CH_2 \cdot CO \end{matrix} \xrightarrow{AlCl_3} C_6H_5 \cdot CO(CH_2)_2 \cdot CO_2H$$

$$\text{thiophene} + CH_3CO \cdot Cl \xrightarrow{SnCl_4} \text{acetylthiophene} + HCl$$

$$C_6H_6 + \begin{matrix} CH_2{-}CH_2 \\ \diagdown \;\; \diagup \\ CH_2 \end{matrix} \xrightarrow{AlCl_3} C_6H_5 \cdot CH_2 \cdot CH_2 \cdot CH_3$$

The reactions are carried out using an excess of the aromatic hydro-carbon as solvent, or in either carbon disulphide or nitrobenzene.

The reaction is clearly an electrophilic substitution, since it is promoted by nucleophilic substituents (e.g. alkyl groups) in the aromatic nucleus and is hindered or suppressed by the presence of electrophilic substituents (e.g. acyl or nitro groups). Under forcing conditions alkyl groups often migrate; also *n*-alkyl groups are converted into branched chains:

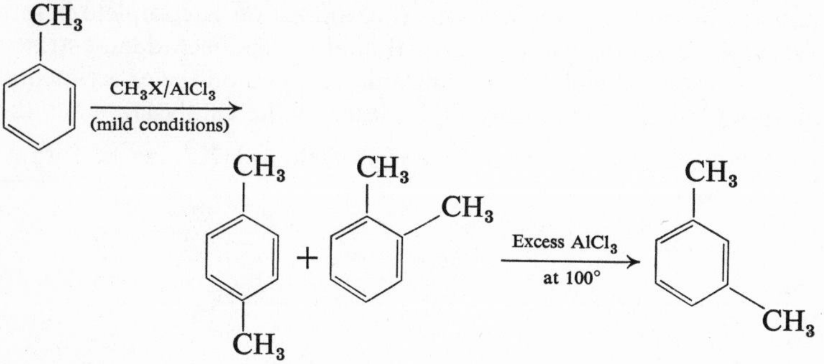

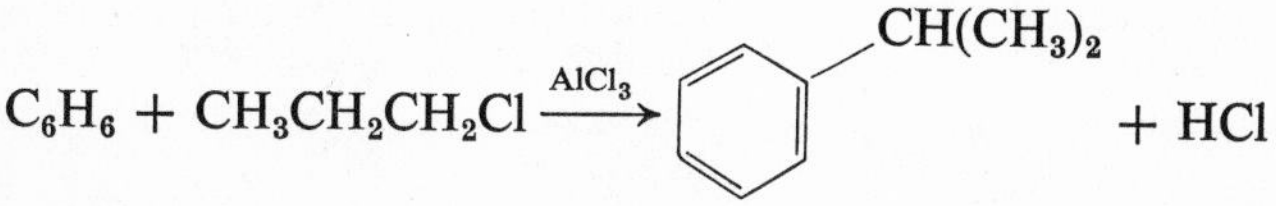

The Friedel–Crafts synthesis, therefore, is not generally used for the preparation of n-alkylbenzenes, though it may be applied indirectly as follows:

$$C_6H_6 + CH_3 \cdot CH_2 \cdot CO \cdot Cl \xrightarrow[(-HCl)]{AlCl_3}$$

$$C_6H_5 \cdot CO \cdot CH_2 \cdot CH_3 \xrightarrow{Zn/Hg, HC} C_6H_5(CH_2)_2 \cdot CH_3$$

The general mechanism of the Friedel–Crafts reaction is an electrophilic substitution of the aromatic nucleus by a carbonium (or potential carbonium) ion, and the function of the acidic catalyst is to facilitate the production of the electrophilic species. Thus consider-ing the general alkylation reaction:

$$R{-}X + AlCl_3 + C_6H_6 \rightarrow C_6H_5 \cdot R + HX + AlCl_3$$

the first step is the interaction between catalyst and halide:

$$R\overset{\curvearrowright}{-}X + AlCl_3 \rightarrow R \overset{\delta+}{\text{-}} \text{-}\text{-}\text{-} \overset{\delta-}{X} \text{-}\text{-}\text{-} AlCl_3 \quad \text{or} \quad R^+ [AlXCl_3]^-$$

In support of this idea, it is known that aluminium halides form conducting solutions with many alkyl and acyl halides and it has been shown, by using radioactive isotopes, that the halogen of the aluminium halide will exchange with the halogen from the organic halide. There is however uncertainty as to the precise degree of polarization involved. In the case of alkylations involving *secondary or tertiary halides* or *acylations*, it seems probable that the attacking species is respectively the carbonium ion R^+ or $R\overset{+}{C}O$ because of the greater stability of these carbonium ions (i.e. ionization is complete before electrophilic substitution occurs), though it has been demonstrated that the degree of polarization may also depend on the experimental conditions (e.g. temperature and nature of the catalyst). Thus the alkylation: $C_6H_6 + R_3CX \xrightarrow{AlX_3} C_6H_5 \cdot CR_3 + HX$, may be formulated as follows:

1.

$$R \text{-} \overset{\overset{R}{|}}{\underset{\underset{R}{|}}{C}} \text{-} X + AlX_3 \rightleftharpoons R_3\overset{+}{C} + AlX_4^-$$

2.

Mesomeric forms

3. abstraction of a proton by AlX_4^-.

$+ AlX_3 + HX$

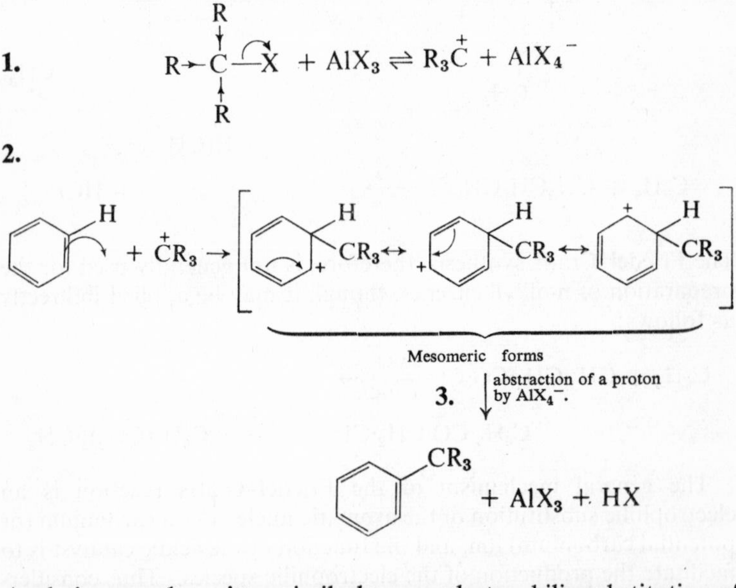

Acylation may be written similarly as an electrophilic substitution of the aromatic nucleus by the acylium cation, $R\overset{+}{C}O$, which is supported by the fact that acetyl perchlorate $(CH_3\overset{+}{C}O)ClO_4^-$ is an extremely effective acetylating agent: e.g.,

$$C_6H_6 + (CH_3\overset{+}{C}O)ClO_4^- \rightarrow C_6H_5 \cdot CO \cdot CH_3 + HClO_4.$$

On the other hand, with *primary alkyl halides*, RCH_2X, the most likely general mechanism involves attack by a *potential* carbonium ion: e.g., $C_6H_6 + R \cdot CH_2X \xrightarrow{AlX_3} C_6H_5 \cdot CH_2R + HX$

Example 1. Preparation of Acetophenone

$$C_6H_6 + CH_3COCl \xrightarrow{AlCl_3} C_6H_5COCH_3 + HCl$$

Benzene   Acetyl chloride   Acetophenone (p. 54)

Set up the apparatus shown in figure 2. Place anhydrous, finely powdered aluminium chloride (20 g.) and *anhydrous* benzene (50 ml.) in the flask and cool in ice-water. Do not use ice; the benzene will solidify. Add acetyl chloride (14 ml.) slowly during 15 minutes by means of the separatory funnel, shaking the flask frequently during the addition. Heat the flask on a water-bath at 50° for one hour to complete the reaction, having first fitted the hydrogen chloride trap to collect the copious volume of hydrogen chloride emitted. Cool and pour into water ($\approx$125 ml.) and a little crushed ice contained in a 500 ml. flask. Decomposition will occur with the evolution of heat and a dark oil separates. Cork the flask and shake to complete the decomposition. (If any solid remains add a small volume of concentrated hydrochloric acid.) Pour into a separatory funnel, and run off the lower aqueous layer, wash the benzene layer with dilute sodium hydroxide (to remove hydrochloric acid), then with water, and finally dry over anhydrous magnesium sulphate. Remove the desiccant by filtration, the filtrate being run directly into a distillation flask. Distil off the excess benzene from a steam-bath, and then distil the acetophenone using an air-condenser. The yield of acetophenone is 14 g.; b.p. 195–202° (70% of theory based upon the weight of acetyl chloride, benzene is in excess).

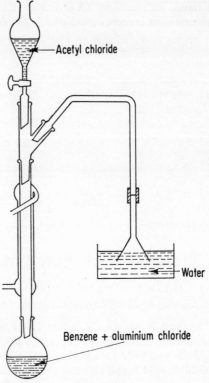

Figure 2

Example 2. Preparation of *o*-Benzoylbenzoic Acid (Benzophenone-2-Carboxylic Acid)

Phthalic anhydride   *o*-Benzoylbenzoic acid

Anthraquinone

Equip a 250 ml. flask with a reflux condenser and place it in a fume cupboard. Place pure phthalic anhydride (8 g.) and sodium-dried benzene (35 ml.) in the flask and mix the contents well by shaking. Add powdered aluminium chloride (17 g.) shaking well. (The reaction generally does not become too vigorous, but cool if necessary in an ice-bath.) After the aluminium chloride has been added and the evolution of hydrogen chloride slackens, warm cautiously on a water-bath at 50–60° for 5 minutes and finally boil the mixture, with frequent shaking, on a steam-bath for 1 hour until practically no more hydrogen chloride is evolved. Cool the flask, add crushed ice (75 g.) gradually until the dark mass is completely decomposed, and thne run in concentrated hydrochloric acid (≃15 ml.) until the solution clears. Steam distil to remove the excess benzene, the residue in the flask will solidify on cooling. Decant the aqueous solution through a Buchner funnel, wash the solid by decantation with a little cold water, and return the filtered solid to the flask. Add a warm solution of anhydrous sodium carbonate (4·5 g.) in water (70 ml.). Heat until all the solid dissolves (apart from particles of aluminium hydroxide and some tarry material.)

Cool slightly and add decolourizing charcoal (0·5 g.). Warm for 2 minutes and filter the solution under suction. Place the filtrate in a 400 ml. beaker and cool in ice-water, and cautiously acidify with concentrated hydrochloric acid (≃5 ml.). The acid first separates as an oil but rapidly solidifies on stirring and cooling. Filter when ice-cold, and wash with a little water. Air-dry on filter papers, the product is the monohydrate m.p. 94°.

To make the anhydrous acid

Dissolve the product in benzene (≃50 ml.) in a 150 ml. round-bottomed flask fitted with a reflux condenser on a water-bath. Boil under reflux for 15 minutes and then transfer to a separatory funnel, run off any water present, and dry over sodium sulphate. Concentrate the benzene solution to (≃20 ml.) on a water-bath and then add petroleum ether (b.p. 60–80°) until a slight turbidity is produced. Allow to cool at room temperature and finally cool by ice to about 5°. Filter off the crystals by suction and dry on filter paper in a desiccator. The yield of pure anhydrous *o*-benzoylbenozic acid is 6·9 g.; m.p. 128° (64% of theory).

Preparation of Anthraquinone

Place polyphosphoric acid (25 ml.) [(made by dissolving phosphoric oxide (18 g.) in commercial orthophosphoric acid (d. 1·75) (10 g.)], and *o*-benzoylbenzoic acid (2·0 g.) in a 150 ml. conical flask fitted with a reflux condenser. Heat on a steam-bath for 2 hours.

Cool the product in ice and add water (40 ml.) with stirring. Filter with suction and wash with water. Boil the residue with concentrated ammonia (10 ml.) for 5 minutes (to remove unchanged acid) and filter at the pump. Recrystallize from boiling glacial acetic acid (60–70 ml.) in the presence of activated charcoal (0·5 g.) and dry at 100°. The yield of pure anthraquinone is 1·8 g.; m.p. 285–286° (85% of theory).

Example 3. Preparation of tert-Butylbenzene

$$\text{Benzene} + (CH_3)_3COH \xrightarrow{\text{AlCl}_3} \overset{C(CH_3)_3}{\text{tert-Butylbenzene}} + H_2O$$

Benzene   tert-Butanol   tert-Butylbenzene

Equip a round-bottomed flask with a mechanical stirrer, a dropping funnel and thermometer dipping into the liquid. Place aluminium chloride (6·7 g.) and anhydrous benzene (39 g.) in the flask, and stir the suspension rapidly. Place tert-butanol (7·4 g.) in the dropping funnel and add this dropwise to the suspension and maintain the temperature at 20–30° with the aid of gentle cooling. Allow the reaction mixture to stand overnight and then pour it onto crushed ice and hydrochloric acid. Transfer the liquid to a separatory funnel and remove the upper benzene layer. Retain the aqueous layer and extract with ether. Combine the ethereal extract and the benzene layer, and remove both the ether and benzene by distillation (care). Fractionally distil the residue and obtain tert-butylbenzene 9·4 g.; b.p. 168–170°/740 mm. (70% of theory).

Example 4. Preparation of Triphenylmethyl Chloride (Trityl Chloride)

$$3C_6H_6 + CCl_4 \xrightarrow{\text{AlCl}_3} (C_6H_5)_3C\cdot Cl + 3HCl$$

Benzene   Carbon   Triphenylmethyl
            tetrachloride   chloride

Dry a mixture of benzene (23 ml.) and carbon tetrachloride (5 ml.) over anhydrous calcium chloride, and filter the solution into a 50 ml. flask. Boil under reflux, then remove the flame and add powdered aluminium chloride (5 g) in small portions, so that the exothermic reaction maintains the solution boiling. Boil for one hour, cool, and pour slowly with stirring onto crushed ice. Separate the benzene layer, wash it twice with 20 % aqueous hydrochloric acid (2 volumes of concentrated acid: 1 volume of water), and finally with concentrated hydrochloric acid. Dry over anhydrous calcium chloride, filter, and distil off the benzene from a water-bath. Pour the residue into a porcelain basin, cool and stir until solidification takes place. Filter off the crystals with suction, and wash them with a little ether. Concentration of the mother-liquor yields a further crop of crystals. Recrystallize the combined product from benzene. Wash the colourless crystals with small amounts of benzene and ether, and dry by suction. The yield of triphenylmethyl chloride is 4·8 g.; m.p. 108–111° (65 % of theory).

Gabriel Synthesis

This is a useful method for the preparation of pure primary amines or amino-acids. Potassium phthalimide is treated with the appropriate alkyl halogen compound, and the resultant N-alkylphthalimide is hydrolysed to yield the amine:

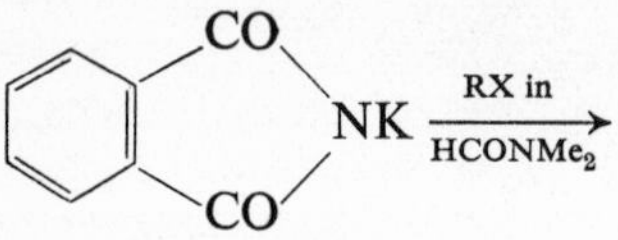

Potassium phthalimide

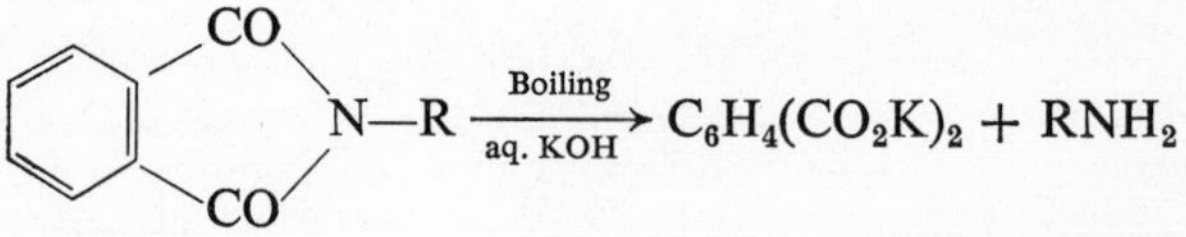

N-Alkylphthalimide   Phthalic acid (Potassium salt)

e.g.,

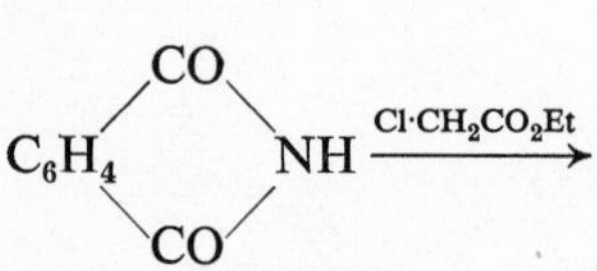

Potassium phthalimide

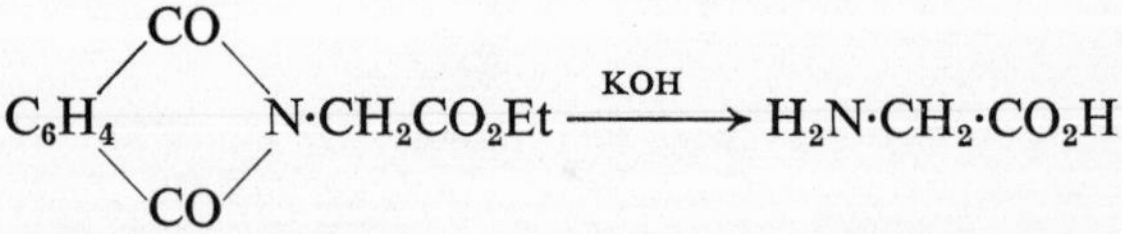

Phthaloylglycine ester   Glycine

A useful modification of the Gabriel synthesis is to react the N-alkylphthalimide with hydrazine hydrate, yielding an intermediate compound which is more easily cleaved than the *N*-alkylphthalimide itself:

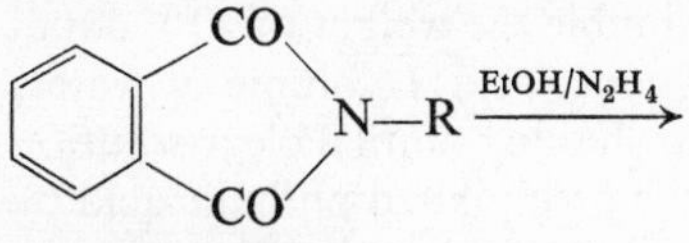

N-Alkylphthalimide

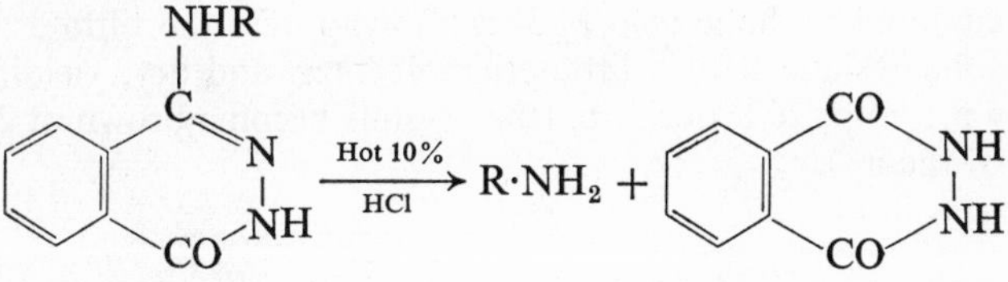

Phthaloylhydrazide

Example. Preparation of Glycine (Amino-acetic Acid)

(*a*) *Potassium phthalimide*
Dissolve phthalimide (10 g.) in hot ethanol (38 ml.), and add a solution of potassium hydroxide (7 g.) in ethanol (40 ml.). Cool the solution and filter off the precipitated salt; wash the solid with a little cold ethanol, and dry in a vacuum desiccator over concentrated sulphuric acid.

(*b*) *Phthaloylglycine ester*
Place potassium phthalimide (10 g.) and chloroacetic ester (6·5 g.) in a 100 ml. round-bottomed flask equipped with a reflux condenser. Heat the mixture in an oil-bath at 150°, with occasional stirring to ensure efficient mixing. After half an hour the mass becomes pasty; cool and dissolve it in hot 50% aqueous ethanol. When cold, filter off the product, wash it with a little cold 50% aqueous ethanol, and finally with ice-cold water (to remove potassium chloride). The yield of phthaloylglycine ester is approximately 7 g.; m.p. 112° after recrystallization from dilute ethanol.

(*c*) *Glycine*
Boil phthaloylglycine ester (5 g.) under reflux with a solution of potassium hydroxide (2·5 g.) in water (25 ml.) until all the ester

dissolves. Cool and add concentrated hydrochloric acid (4·5 ml.), keep at 0° for a short period, then filter off the precipitate of phthaloylglycine, and wash it with ice-water, until the filtrate no longer gives a positive test for chloride ion. Add double the weight of 20% aqueous hydrochloric acid (2 volumes of conc. acid:1 volume of water) and boil under reflux, with occasional shaking, until a clear solution is obtained. After 2 hours remove the precipitated phthalic acid by filtration; cool, dilute with water and evaporate the filtrate on a water-bath. Add a small volume of cold water, filter off any precipitated phthalic acid and again evaporate the filtrate. Wash the solid residue with a little ethanol, filter, and dry, yielding glycine, 4 g.; m.p. 262° decomp. (the crystals become brown at 228°) (86% of theory).

Gattermann Reaction

This is a modification of the Sandmeyer reaction in which the cuprous salt is replaced by freshly prepared, finely divided copper, or by powdered copper bronze. In general for the introduction of chlorine, bromine and iodine the yields are less than those obtained in the corresponding Sandmeyer reaction. But the Gattermann reaction affords better yields of aromatic nitriles; and may also be used for the introduction of the sulphinic acid group —SO_2H. The mechanism is believed to be similar to that of the Sandmeyer reaction.

Example 1. Preparation of Benzonitrile (Phenyl Cyanide)

$$C_6H_5\overset{+}{N_2}\overset{-}{H}SO_4 \quad + KCN \xrightarrow{Cu} C_6H_5CN + KHSO_4 + N_2$$

Benzenediazonium   Potassium   Benzonitrile
sulphate   cyanide

Dissolve aniline (15·5 g.) in 50% sulphuric acid (40 g.) in an *efficient fume cupboard.* Cool to 0° in an ice-salt bath and diazotize the amine by gradual addition of sodium nitrite (11·5 g.) in water (20 ml.), keeping the temperature below 5°. Add a solution of potassium cyanide (40 g.) in water (80 ml.), followed by gradual addition of copper powder† with stirring. Stir until nitrogen ceases to be evolved. Allow to stand for 10 minutes, then steam distil, and extract the aqueous distillate with ether. Wash the ethereal extract repeatedly with dilute sodium hydroxide, and then dilute sulphuric acid. Dry it over anhydrous potassium carbonate, remove the desiccant, and distil off the ether. Fractionally distil the residual liquid, collecting benzonitrile 6 g. at 191° (60% of theory).

The Gattermann Reaction may also be used to prepare sulphinic acids, by the action of sulphur dioxide on diazonium compounds:

$$2R\overset{+}{N_2}\overset{-}{Cl} + 2SO_2 + 2Cu \rightarrow 2RSO_2H + 2CuCl + N_2$$

Sulphinic acids are unstable compounds, which are readily oxidized to the corresponding sulphonic acids with alkaline permanganate. This procedure gives pure sulphonic acids, whereas direct sulphonation yields a mixture of isomers; thus *o*-toluidine can be converted into *o*-toluene-sulphonic acid.

Example 2. Preparation of Naphthalene-1,4-Sulphosulphinic Acid (Sodium Salt).

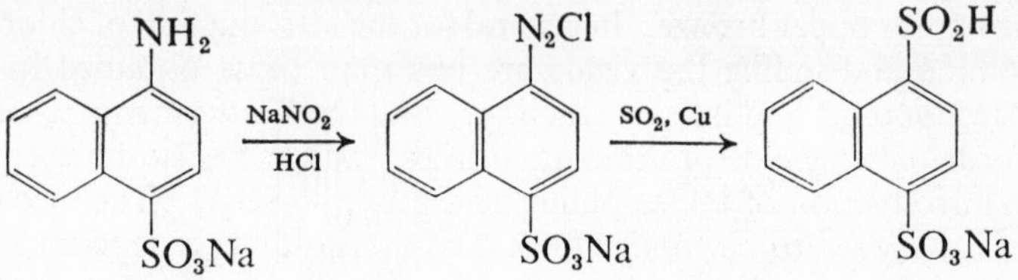

Sodium naphthionate   Naphthalene-1,4-sulphosulphinic acid (sodium salt)

Sodium naphthionate (10 g.) is diazotized with sodium nitrite (3·5 g.) in dilute hydrochloric acid solution and then sulphur dioxide is passed into the solution until it is saturated. Copper powder† is gradually added until nitrogen ceases to be evolved, a slow stream of sulphur dioxide being passed through the solution during the addition. Filter and saturate the filtrate with sodium chloride. Filter off the sodium salt of 1,4-sulphosulphinic acid and recrystallize it from water giving 6 g. (100% of theory).

† *Preparation of finely the divided Copper Powder*
Dissolve cupric sulphate (100 g.) in water (350 ml.) in a 600 ml. beaker, and allow the solution to cool to room temperature. Stir mechanically and add zinc dust ($\simeq$ 35 g.); until the solution is decolourized (more zinc dust may be added if required). The precipitated copper is washed with water by decantation and then thoroughly washed with dilute hydrochloric acid to remove any remaining zinc. Filter off the suspension at the pump and wash it with water. Keep the copper powder moist for the best results.

Gomberg–Bachmann–Hey Reaction

This is the synthesis of biaryls by addition of alkali to a mixture of a liquid aromatic compound and a diazonium salt, e.g.

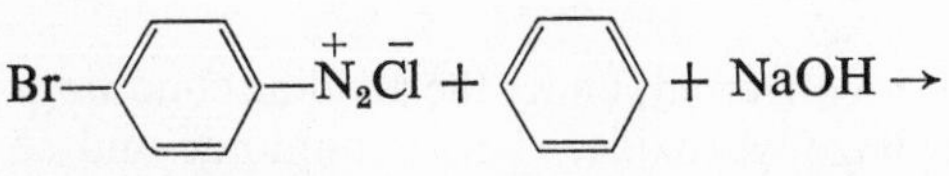

$$Br-\langle\bigcirc\rangle-\overset{+}{N_2}\overset{-}{Cl} + \langle\bigcirc\rangle + NaOH \rightarrow$$

p-Bromobenzene-   Benzene
diazonium chloride

$$Br-\langle\bigcirc\rangle-\langle\bigcirc\rangle + NaCl + H_2O + N_2$$

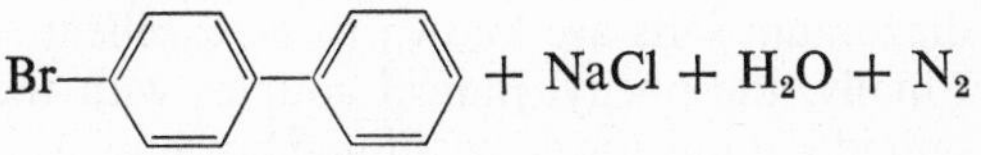

p-Bromobiphenyl

The reaction will also proceed with heterocyclic compounds. The yields are generally poor owing to the two-phase system involved, but may be improved by employing sodium acetate instead of the hydroxide; and in phenylation reactions by addition of compounds, like dibenzoyl peroxide, which are known to furnish phenyl radicals. The synthesis always gives o-/p-substitution, irrespective of the nature of the nuclear substituent, e.g.

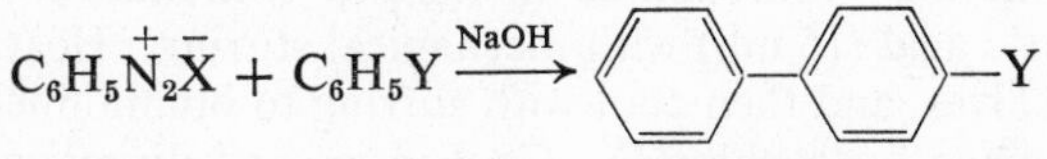

$$C_6H_5\overset{+}{N_2}\overset{-}{X} + C_6H_5Y \xrightarrow{NaOH} \langle\bigcirc\rangle-\langle\bigcirc\rangle-Y$$

(mainly)

(where Y = Br, CH$_3$, NO$_2$). These experiments indicate a free-radical mechanism, probably as follows for the above general reaction:

$$C_6H_5\overset{+}{N_2}\overset{-}{X} \xrightarrow{NaOH} [C_6H_5N_2OH] \longrightarrow C_6H_5\cdot + OH\cdot + N_2$$

then:

$$C_6H_5\cdot + \underset{}{\bigcirc}\!\!-Y \rightarrow$$

$$\left[\; \underset{H}{\overset{C_6H_5}{\bigcirc}}\!\!-Y \leftrightarrow \underset{H}{\overset{C_6H_5}{\bigcirc}}\!\!\overset{Y}{\cdot} \leftrightarrow \underset{H}{\overset{C_6H_5}{\bigcirc}}\!\!-Y \;\right]$$

Mesomeric | structures

$-H\cdot$ (rapidly removed)

$$\bigcirc\!\!-\!\!\bigcirc\!\!-Y$$

First the diazonium salt is converted, under the alkaline conditions of the reaction, into the diazohydroxide. This is nonionic and so passes into the aromatic layer, where it decomposes into phenyl radicals and probably to hydroxyl radicals. Alkaline solutions of diazonium salts are known to be excellent sources of aryl radicals. Finally, the phenyl radical couples with the liquid aromatic compound yielding the p-substituted biphenyl by loss of atomic hydrogen. The hydrogen atom must immediately combine, possibly with the hydroxyl radical yielding water; because when easily reducible compounds are added to the reaction mixture they are not reduced indicating the absence of free hydrogen atoms.

Example. Preparation of p-Bromobiphenyl

Warm together p-bromoaniline (10 g.) and water (5 ml.) in a 50 ml. beaker until the bromoaniline melts and then add concentrated hydrochloric acid (15 ml.) with mechanical stirring. Heat, until the amine dissolves, and then cool with stirring to obtain finely divided p-bromoaniline hydrochloride. Cool in ice and diazotize by drop-wise addition of sodium nitrite (4·5 g.) in water (10 ml.). Allow to stand for ten minutes and then transfer the solution to a cooled 250 ml. beaker and then slowly add benzene (75 ml.) with stirring. Cool and stir, and then add dropwise 5N sodium hydroxide solution (15 ml.), so that the temperature does not exceed 0°. Allow the flask to warm up to room temperature and then acidify with hydrochloric acid. Remove the upper benzene layer and dry with anhydrous sodium sulphate. Filter off the desiccant, and distil off the benzene. Dissolve the residue in the minimum quantity of hot ethanol ($\simeq$50ml.) and add zinc dust (1 g.) and concentrated hydrochloric acid (1 ml.). Filter and allow to crystallize, yielding pure *p*-bromobiphenyl 5 g.; m.p. 89·5–90° (35% of theory).

Grignard Reaction

This represents the formation of a Grignard reagent (RMgX) and its subsequent reaction with a second component. These organo-magnesium halides are of great importance in organic synthesis, because they can react with a number of functional groups. Grignard reagents are prepared by the action of magnesium turnings on an ethereal solution of an alkyl or aryl halide under strictly anhydrous conditions.

$$R—X + Mg \xrightarrow{\text{Ether}} R—Mg—X \quad (X = halogen; \; preferably \; Br \; or \; I)$$

The organo-magnesium halide is not isolated but is used in the form of an ethereal solution in further reactions, as illustrated by the following examples:

(*a*) *With compounds containing reactive (acidic) hydrogen atoms* (e.g. water, alcohols, ammonia, primary and secondary amines, carboxylic acids, or acetylenes containing the ethynyl group), they yield hydrocarbons:

$$\overset{\delta^-}{R} \cdot \overset{\delta^+}{Mg} X + H_2O \xrightarrow{\text{Ether}} R \cdot H + Mg(OH)X$$

$$R \cdot MgX + R' \cdot NH_2 \longrightarrow R \cdot H + Mg(NHR')X$$

$$R \cdot MgX + R'CO_2H \longrightarrow R \cdot H + R'CO_2MgX$$

$$RMgX + R' \cdot C \equiv CH \longrightarrow$$
$$R \cdot H + R' \cdot C \equiv C \cdot MgX \xrightarrow{R''X} R'C \equiv CR'' + MgX_2$$

The latter reaction yields acetylenic Grignard reagents which can be used for making unsymmetrical acetylenes and acetylenic acids. All these reactions may be regarded as the neutralization of the base ($\bar{R}$ of RMgX) by the acidic hydrogen atom of the other component.

By reaction with methylmagnesium iodide under controlled conditions, the number of reactive hydrogen atoms in a compound can be quantitatively determined (*Zerevitinoff method*).

(b) With carbonyl compounds
Here nucleophilic addition of the Grignard reagent to the carbonyl group occurs.

With aldehydes and ketones the adduct on hydrolysis yields an alcohol and, indeed, all three classes of monohydric alcohols may be obtained by this route:

$$
\begin{matrix}
R \\
\diagdown \\
\diagup C{=}O \\
R'
\end{matrix}
+ R''MgX \xrightarrow{\text{Ether}}
\begin{matrix}
R \quad OMgX \\
\diagdown \diagup \\
C \\
\diagup \diagdown \\
R' \quad R''
\end{matrix}
$$

$$
\xrightarrow{\text{H}_2\text{O/H}^+}
\begin{matrix}
R \quad OH \\
\diagdown \diagup \\
C \\
\diagup \diagdown \\
R' \quad R''
\end{matrix}
+ \text{Mg(OH)X}
$$

Similarly reaction with *solid carbon dioxide* gives excellent yields of carboxylic acids:

$$
R{\cdot}MgX + O{=}C{=}O \longrightarrow R{\cdot}CO{\cdot}OMgX \xrightarrow{\text{H}_2\text{O/H}^+} R{\cdot}CO_2H
$$
$$
+ \text{Mg(OH)X}
$$

By this route acids, like trimethylacetic acid, which are not readily accessible by other methods can be obtained.

With esters and *only one mole* of the Grignard reagent, the main product is the ketone; provided that the Grignard reagent is added to the ester and *not vice-versa*.

$$
R{\cdot}MgX + R'{\cdot}C{\cdot}OEt \xrightarrow{\text{Ether}}
\left[
\begin{matrix}
OMgX \\
| \\
R'{-}C{-}OEt \\
| \\
R
\end{matrix}
\right]
\xrightarrow[{[-\text{MgX(OEt)}]}]{}
\begin{matrix}
O \\
\| \\
R'{-}C \\
| \\
R
\end{matrix}
$$

(c) With nitriles
Nucleophilic addition to cyano-group takes place, and subsequent hydrolysis yields a ketone *provided* only one mole of the Grignard

reagent is employed:

$$R \cdot \overset{\delta-}{M}g\overset{\delta+}{X} + R' - C \overset{\cdot\curvearrowleft}{\equiv} N \longrightarrow \left[\underset{\underset{R}{|}}{R' - C} = N \cdot MgX \overset{H_2O}{\longrightarrow} \underset{\underset{R}{|}}{R' - C} = N \cdot H \right]$$

$$\left[-Mg(OH)X \right]$$

$$\overset{H_2O}{\longrightarrow} \underset{\underset{R}{|}}{R' - C} = O + NH_3$$

The Grignard reaction has been extended by the use of tetra-hydrofuran (T.H.F.), and ethers of di- and triethylene glycol as solvents. In these solvents the reactivity of the organic halide is enhanced; so that, for instance, relatively unreactive halides, like vinyl halides, easily yield organomagnesium derivatives which with acetic anhydride give vinyl ketones:

$$CH_2 = CH - X \xrightarrow[\text{T.H.F.}]{Mg} CH_2 = CH - MgX \xrightarrow[\text{at } -70°]{(CH_3CO)_2O}$$

$$CH_2 = CH \cdot CO \cdot CH_3$$

The Mechanism of the Grignard Reaction

The first part of the reaction, namely the formation of the Grignard reagent is probably a free-radical process initiated by formation of a trace of magnesium halide

1. $2RX + Mg \rightarrow R - R + MgX_2$

2. $Mg + MgX_2 \rightleftharpoons 2\dot{M}gX$

3. $RX + \dot{M}gX \rightarrow \dot{R} + MgX_2$

4. $\dot{R} + \dot{M}gX \rightarrow R \cdot MgX$

A crystal of iodine is often added as a catalyst in the preparation of Grignard reagents and its effect may be due to the reaction:

$$Mg + I_2 \rightarrow MgI_2$$

In the majority of their subsequent reactions Grignard reagents behave as though they are polarized in the form $\overset{- \quad +}{RMgX}$. The most important reaction from the synthetic view point is their addition to carbonyl compounds and there is evidence that *two moles* of the Grignard reagent are involved in this process, which may accordingly be formulated as below:

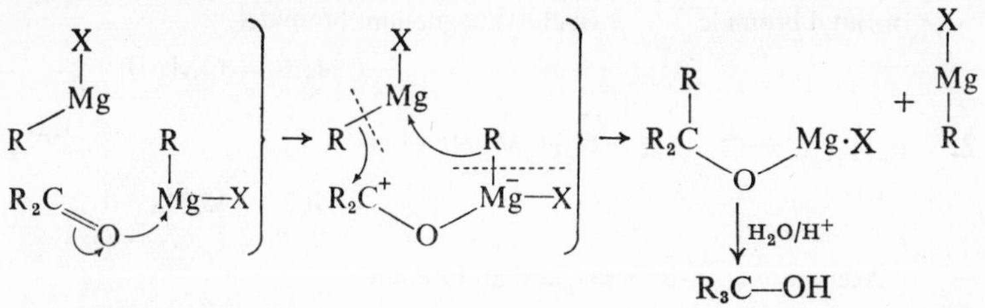

If this general reaction mechanism is valid, it would be anticipated that Grignard reagents containing β-hydrogen atoms would be also yield olefins as by-products due to the operation of the following side-reaction:

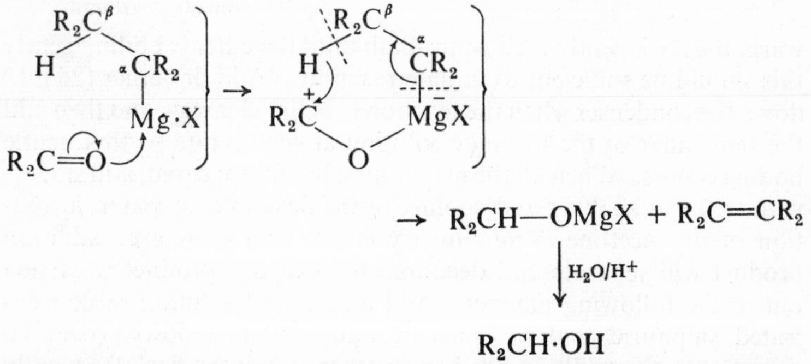

$$\rightarrow R_2CH-OMgX + R_2C=CR_2$$

$$\downarrow_{H_2O/H^+}$$

$$R_2CH\cdot OH$$

This is supported by the experimental observation that secondary alcohols are obtained as by-products in this reaction (cf. the Meerwein–Ponndorf reduction).

Example 1. Preparation of n-Butyldimethyl-carbinol (or 2-Methyl-n-Hexanol)

Dry all apparatus and reagents prior to use, and free the magnesium from grease by washing with anhydrous ether, filter, and finally dry in an oven at 110–120°. Equip a 500 ml. two-necked round-bottomed flask with a double-surface reflux condenser and a 50 ml. separatory funnel, each bearing a calcium chloride tube. Place a mixture of n-butyl bromide (14 ml.) in dry ether (15 ml.) in the separatory funnel, and add this dropwise to a mixture of magnesium turnings (3·1 g.) and dry ether (15 ml.) in the flask. (The reaction should start after the addition of 5 ml. of solution, if it does not do so,

1. $n—C_4H_9Br + Mg \xrightarrow{Et_2O} n — C_4H_9MgBr$

n-Butyl bromide   n-Butylmagnesium bromide

2. $(CH_3)_2C \overset{\frown}{=} \overset{\delta-}{O} + n - \overset{\delta+}{C_4H_9}MgBr \longrightarrow$

$\xrightarrow{H_2O}$

Acetone   n-Butylmagnesium bromide

n-Butyldimethylcarbinol.

warm the flask gently on a water-bath until the ether is boiling gently this should be sufficient to initiate reaction.) Add dry ether (25 ml.) down the condenser when the reaction is well under way, and then add the remainder of the bromide solution at such a rate so that gentle boiling occurs. When all the magnesium has disappeared, add slowly, with frequent shaking and cooling of the flask in cold water, a solution of dry acetone (9 ml.) in dry ether (8 ml.). A grey addition product will separate and decomposition of this product is carried out in the following manner. Add an ice-cold solution of concentrated sulphuric acid (8·7 ml.) in water (88 ml.) slowly (over 20 minutes) to the addition product in ether. Cool the flask frequently during this addition. Separate the upper ethereal layer, and extract the aqueous layer several times with ether. Combine the ethereal extracts, dry over anhydrous potassium carbonate, filter off the desiccant, and distil off the ether (*care*). Finally distil the residue, and collect n-butyldimethylcarbinol at 137–141°. The yield is 7 g. (60% of theory based on n-butyl bromide).

Example 2. Carbonation of a Grignard Reagent

$$RMgX \xrightarrow{CO_2} RCOOMgX \xrightarrow{H_2O} R·COOH$$

Preparation of Benzoic Acid

Equip a 200 ml. round-bottomed flask with a double surface reflux condenser, a 50 ml. dropping funnel, and close the open ends of each with calcium chloride drying tubes. (Dry all apparatus at 110° before use.) Place clean dry magnesium turnings (2 g.), a crystal of iodine, and dry bromobenzene (3·8 g.≡2·5 ml.), together with sodium-dried ether (5 ml.) in the flask. If the magnesium does not react within a few minutes, warm the flask on a water-bath so that the ether boils gently under reflux then remove from the bath. The formation of the Grignard reagent will be indicated by the disappearance of the colour due to iodine, the development of a faint turbidity, and gentle boiling of the ether. When the initial reaction begins to subside place dry bromobenzene (9·5 g.≡6·4 ml.) in dry ether (35 ml.) in the dropping funnel and add the solution at such a rate so as to maintain gentle reflux. This operation will take approximately 15 minutes. Boil the solution for one hour on a water-bath to complete the reaction. The solution will be cloudy or slightly dark and only a little magnesium should remain unattacked. Place 'dry ice' (solid carbon dioxide) (approximately 20 g.) in small lumps in a dry 600 ml. beaker. (*Handle the 'dry ice' with caution using a cloth or gloves, as it will burn the skin.*) Pour the solution of the Grignard reagent slowly and steadily onto the solid carbon dioxide with stirring, taking care to keep any unreacted magnesium in the flask. A vigorous reaction will occur and a solid mass of the Grignard adduct results. Stir this mixture, until all of the carbon dioxide has evaporated, and add crushed ice (100 g.), then 1:1 aqueous hydrochloric acid (1 volume of conc. acid:1 volume of water) (15 ml.), and continue stirring until most of the solid has decomposed.

Transfer the mixture to a separatory funnel, wash the beaker with ether (15 ml.), and then add it to the mixture in the funnel. Remove the lower aqueous layer, then wash the ethereal layer twice with water (10 ml.) and finally extract it twice with 5% aqueous sodium hydroxide (25 ml.) and run the extracts into a clean beaker. Treat the alkaline extract with activated charcoal (0·5 g.) and filter at the pump with the aid of a little 'Hyflo-supercel.' Acidify the filtrate with dilute hydrochloric acid, filter off the precipitated benzoic acid at the pump, and recrystallize it from boiling water. Air-dry the product after pressing on filter paper.

The yield of benzoic acid is 4·6 g.; m.p. 121° (66% of theory).

Example 3. Preparation of Benzhydrol (Diphenylmethanol)

1. $Ph \cdot Br + Mg \rightarrow Ph \cdot Mg \cdot Br$
  Bromobenzene   Phenylmagnesium bromide

2.

$$Ph \cdot Mg \cdot Br + Ph \cdot CH \!=\! O \rightarrow Ph - CH \begin{matrix} OMgBr \\ \\ Ph \end{matrix}$$

Phenylmagnesium   Benzaldehyde
bromide

$$\downarrow H_2O$$

$$Ph_2CH \cdot OH + MgBr \cdot OH$$

Benzhydrol

(a) Preparation of phenylmagnesium bromide

In this preparation it is essential that all reagents must be thoroughly dry. Wash the magnesium turnings with ether and dry in an oven at 110–120°. Place magnesium (1·2 g.) in a dry 150 ml. flask, together with anhydrous ether (30 ml.) and monobromobenzene (8·8 g.). Equip the flask with a reflux condenser, the inner tube of which has been well dried, and fit a calcium chloride tube. Heat the flask on a water-bath. If the reaction does not commence quickly, add a crystal of iodine to facilitate the reaction, and then heat until all (or nearly all) of the magnesium dissolves.

(b) Preparation of benzhydrol

Place freshly distilled benzaldehyde (5·3 g.) in anhydrous ether (12 ml.) in a dry flask, fitted with a reflux condenser. Gradually add the Grignard reagent (prepared above), a vigorous reaction occurs as the organo-magnesium intermediate precipitates. Complete the reaction by heating on the water-bath for 30 minutes. Cool the flask and pour the contents slowly with stirring and cooling into an excess of dilute hydrochloric acid. Stir until all the precipitate dissolves, and then separate the aqueous layer and extract it with ether. Add this extract to the original ethereal solution and shake with a dilute aqueous solution of sodium bisulphite (to remove any unchanged benzaldehyde). Dry the ethereal solution over anhydrous potassium carbonate and then remove the desiccant by filtration. Distil off the ether from a water-bath (care). The oily residue will solidify on standing; it may be recrystallized from petroleum ether. The yield is 6·5 g.; m.p. 68° (72% of theory based upon benzaldehyde).

Hantzsch Pyridine Synthesis

This consists in heating a mixture of a β-keto-ester (2 moles), ammonia (1 mole), and an aldehyde (1 mole) giving a dihydropyridine derivative, which is subsequently oxidized to the corresponding pyridine. Consider, as an example, the formation of 2,4,6-trimethylpyridine (collidine) from acetoacetic ester, acetaldehyde, and ammonia:

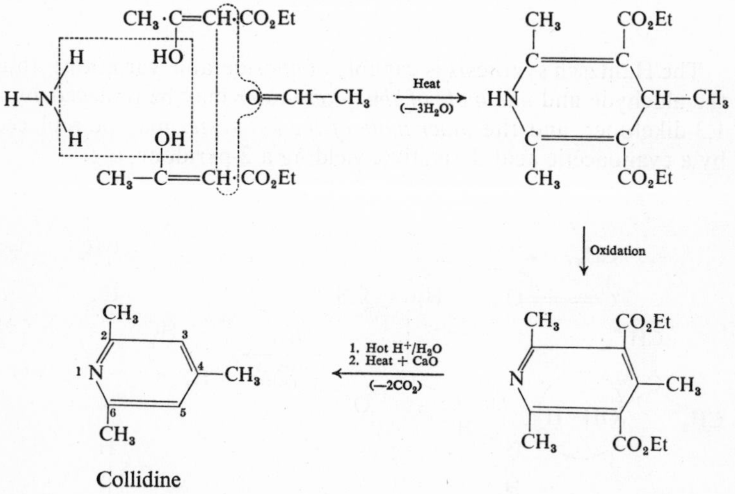

Collidine

In this condensation, the ammonia also functions as a basic catalyst converting acetoacetic ester into the enolic form; and the reaction may proceed as above.

The last stage is the condensation of the reactive α-hydrogen atoms of the imino intermediate with the carbonyl oxygen atom of the aldehyde, leading to the formation of the dihydropyridine derivative.

73

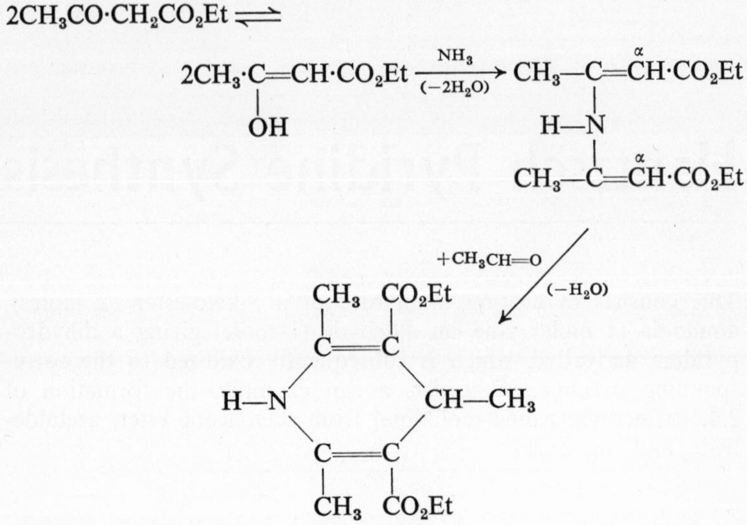

$$2CH_3CO \cdot CH_2CO_2Et \rightleftharpoons$$

The Hantzsch synthesis is capable of considerable variation: thus the aldehyde and *one mole of the β-keto-ester* may be replaced by a 1,3-diketone; and the *other mole of the keto-ester* may be replaced by a cyanoacetic acid derivative, yielding a 2-pyridone, e.g.

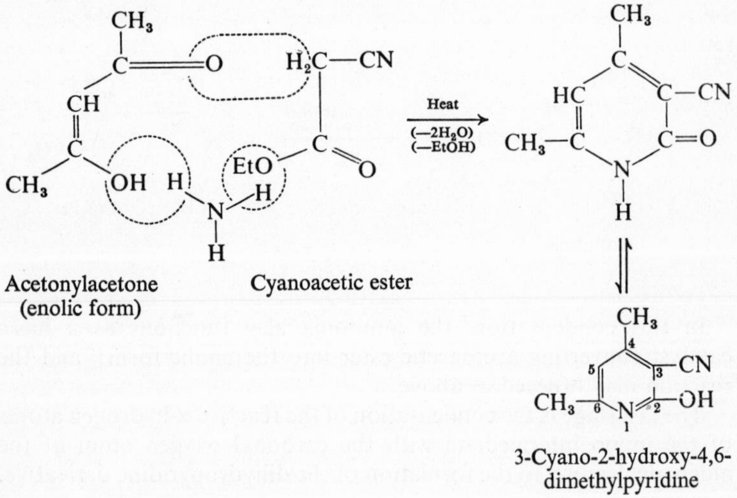

Acetonylacetone
(enolic form)

Cyanoacetic ester

3-Cyano-2-hydroxy-4,6-
dimethylpyridine

Example. Preparation of 3,5-Dicarbethoxy-2,6-Dimethyl-4-Phenylpyridine

(a) *Preparation of* 3,5-*Dicarbethoxy*-2,6-*Dimethyl*-4-*Phenyl*-1,4-*Dihydropyridine*

$$Ph \cdot CHO + 2CH_3 \cdot CO \cdot CH_2CO_2Et + NH_3 \xrightarrow{\text{Heat}}$$

Benzaldehyde Acetoacetic ester

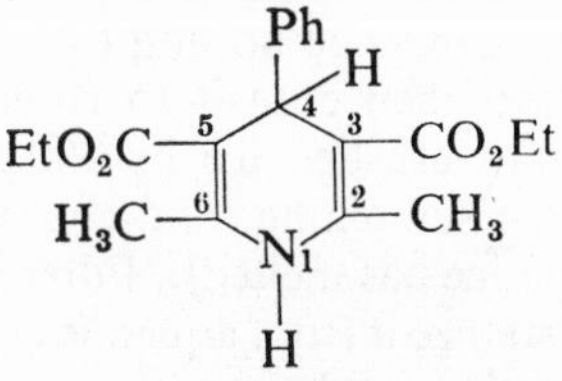

$$+ 3H_2O$$

3,5-Dicarbethoxy-2,6-dimethyl-
4-phenyl-1,4-dihydropyridine

Place acetoacetic ester (9 ml.) and ammonium carbonate ($\simeq$6 g.) in a 25 ml. conical flask, and warm the mixture just enough to decompose the ammonium carbonate liberating ammonia. Continue occasional warming, and stirring for one and a quarter hours, with addition of further amounts of ammonium carbonate, as is required, in order to maintain a constant supply of ammonia. If any water is produced as a separate layer, remove it by means of a pipette and rubber teat. Add benzaldehyde (3·5 ml.), and more ammonium carbonate (3 g.), and heat the mixture on a steam-bath for 2 hours. Then set it aside at room temperature overnight. Now add methanol (30 ml.), warm (to dissolve any precipitated solid), and cool the solution in ice/water. Filter off the yellow crystals at the pump, wash them with a small volume of cold methanol, and dry in an oven at 100°. The yield of 3,5-dicarbethoxy-2,6-dimethyl-4-phenyl-1,4-dihydropyridine is 4·7 g. (41 % of theory based on acetoacetic ester).

(b) *Preparation of* 3,5-*Dicarbethoxy*-2,6-*Dimethyl*-4-*Phenylpyridine*

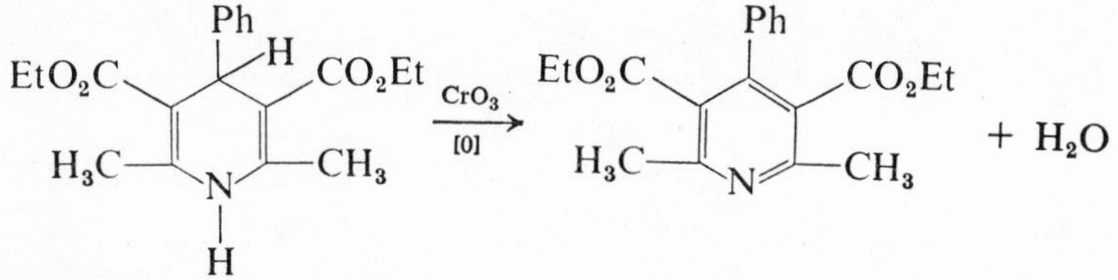

$$+ H_2O$$

3,5-Dicarbethoxy-2,6-dimethyl-
4-phenyl-1,4-dihydropyridine

3,5-Dicarbethoxy-2,6-dimethyl-
4-phenylpyridine

Dissolve   3,5-dicarbethoxy-2,6-dimethyl-4-phenyl-1,4-dihydropyridine (3 g.) in glacial acetic acid (15 ml.) in a 50 ml. round-bottomed flask. Dissolve solid chromium trioxide ($\approx$1·5 g.) in the minimum volume of cold water, and dilute the solution to a volume of 15 ml. with glacial acetic acid. Gradually add the chromium trioxide solution from a dropping funnel into the boiling dihydropyridine solution with swirling, until the orange colour of the oxidizing agent can be clearly observed as well as the green chromic salt formed during oxidation. Continue boiling the mixture under reflux for a further 15 minutes; then cool it to room temperature, and pour it with stirring onto crushed ice ($\approx$100 g.) in a 250 ml beaker. The oil solidifies on scratching, and cooling (though this may not occur as soon as the ice has melted). Filter off the solid product at the pump, and recrystallize it from aqueous ethanol. Filter and dry the crystals, first by suction, and then in a vacuum desiccator, giving 3,5-dicarbethoxy-2,6-dimethyl-4-phenylpyridine, as colourless crystals, 1·9 g.; m.p. 62° (60% of theory based on the dipydropyridine).

Haworth Synthesis

This refers to the preparation of polynuclear aromatic compounds (e.g. naphthalene and phenanthrene and their derivatives), by the below reaction sequence:

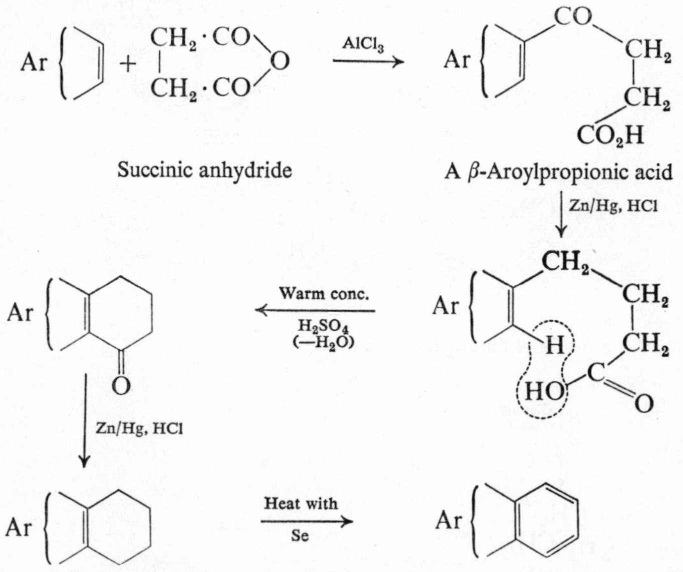

$$Ar \left\{ \begin{array}{c} \\ \end{array} \right\rangle + \begin{array}{c} CH_2 \cdot CO \\ | \\ CH_2 \cdot CO \end{array} \Big\rangle O \xrightarrow{AlCl_3} Ar \left\{ \begin{array}{c} CO \\ CH_2 \\ CH_2 \\ CO_2H \end{array} \right.$$

Succinic anhydride	A β-Aroylpropionic acid

$$\downarrow Zn/Hg, HCl$$

$$Ar \left\{ \begin{array}{c} CH_2 \\ CH_2 \\ H \quad CH_2 \\ HO \quad C \\ O \end{array} \right.$$

Warm conc. H$_2$SO$_4$ (—H$_2$O)

$$Ar \left\{ \begin{array}{c} \\ O \end{array} \right.$$

$$\downarrow Zn/Hg, HCl$$

$$Ar \left\{ \begin{array}{c} \\ \end{array} \right. \xrightarrow[Se]{Heat with} Ar \left\{ \begin{array}{c} \\ \end{array} \right.$$

(Ar = The remainder of the initial aromatic system.) Thus phenanthrene can be synthesized by this reaction starting from naphthalene and succinic anhydride:

77

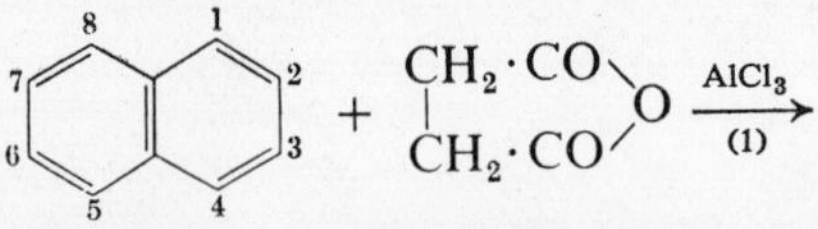
AlCl$_3$
(1)

Naphthalene Succinic anhydride

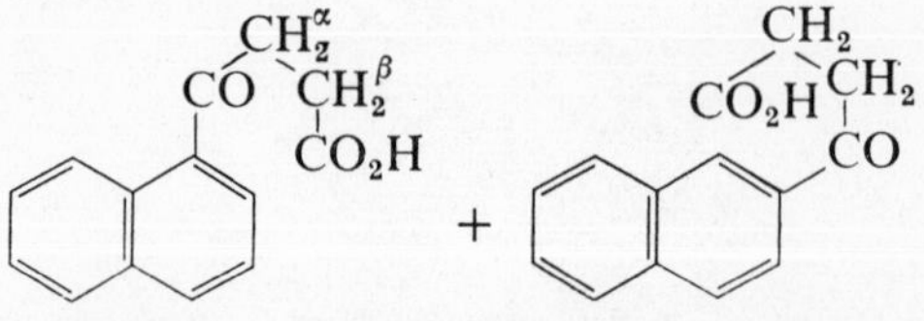

β-1-Naphthoyl- and β-2-Naphthoylpropionic acids

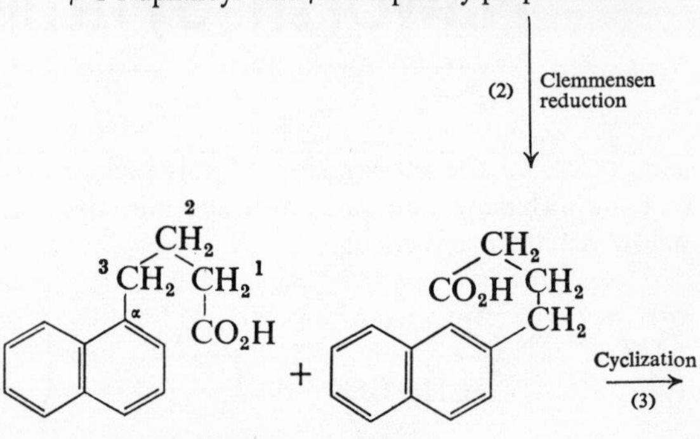
(2) Clemmensen reduction
Cyclization
(3)

3-α- and 3-β-Naphthylbutyric acids.

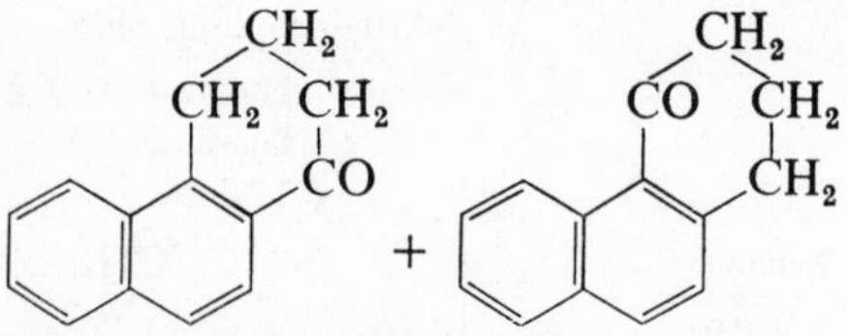

1- and 4-Keto-1,2,3,4-tetrahydrophenanthrene

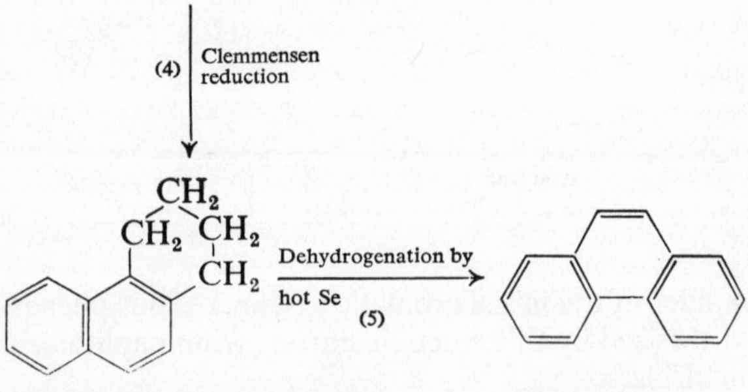
(4) Clemmensen reduction
Dehydrogenation by hot Se
(5)

1,2,3,4-Tetrahydrophenanthrene Phenanthrene

The mechanism of the Friedel–Crafts acylation and the Clemmensen reduction, (stages (1), (2) and (4)) have already been given (pp. 50 and 31 respectively).

Substituted phenanthrenes may be prepared by treatment of the ketonic products of stages (1) or (3) with Grignard reagents, yielding the corresponding secondary alcohols which may be dehydrated and the unsaturated products converted into the corresponding phenanthrenes by dehydrogenation.

Example. Preparation of Phenanthrene

Stage 1. *Preparation of β-1-Naphthoyl- and β-2-naphthoylpropionic acid*

Add naphthalene (40 g.) and succinic anhydride (20 g.) to a cold stirred solution of anhydrous aluminium chloride (55 g.) in anhydrous nitrobenzene (150 ml.). Stir the solution for 12 hours, then acidify with concentrated hydrochloric acid, and steam distil to remove unchanged nitrobenzene and naphthalene. Wash the solid residue with water and dissolve it in warm aqueous sodium carbonate, filter the solution and acidify with concentrated hydrochloric acid. Filter off the precipitated acid and recrystallize it from glacial acetic acid, giving a crystalline product 14 g.; m.p. 165–171°. A further recrystallization from methanol gives pure β-2-naphthoylpropionic acid 13 g., m.p. 171–173°. Dilute the acetic acid mother liquor with boiling water (3 volumes) and boil the solution with decolourizing charcoal. Filter, cool, and recrystallize the solid from methanol giving β-1-naphthoylpropionic acid 16 g., m.p. 129–131°.

Stage 2. *Preparation of 3α- and 3β-naphthylbutyric acids*

These are prepared by Clemmensen reduction as follows:

Boil each of the keto-acids (1 part), zinc amalgam (5 parts) and concentrated hydrochloric acid (5 volumes) under gentle reflux for 12 hours. Cool the mixture, dilute it with water, and filter off the crude product. Dissolve it in aqueous sodium carbonate, filter (to remove insoluble zinc salts), and finally acidify with concentrated hydrochloric acid yielding 3α- and 3β-naphthylbutyric acid. Purify the product by fractional recrystallization, from petroleum ether (b.p. 60–80°) or aqueous ethanol, giving the acids having m.p. of 106–107° and 94–95°, respectively.

Stage 3. Preparation of 1-*keto and* 4-*keto*-1,2,3,4-*tetrahydrophenanthrene*

Gradually add 3α or 3β-naphthylbutyric acid (1 part) to a well stirred mixture of concentrated sulphuric acid (3 volumes) and water (1 volume). Heat with stirring on a boiling water-bath for one hour. Cool the red solution and extract it with ether; wash the ethereal extract well with water, ammonium hydroxide, and finally dry it over anhydrous potassium carbonate. Filter off the desiccant, and distil off the ether taking the normal precautions. Recrystallize the solid product from a chloroform–petroleum ether mixture giving 1-keto-1,2,3,4-tetrahydrophenanthrene m.p. 95–96°, and 4-keto-1.2.3.4-tetrahydrophenanthrene m.p. 69° (from methanol).

Stage 4. Preparation of 1,2,3,4-*Tetrahydrophenanthrene*

This may be prepared by Clemmensen reduction of either of the keto-acids above or a mixture, following the directions given under stage 2. Purify the crude product by distillation under reduced pressure, collecting 1,2,3,4-tetrahydrophenanthrene at 173°/11 mm., m.p. 33–34° (from methanol).

Stage 5. Preparation of phenanthrene

In an efficient fume cupboard with the hood down, heat a mixture of 1,2,3,4-tetrahydrophenanthrene (1 part) and finely-divided selenium. (*Selenium metal and hydrogen selenide (evolved in this reaction) are both poisonous.*) (1·3 parts) in a metal-bath at 300–340° for 24 hours. Cool the mixture, then extract it with ether and distil off the solvent taking the normal precautions. Recrystallize the crude product from ethanol, giving phenanthrene m.p. 101°, b.p. 215°/12 mm.

Hofmann Rearrangement

This refers to the conversion of an amide into a primary amine by treatment with chlorine or bromine in the presence of alkali, or hypohalite. The overall reaction may be written as:

$$R \cdot CO \cdot NH_2 + 4NaOH + X_2 \rightarrow R \cdot NH_2 + 2NaX + Na_2CO_3$$
$$+ 2H_2O$$

(where X = Cl or Br)

It almost certainly involves initial formation of the N-halogenoamide, since these compounds have been isolated and have been shown to undergo the rearrangement in the presence of alkali. The halogeno-amide then forms its conjugate base (I), and it has been demonstrated that these compounds rapidly rearrange yielding isocyanates (II). In this rearrangement it is likely that migration of the hydrocarbon radical R and the loss of the halide anion are simultaneous; also the migration is *intra*molecular because R migrates with complete retention of configuration. This mechanism accounts both for the absence of hydroxamic acids in the product, and for the accelerating influence of electron-donor groups on the rate of reaction. The mechanism of the Hofmann rearrangement may therefore be represented as:

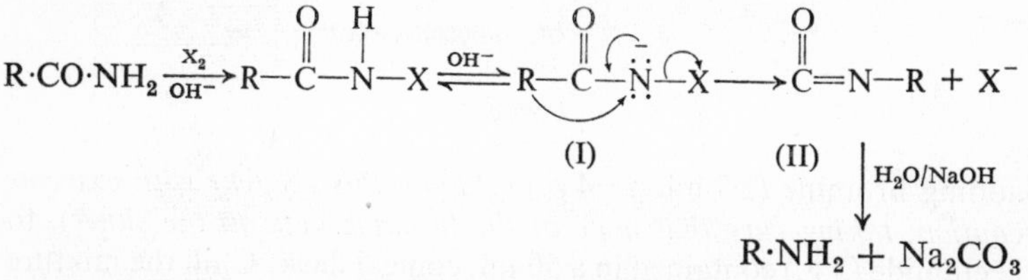

In the final stage the isocyanate (II) is hydrolysed to the primary amine; when ethanol is employed as the solvent a urethan (III) is formed which also yields the amine on hydrolysis:

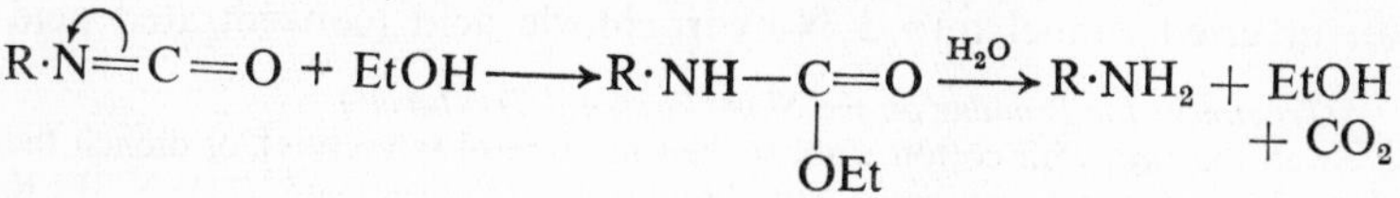

The Hofmann rearrangement can be applied to the preparation of aliphatic, aromatic, and heterocyclic primary amines and they are generally obtained in excellent yields. Since the conversion $RCONH_2 \rightarrow R \cdot NH_2$ involves the loss of one carbon atom, the reaction is often a useful method of descending a homologous series.

Example 1. Preparation of Methylamine Hydrochloride

Set up the apparatus shown in Figure 3 in a fume cupboard using a 100 ml. distillation flask. Prepare the bromoacetamide solution by

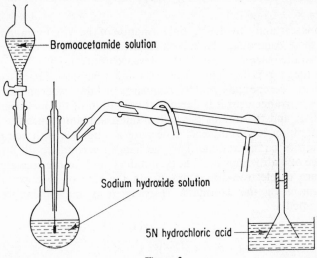

Bromoacetamide solution

Sodium hydroxide solution

5N hydrochloric acid

Figure 3

adding bromine (2·7 ml.≡8·4 g.) (*Handle this reagent with extreme caution, taking care that none of the bromine gets on the skin†*), to acetamide (3 g.) contained in a 50 ml. conical flask. Chill the mixture in an ice-bath, and add 10% aqueous sodium hydroxide solution (25 ml.) and mix the solutions well. Dissolve sodium hydroxide pellets (7·5 g.) in water (20 ml.) in the distillation flask, and arrange an inverted funnel into 5 N-hydrochloric acid [concentrated acid

† *Treatment for Bromine on the Skin* (*First-Aid Treatment*)
Swab the skin with cotton wool soaked in glycerol (glycerine), or drench the skin with water and then bathe with dilute sodium thiosulphate. THEN SEEK MEDICAL ATTENTION.

(6 ml.) and water (6 ml.)]. Warm the sodium hydroxide solution to 60° and run in the previously prepared solution of bromoacetamide slowly from the top funnel, at such a rate that the temperature remains between 60–70°. After the addition is complete, maintain the temperature at 60–70° for 15 minutes, and then distil until no more methylamine passes over (i.e. the distillate is no longer alkaline). Add boiling chips, and evaporate the distillate almost to dryness by heating over a wire-gauze with a clock glass placed over the top of the beaker to prevent splashing. Purify the product by recrystallization from boiling absolute ethanol (15 ml.) (in which the contaminating ammonium chloride is insoluble). Dry the product which is deliquescent, in a desiccator yielding methylamine hydrochloride 1·5 g. (44% of theory based upon acetamide).

N-*Methyl-p-toluenesulphonamide*

$$CH_3NH_2 \cdot HCl + 2NaOH + p\text{-}CH_3 \cdot C_6H_4SO_2Cl \rightarrow$$

Methylamine hydrochloride   p-Toluenesulphonyl chloride

$$CH_3 - \langle\!\!\!\bigcirc\!\!\!\rangle - SO_2NH \cdot CH_3 + 2NaCl + 2H_2O$$

N-Methyl-*p*-toluenesulphonamide

Treat methylamine hydrochloride (0·5 g.) with 5% aqueous sodium hydroxide (20 ml.) and then add p-toluenesulphonyl chloride (1·4 g.) dissolved in the minimum volume of acetone. Shake the corked test-tube† for five minutes, then warm (*after removing the cork*) until all the solid is dissolved. Cool the tube, acidify with dilute hydrochloric acid, and filter off the solid product. Wash it with dilute hydrochloric acid and then recrystallize from aqueous ethanol (1:1). Dry by pressing on filter paper, yielding *N*-methyl-p-toluene-sulphonamide 1·3 g., m.p. 75° (95% of theory). (This is an example of the Schotten–Baumann reaction, and it enables an assessment of the purity of methylamine hydrochloride to be made.)

Example 2. Preparation of Anthranilic Acid (o-Aminobenzoic Acid)

Prepare a solution of sodium hydroxide (7·5 g.) in water (30 ml.) in a 100 ml. conical flask and cool to 0° or below in an ice-salt bath. Add bromine (6·6 g.≡2·1 ml.) in one portion, and shake until all

† Release the cork from time to time to prevent the build up of pressure.

Phthalimide   Anthranilic acid

the bromine has reacted (*work in a fume cupboard*). The temperature of the solution will rise; cool it again to 0° or below. Add finely-powdered phthalimide (6 g.) in one portion to the cold sodium hypobromite solution, shake vigorously and add a solution of sodium hydroxide (5·5 g.) in water (20 ml.) with swirling. The solid will dissolve and the temperature increases to ≏70°. Warm the mixture at 80° for about two minutes, filter, if necessary, and then cool in ice and add concentrated hydrochloric acid slowly with shaking until the solution is just neutral (≏15 ml. will be required). (It is recommended that a little of the alkaline solution is set aside in case of the addition of too much acid.) Transfer the mixture to a 250 ml. beaker (foaming occurs in the next operation), and completely precipitate the anthranilic acid by the gradual addition of glacial acetic acid (≏5 ml.). Filter off the acid at the pump, wash with a *little* cold water, and recrystallize from hot water with the addition of a little activated charcoal. Filter off the pure acid at the pump, and dry in an air-oven at 100°, yielding anthranilic acid 3·5 g., m.p. 145° (63% of theory based on phthalimide).

Example 3. Preparation of 3-Aminopyridine

Nicotinamide   3-Aminopyridine

Place sodium hydroxide solution, prepared by dissolving sodium hydroxide (15 g.) in water (140 ml.), in a 250 ml. beaker equipped with a mechanical stirrer and immersed in an ice-salt bath. Add bromine (5·2 ml.) to this solution with stirring, and when the temperature reaches 0° add nicotinamide (10 g.) in one portion with vigorous stirring. Stir for 15 minutes, when the solution should be practically clear. Replace the ice-salt bath with a water-bath, and heat the solution at 70–75° for 45 minutes with occasional stirring. Cool the solution to room temperature, saturate it with sodium chloride ($\simeq$30 g.), and then extract the mixture with ether (5 × 60 ml.) shaking vigorously each time. Combine the ethereal extracts and dry over sodium hydroxide pellets ($\simeq$4 g.), filter, and distil off the ether from a water-bath (*care*). The hygroscopic residue solidifies on cooling. Purify this crude material by dissolving it in a mixture of benzene (50 ml.), and petroleum ether (12 ml.), followed by heating on a steam-bath with activated charcoal (2 g.) and sodium hydrosulphite (0·5 g.) for 20 minutes. Then filter the hot solution under gravity† and cool preferably in a refrigerator. Filter off the product under gravity†, and dry it in a desiccator over paraffin wax shavings yielding 3-aminopyridine 2·4 g,. m.p. 61–63° (31% of theory).

† Filtration under gravity, rather than at the pump, is recommended because of the hygroscopic nature of the product.

Knoevenagel Reaction

This is a general condensation between aldehydes or ketones and compounds containing activated methylene groups in the presence of an organic base such as pyridine or piperidine. The reaction is normally associated with the production of $\alpha\beta$-unsaturated compounds, e.g.

$$R_2CO + \overset{\overset{\displaystyle CN}{\displaystyle |}}{CH_2 \cdot COOEt} \xrightarrow[(-H_2O)]{Base} R_2C{=}C(CN)CO_2Et$$

The manner in which the reaction proceeds depends on the proportion of the reactants:

(a) $RCHO + CH_2(CO_2Et)_2 \xrightarrow{Base} RCH{=}C(CO_2Et)_2 + H_2O$

or

(b) $RCHO + 2CH_2(CO_2Et)_2 \xrightarrow{Base} RCH \underset{CH(CO_2Et)_2}{\overset{CH(CO_2Et)_2}{\big\langle}} + H_2O$

Equation (a) is obeyed when equivalent amounts of the reactants are used in the presence of pyridine. Whereas (b) generally holds for aliphatic aldehydes in the presence of an excess of the active methylene compound and piperidine as the basic catalyst. When tertiary amines are used as catalyst, the mechanism of the reaction is known to be similar to the aldol condensation. Considering the reaction, $RCHO + CH_2(CO_2Et)_2 \xrightarrow{B} R \cdot CH{=}C(CO_2Et)_2 + H_2O$, the mechanism is as shown at top of facing page.

The initial formation of the carbanion by abstraction of the hydrogen by the base from the active methylene group of the malonic ester, is followed by nucleophilic attack by this carbanion on the

$$CH_2(CO_2Et)_2 + B \rightleftharpoons \bar{C}H_2(CO_2Et)_2 + BH^+$$

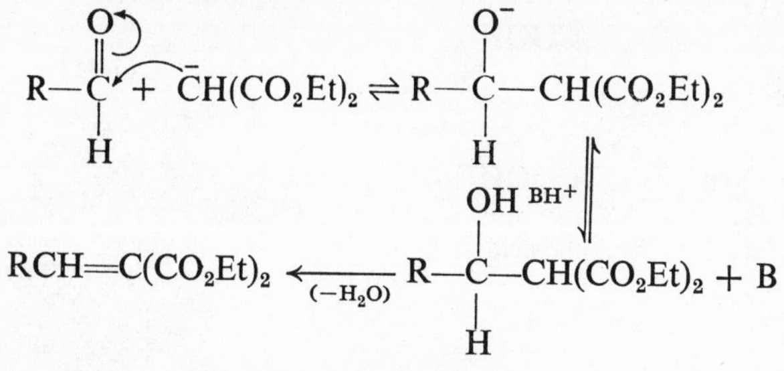

$$RCH{=}C(CO_2Et)_2 \xleftarrow[(-H_2O)]{} R{-}\underset{H}{\overset{OH}{\underset{|}{\overset{|}{C}}}}{-}CH(CO_2Et)_2 + B$$

(B = Basic catalyst)

aldehyde. Protonation of the adduct regenerates the basic catalyst; and the final step is dehydration yielding the $\alpha\beta$-unsaturated ester.

Example 1. Preparation of Cinnamic Acid (β-Phenylacrylic Acid)

$$C_6H_5CHO + CH_2(CO_2H)_2 \xrightarrow{NH_3}$$

Benzaldehyde   Malonic acid

$$C_6H_5CH{=}C(CO_2H)_2 \xrightarrow{(-CO_2)} C_6H_5CH{=}CHCO_2H$$

Benzalmalonic acid   Cinnamic acid

Add benzaldehyde (10 g.) and an 8% solution of ammonia in ethanol (40 g.) to malonic acid (10 g.) and heat on a water-bath until a clear solution is obtained. Remove ethanol by evaporation and then heat at 130–150° until carbon dioxide ceases to be evolved. Dissolve the residue in water, and acidify the solution with dilute hydrochloric acid. Filter off the precipitate at the pump and recrystallize it from hot water, yielding cinnamic acid 3·5 g.; m.p. 134° (50% of theory).

Example 2. Preparation of *p*-Methoxycinnamic Acid

Dissolve anisaldehyde (*p*-methoxybenzaldehyde) (1·2 ml.) and malonic acid (1·0 g.) in redistilled pyridine (20 ml.). Add 2 drops of piperidine and boil under reflux for 2 hours. Cool, dilute with water,

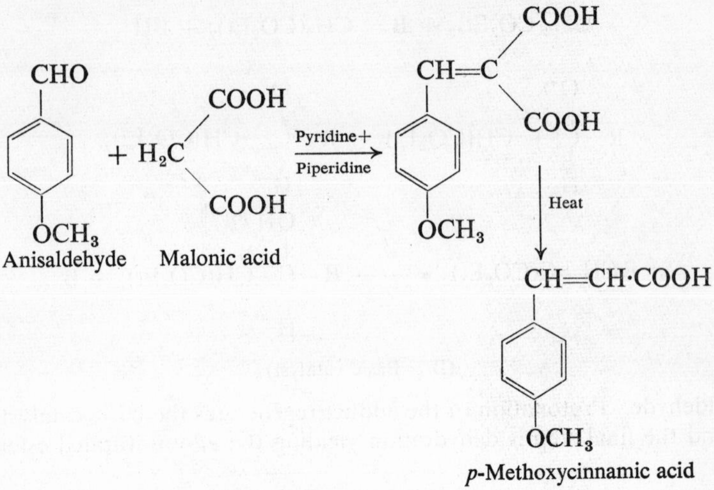

p-Methoxycinnamic acid

and acidify the solution with dilute hydrochloric acid. Filter off the product at the pump. Recrystallize *p*-methoxycinnamic acid from aqueous ethanol, giving 1·3 g., m.p. 172° (76% of theory).

Liebermann Nitroso Reaction

This is the nuclear nitrosation of NN-dialkylarylamines on treatment with nitrous acid in weakly acid solution, e.g.

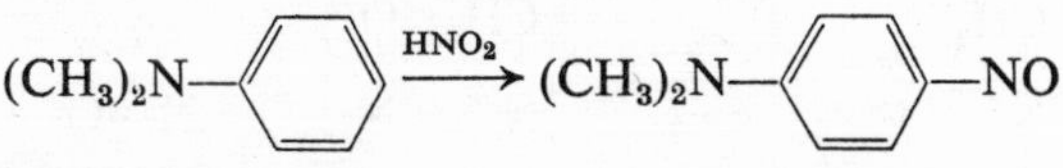

$$(CH_3)_2N-\underset{}{\bigcirc}\xrightarrow{HNO_2}(CH_3)_2N-\underset{}{\bigcirc}-NO$$

One possible mechanism for the process would be a direct electrophilic substitution by the nitrosonium ion NO^+:

1. $HONO \underset{}{\overset{H^+}{\rightleftharpoons}} H_2O + \overset{+}{N}O$

2.

Mesomeric forms

$(-H^+)$

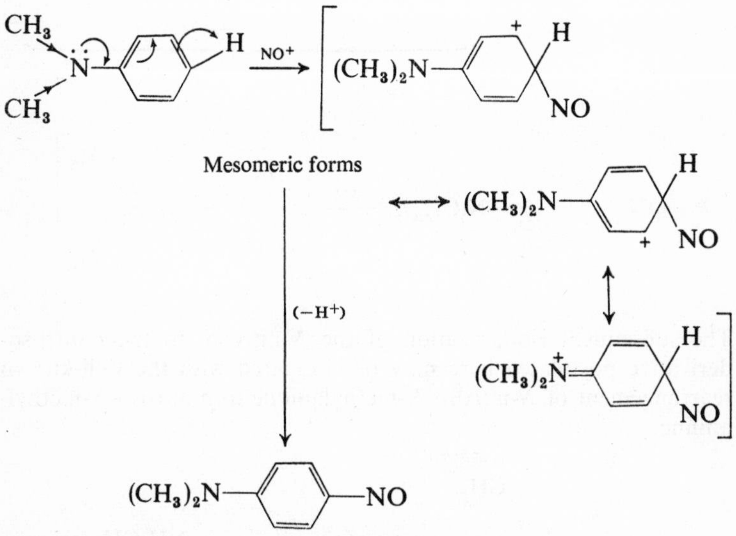

Liebermann's reaction fails with certain NN-dialkylanilines containing bulky alkyl groups, or those in which an o-substituent is present. This observation provides some support for the above mechanism, since in such cases the activating mesomeric (+M) effect of the dialkylamino-group would be considerably reduced, possibly inhibiting electrophilic attack by the nitrosonium ion. An alternative mechanism for the Liebermann reaction involves initial formation of the N-nitroso-compound. Nitrous acid is slowly converted into the anhydride N_2O_3 which then reacts with the dimethylaniline:

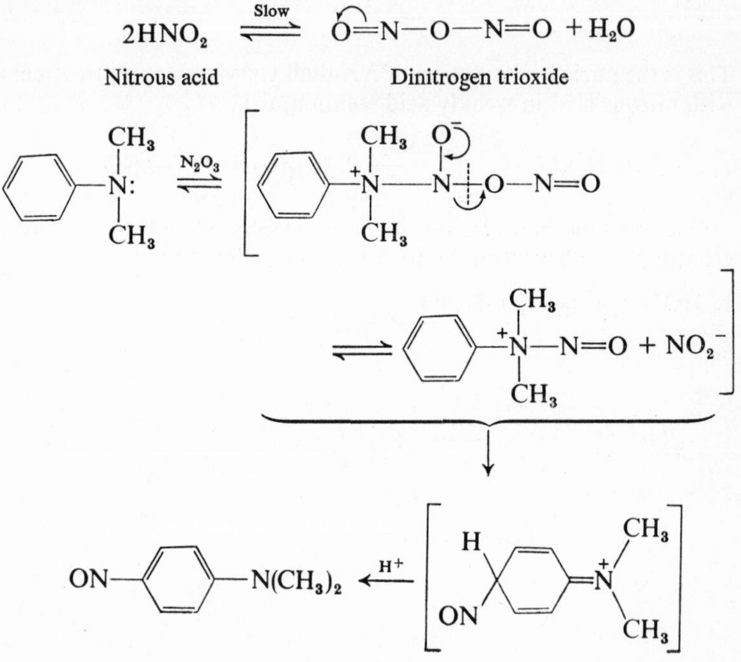

The subsequent isomerization of the N-nitroso- to the p-nitroso-derivative postulated here may be compared with the well-known rearrangement of N-nitroso-N-methylaniline to p-nitroso-N-methylaniline:

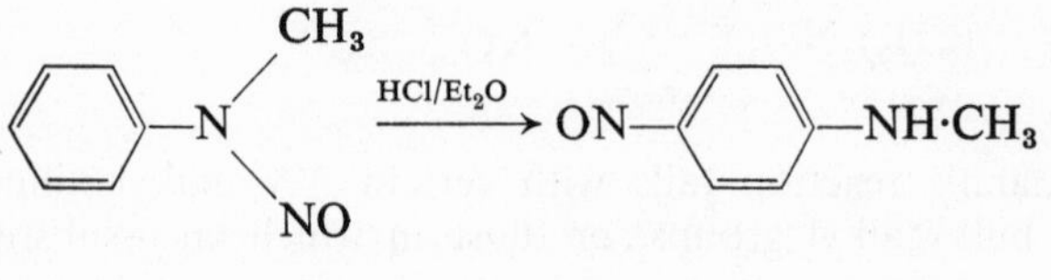

Example. Preparation of *p*-Nitroso-*N,N*-dimethylaniline

$$(CH_3)_2N-\!\!\!\left\langle\ \right\rangle \xrightarrow{\ HNO_2\ } (CH_3)_2N-\!\!\!\left\langle\ \right\rangle-\!NO$$

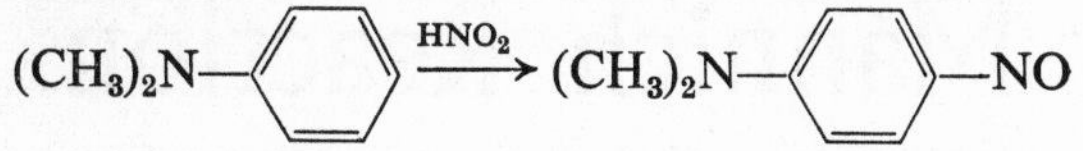

N,N-Dimethylaniline   *p*-Nitroso-*N,N*-dimethylaniline

Dissolve *N,N*-dimethylaniline (2 g.) in a mixture of water (10 ml.) and concentrated hydrochloric acid (5 ml.) in a small beaker. Cool the beaker in an ice-salt bath and add sodium nitrite (1·5 g.) in water (3 ml.) slowly with stirring. Small yellow needles of *p*-nitroso-*N,N*-dimethylaniline hydrochloride will separate out and a thick crystalline deposit will be soon observed. Allow the mixture to stand for 15 minutes (or until no further increase in the quantity of crystals is observed), then filter off the solid at the pump and dry by suction. Mix the crude solid with sodium hydroxide solution until alkaline, giving a thick green paste of the free base. Add sufficient ether to dissolve the green precipitate and transfer the solution to a separatory funnel. Separate, wash the ether layer with water (× 2), and finally dry over anhydrous sodium sulphate. Filter the ethereal solution from the desiccant and concentrate the filtrate by distillation from a water-bath (*care*). Place the concentrate in a small beaker and set aside to crystallize; *p*-Nitroso-*N,N*-dimethylaniline separates as large green foliated crystals 2·3 g., m.p. 85° (93% of theory).

Mannich Reaction

This is the acid-catalysed condensation of formaldehyde with ammonia, or a primary or secondary amine, and a compound containing at least one reactive hydrogen atom, often an aldehyde, ketone, or ester. The reactive hydrogen is replaced by an aminomethyl or substituted aminomethyl group, e.g.,

$$PhCOCH_3 + CH_2{=}O + (CH_3)_2NH{\cdot}HCl$$

Acetophenone	Formaldehyde	Dimethylamine
(Methyl phenyl ketone)		hydrochloride

$$PhCOCH_2CH_2N(CH_3)_2{\cdot}HCl + H_2O$$

β-Dimethylaminopropiophenone
hydrochloride

The most probable mechanism is first reaction of formaldehyde and the amine to yield an imine:

1. $CH_2{=}O + (CH_3)_2\overset{+}{N}H_2 \rightleftharpoons CH_2{=}\overset{+}{N}(CH_3)_2 + H_2O$

Then the enol attacks the imine giving the final product:

$$2\ Ph{\cdot}CO{\cdot}CH_3 \rightleftharpoons Ph{-}C{=}CH_2 + CH_2{=}\overset{+}{N}(CH_3)_2 \rightarrow$$
$$\overset{|}{O}{-}H$$

$$Ph{\cdot}C{\cdot}\overset{\alpha}{C}H_2\overset{\beta}{C}H_2N(CH_3)_2 + H^+$$
$$\overset{\|}{O}$$

The reaction is third order; the second step being the rate-determining one, $V = k[CH_2O][Me_2\overset{+}{N}H_2][Ph{\cdot}CO{\cdot}CH_3]$. There is considerable evidence for the initial reaction between formaldehyde and the amine.

Example. Preparation of β-Dimethylaminopropiophenone Hydrochloride

Place dry dimethylamine hydrochloride (5·3 g.), powdered paraformaldehyde (2·0 g.) and acetophenone (6·0 g. ≡ 5·9 ml.) in a 50 ml. round-bottomed flask fitted with a reflux condenser. Add ethanol (8 ml.) containing 2–3 drops of concentrated hydrochloric acid, and boil the mixture under reflux for 1 hour. It should then be clear and homogeneous; but if necessary filter the solution through a preheated Buchner funnel. Transfer the filtrate to a 100 ml. conical flask and add acetone (40 ml.) to the warm solution. Allow to cool to room temperature and further cool in ice. Filter off the crystals at the pump, wash them with acetone (2–3 ml.), and dry with suction. Then dry at 100° for half an hour giving 7·4 g., m.p. 153–155°. Recrystallize by dissolving in hot absolute ethanol (9 ml.) followed by the slow addition of acetone (45 ml.) yielding pure β-dimethylaminopropiophenone hydrochloride, 6·4 g., m.p. 155–156° (61% of theory).

Meerwein-Ponndorf-Verley Reduction

This is the specific reduction of a carbonyl compound to an alcohol, by treatment with an aluminium alkoxide (isopropoxide) in excess of the corresponding alcohol (isopropanol):

$$RR'C{=}O + (CH_3)_2CHOH \xrightleftharpoons{Al[O \cdot HC(CH_3)_2]^3} RR'CH \cdot OH + (CH_3)_2CO$$

The method has been successfully applied to the reduction of aliphatic and aromatic aldehydes and ketones; generally the carbonyl compound is boiled with excess isopropanol in the presence of aluminium isopropoxide, with simultaneous removal of the acetone produced to force the reaction to completion. However, in many cases it is found that satisfactory yields can be obtained without distilling off the acetone. The mechanism of this reduction may be depicted as follows:

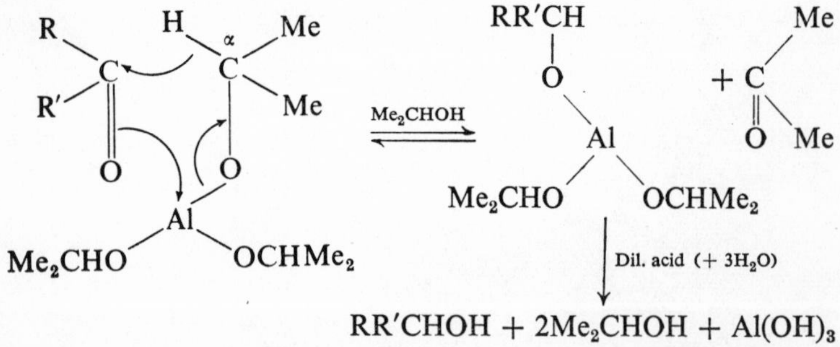

This scheme involves the co-ordination of the carbonyl oxygen atom to the aluminium of the propoxide, and transfer of a hydride ion from the propoxide to the carbonyl carbon atom which is facilitated by the cyclic transition state. The products of these electron shifts are acetone and the aluminium complex of the secondary alcohol corresponding to the carbonyl compound, which by treatment with

94

dilute acid gives the required product, RR'CHOH. It has been proved that an α-hydrogen is transferred by performing the reduction using deuterium labelled isopropoxide, when the resultant alcohol was discovered to contain deuterium in the α-position.

Example 1. Reduction of Benzophenone (Diphenyl Ketone)

Benzophenone   Benzhydrol

Add aluminium foil (2·7 g.) and mercuric chloride (0·05 g.) (*poisonous*) to dry isopropanol† (100 ml.), and boil the mixture under gentle reflux in a round-bottomed flask bearing a water condenser fitted with a calcium chloride tube. Heat on a hot-plate or in an isomantle until the aluminium dissolves. Allow to cool, and then add benzophenone (9 g.) to the mixture in the flask. Boil this mixture for a further 30 minutes, and then arrange the apparatus for distillation. Distil off the excess isopropanol and the acetone formed during the reaction. Test the filtrate with Brady's reagent (2,4-dinitrophenylhydrazine in aqueous methanol/sulphuric acid) to confirm the presence of acetone. Remove the final traces of isopropanol by distillation under slightly reduced pressure. Cool, and pour the viscous liquid into a mixture of concentrated hydrochloric acid (17 ml.) and water (90 ml.). Stir manually and then filter at the pump, and recrystallize from petroleum ether (b.p. 60–80°)(≃ 80 ml.). (If a coloured solution appears at this stage, add benzene (10 ml.), and filter the hot solution. Cool in ice-water and filter off the benzhydrol at the pump. The yield is 8·0 g., m.p. 67–69° (88% of theory).

Example 2. Reduction of *m*-Nitroacetophenone (Methyl-*m*-Nitrophenyl Ketone)

This is an example of the specificity of aluminium isopropoxide for the reduction of carbonyl groups. The other reducible group in

† Commercial Avantine may be dried over anhydrous potassium carbonate.

the molecule, the nitro group, remaining unaffected.

m-Nitroacetophenone   Methyl-m-nitrobenzyl alcohol

(a) Preparation of m-Nitroacetophenone

Equip a 2 litre Pyrex beaker with an efficient multispeed mechanical stirrer, a dropping funnel, and a thermometer capable of reading to $-20°$. Immerse the beaker in a large ice-salt bath and place in it sulphuric acid (d. 1·84, 141 ml.) and cool the acid with stirring to $-5°$ when it will solidify. Place redistilled acetophenone (48 g., b.p. 93°/21 mm.) in the dropping funnel, and add it at such a rate that the temperature does not exceed 5°. The sulphuric acid melts and will become dark red in colour and stirring will again be possible. Cool the mixture to $-10°$ by the addition of solid carbon dioxide chippings to the ice-salt bath, and directly to the reaction mixture. Now carefully add the nitration mixture of nitric acid (d. 1·42, 20 ml.) and fuming nitric acid (d. 1·50, 21 ml.) dissolved in sulphuric acid (d. 1·84; 98 ml.), at such a rate (dropwise) that the temperature does not exceed $-5°$. (Solid carbon dioxide chippings will be required to be added to the reaction mixture to maintain this temperature.) On completion of the addition, keep the mixture at $-5°$ while stirring for 15 minutes. Then pour the reaction mixture onto ice (750 g.) in water (1 litre) with vigorous manual stirring and continue this for a further 5 minutes. Filter off the product, a cream solid, at the pump, dry by suction and transfer it to a mortar and triturate it with water (3 × 50 ml.) and cold ethanol (2 × 15 ml.). Air-dry on a porous plate, and then recrystallize from ethanol. A further crop of crystals will be obtained by reducing the mother liquor to half its original volume. The yield of m-nitroacetophenone is 49 g., m.p. 78–79° (75% of theory based on acetophenone).

(b) Preparation of Methyl-m-Nitrobenzyl Alcohol

Dissolve aluminium foil (3 g.), in dry† isopropanol (120 ml.) containing mercuric chloride (0·04 g.), by heating gently under

† Dried over anhydrous potassium carbonate.

reflux in a 250 ml. round-bottomed flask fitted with a reflux condenser bearing a calcium chloride tube. When the aluminium has completely dissolved, add *m*-nitroacetophenone (33 g. dried *in vacuo*) and boil under reflux for 1 hour after all the ketone has dissolved. Distil off the excess isopropanol and the acetone formed during the reaction; the last traces should be removed under reduced pressure. Cool the flask to about 50° and add its viscous contents to mechanically stirred ice-cold 3*N*-sulphuric acid (350 ml.). Add a portion of the cold acid to the residue in the flask and add this to the main bulk. Stir until the viscous oil solidifies giving a pale buff product. Filter off the product at the pump, triturate it twice with water (50 ml., 30 ml.) in a mortar, and then filter at the pump and air-dry. Recrystallize from benzene; a second crop of crystals will be obtained from the mother liquor by evaporation to half its original volume. The yield is 24·5 g., m.p. 61·5–62° (78 % of theory).

Michael Condensation

This is the base-catalysed addition of compounds containing a reactive α-hydrogen atom to compounds with activated double or triple bonds, e.g.

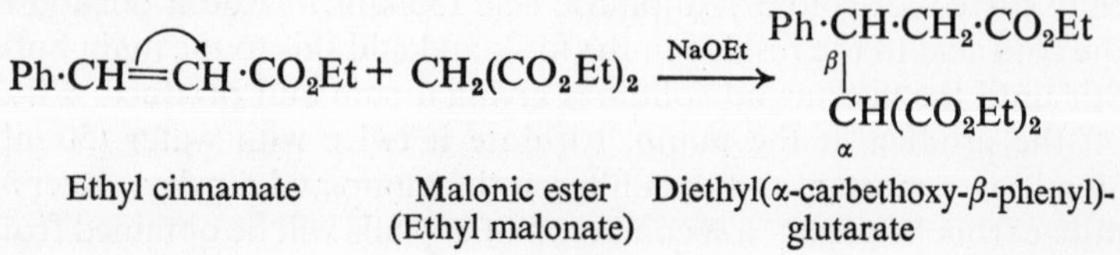

Ph·CH=CH·CO2Et + CH2(CO2Et)2
NaOEt
Ph·CH·CH2·CO2Et
β
CH(CO2Et)2
α
Ethyl cinnamate
Malonic ester
(Ethyl malonate)
Diethyl(α-carbethoxy-β-phenyl)-
glutarate

The reaction is capable of very wide variation; thus the methylene compounds may be, e.g. malonic ester, acetoacetic ester, cyanoacetic ester, benzyl cyanide, or ω-nitrostyrene. The other reactant is an unsaturated compound, in which the multiple bond is activated by the presence of an attached electron-withdrawing group, e.g. αβ-unsaturated aldehydes, ketones, esters, or nitriles.

An example of an intramolecular Michael reaction is given below:

CH=CH·CO2Et
CH2·CO2Et
Base
CH2·CO2Et
CO2Et

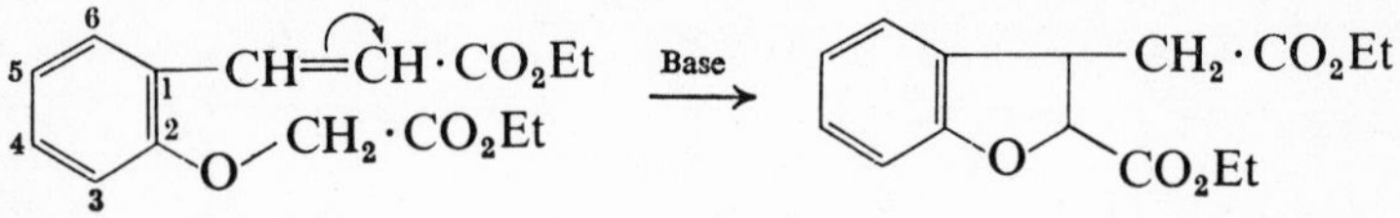

Cyclic products may also be formed by a subsequent cyclisation, e.g.

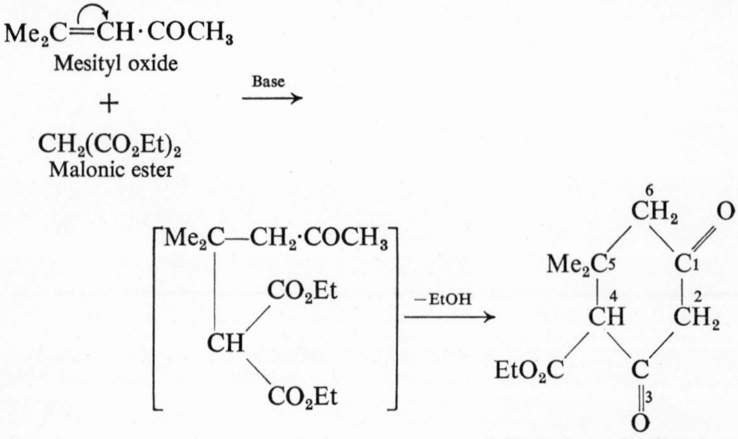

Me2C=CH·COCH3
Mesityl oxide
+
CH2(CO2Et)2
Malonic ester
Base
Me2C—CH2·COCH3
CO2Et
CH
CO2Et
−EtOH
CH2
O
Me2C5
C1
CH
CH2
EtO2C
C
O

4-Carbethoxy-5,5-dimethyl-
1,3-cyclohexadione

The basic catalysts used may be sodium alkoxides, diethylamine, piperidine, or quaternary bases.

Considering, for instance, the Michael reaction between ethyl cinnamate and malonic ester: the mechanism involves attack of the carbanion (from malonic ester) on the more positive end of ethyl cinnamate giving an intermediate anion, which on subsequent treatment with water, yields the final isolated product:

$$CH_2(CO_2Et)_2 + B: \rightleftharpoons \bar{C}H(CO_2Et)_2 + \overset{+}{B}:H$$

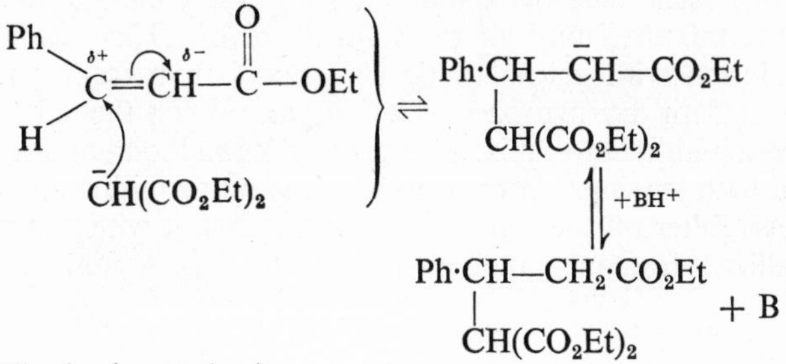

$$Ph \cdot CH - \bar{C}H - CO_2Et$$
$$| \\ CH(CO_2Et)_2$$

$$\Bigg\} \rightleftharpoons$$

$$\Big\Vert +BH^+$$

$$Ph \cdot CH - CH_2 \cdot CO_2Et$$
$$| \qquad\qquad + B \\ CH(CO_2Et)_2$$

(B = The basic catalyst)

Example 1. Preparation of Diethyl-αβ-Diphenylglutarate

$$Ph \cdot CH{=}CH \cdot CO_2Et + Ph \cdot CH_2CO_2Et \xrightarrow{\text{NaOEt}} \overset{\beta}{Ph \cdot CH} \cdot CH_2CO_2Et$$
$$\underset{\alpha}{|} \\ Ph \cdot CH \cdot CO_2Et$$

Ethyl cinnamate   Ethyl phenylacetate   Diethyl-αβ-diphenylglutarate

Mix ethyl cinnamate (10 g.) and ethyl phenylacetate (10 g.) with a solution of sodium (0·4 g.) in dry ethanol (6 ml.); and then boil the mixture under reflux for two and half hours. Cool, and neutralize it with the calculated quantity of dilute hydrochloric acid, then add sufficient water to produce turbidity. Cool the mixture in ice-water, and filter off the crystalline precipitate at the pump. Recrystallize it twice from aqueous ethanol, giving pure diethyl-αβ-diphenyl-glutarate as needles 15 g., m.p. 92–93° (75% of theory).

Example 2. Diethyl-(α-phenyl-β-nitroethyl)-Malonate

$$Ph \cdot CH{=}CH{-}NO_2 + CH_2(CO_2Et)_2 \xrightarrow{\text{NaOEt}} \begin{array}{c} Ph \cdot CH \cdot CH_2 \cdot NO_2 \\ | \\ CH \cdot (CO_2Et)_2 \end{array}$$

ω-Nitrostyrene	Malonic ester	Diethyl-(α-phenyl-
(ω-Nitrophenylethylene)		β-nitroethyl)-malonate

Add finely powdered ω-nitrostyrene (5 g.) to an ice-cold solution of malonic ester (26 g.) and sodium (1 g.) in dry ethanol (30 ml.). Shake the mixture, until all the solid dissolves. Then acidify the clear solution with glacial acetic acid; cool it in ice-water, and saturate it with dry hydrogen chloride gas. When the solution is colourless, pour it onto a mixture of crushed ice and sodium carbonate solution with stirring. After scratching the oil for a few minutes it solidifies. Filter off the solid with suction, wash it with water, and recrystallize it from methanol, giving the ester 5 g., m.p. 57° (51% of theory).

Oppenauer Oxidation

This is the reversal of the Meerwein–Ponndorf–Verley reduction; namely, the specific oxidation of a primary or secondary alcohol in the presence of an aluminium alkoxide (the tertiary butoxide is most generally used) and excess acetone which functions as an hydrogen acceptor:

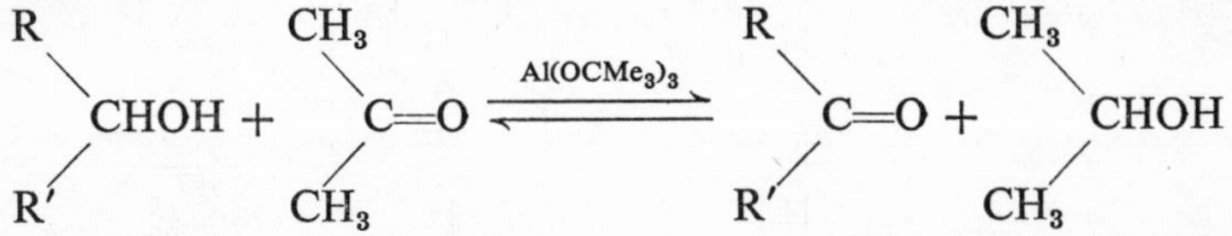

Benzoquinone is also used as an acceptor, especially in the oxidation of primary alcohols to aldehydes. The mechanism involves a cyclic transition state† which accounts for the stereospecificity of the oxidation. Unsaturated alcohols may be oxidized in this manner, though migration of the double bond may occur as in example 1.

Example 1. Preparation of Cholestenone (Cholest-4-en-3-one).

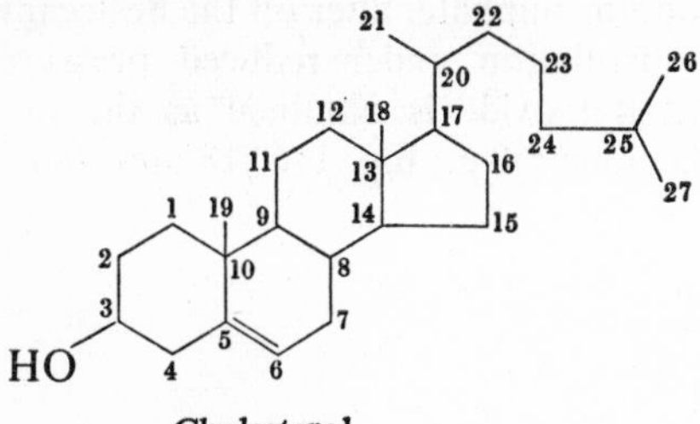

Cholesterol

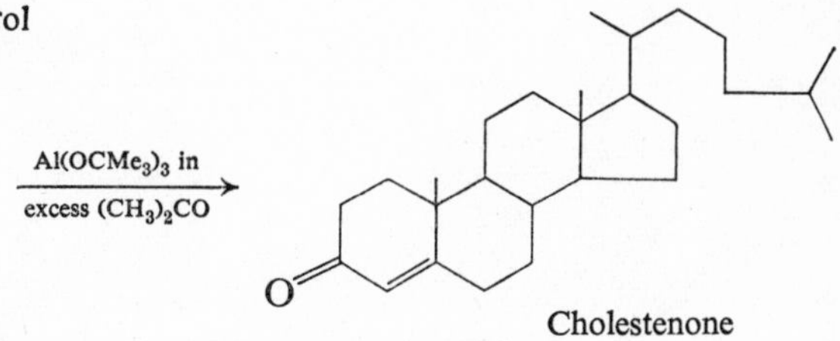

Cholestenone

† See the Meerwein–Ponndorf–Verley reduction (p. 94).

Add a solution of cholesterol (10 g.) in hot acetone (150 ml.) to a solution of crystalline aluminium tert.-butoxide (12 g.) in benzene (300 ml.) and boil under reflux for 10 hours. Cool, and shake the reaction mixture with dilute sulphuric acid to remove aluminium salts. Wash the benzene layer with water, dry it over anhydrous sodium sulphate, filter off the desiccant, and concentrate by evaporation. The yield is 8·9 g., m.p. 79–80° (89 % of theory).

Example 2. Preparation of cis-α-Decalone

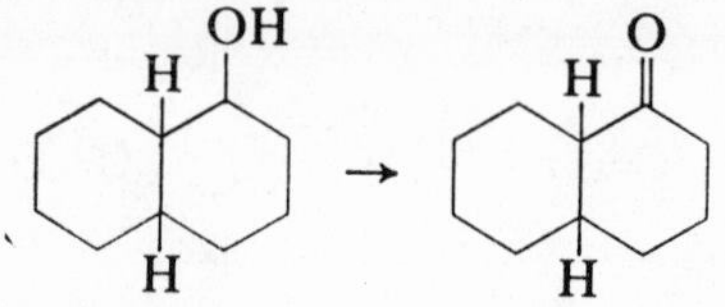

cis-α-Decalol   cis-α-Decalone
(1-Hydroxy-cis-decahydronaphthalene)

Add freshly distilled aluminium isopropoxide (15 g.) to a solution containing cis-α-decalol (7·5 g.), benzene (thiophen-free, 750 ml.) and acetone (500 ml.). Boil the solution under reflux for 12 hours during which time the open end of the condenser is protected by a calcium chloride tube. Cool to room temperature and wash the reaction mixture successively with 30 % aqueous sulphuric acid and water. Dry over anhydrous sodium sulphate, filter off the desiccant, and remove the solvent by distillation under reduced pressure. Finally distil the residue; mesityl oxide is obtained as the first fraction; followed by cis-α-decalone 6·0 g., b.p. 116°/18 mm. (80 % of theory).

Orton Rearrangement

This is the conversion of N-halogenoacetanilides into a mixture of o- and p-halogenoacetanilides by treatment with hydrochloric acid, usually in a hydroxylic solvent, e.g.

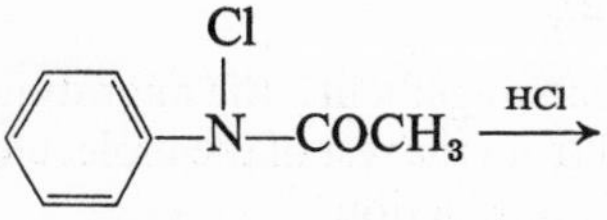

N-Chloroacetanilide

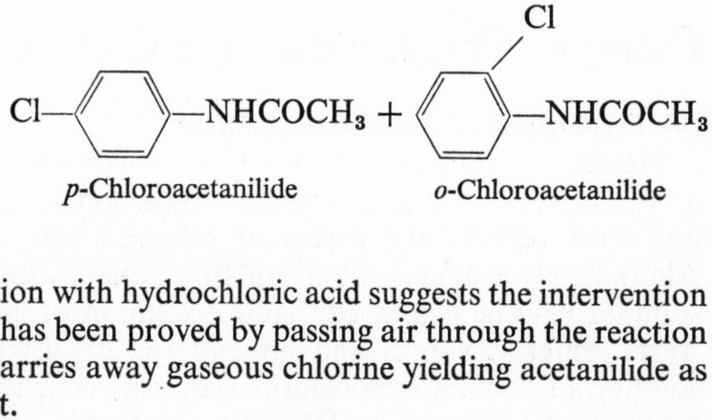

p-Chloroacetanilide o-Chloroacetanilide

The specific reaction with hydrochloric acid suggests the intervention of chlorine; this has been proved by passing air through the reaction medium, which carries away gaseous chlorine yielding acetanilide as the other product.

When chlorine is not removed, it chlorinates the acetanilide in the o- and p-positions; and the ratio of isomers obtained is the same as that from direct chlorination of acetanilide in the same solvent. The use of radioactive labelled chlorine, in the hydrogen chloride molecule has confirmed that the reaction occurs by the formation of chlorine, since, the calculated proportion of labelled chlorine was found in the rearranged product.

If hydrochloric acid is replaced by hydrogen bromide or hydrogen iodide, bromination or iodination results *via* the intermediate formation of $\overset{\delta^+}{\text{Br}}\text{-}\overset{\delta^-}{\text{Cl}}$ and $\overset{\delta^+}{\text{I}}\text{-}\overset{\delta^-}{\text{Cl}}$ respectively. The mechanism of the Orton rearrangement is shown at top of next page.

$$\underset{\text{(H}^+\text{ from HCl)}}{\overset{\text{X}}{\underset{|}{\text{Ph—N—COCH}_3}}} + \text{H}^+ \rightleftharpoons \overset{\text{X}}{\underset{|}{\text{Ph—NH—COCH}_3}}$$
$$+$$

$$\text{Cl}^- + \overset{\text{X}}{\underset{\underset{+}{|}}{\text{Ph—NH—COCH}_3}} \xrightarrow{\text{Slow}} \overset{\delta^+}{\text{X}}\text{—}\overset{\delta^-}{\text{Cl}} + \text{PhNHCOCH}_3$$

$$\downarrow \text{Fast}$$

—NHCOCH$_3$ + X——NHCOCH$_3$

(X = Cl, Br, I).

It is an example of an *intermolecular* rearrangement: the migrating halogen atom being completely detached from the rest of the molecule for a significant interval of time during the reaction.

Example. Preparation of *p*-Chloroacetanilide

(a) Preparation of N-chloroacetanilide

Prepare a solution of sodium hypochlorite (500 ml.) by saturating a 10% aqueous solution of sodium bicarbonate with chlorine at 0°, and then remove the excess of chlorine with a current of air. Alternatively a similar volume of 10% aqueous sodium hypochlorite solution may be employed. Add a solution of acetanilide (9 g.) in warm water (250 ml.) and ethanol (≃ 20 ml.) to a well stirred solution of sodium hypochlorite (500 ml.) which is kept below 10° by external cooling. A solid will separate, filter this off, dissolve in chloroform, and dry it over anhydrous sodium sulphate for 20 minutes. Filter, and then remove the solvent under reduced pressure (keeping the temperature <40°). The residue is *N*-chloroacetanilide. Recrystallize it rapidly from chloroform petroleum ether mixture, with the minimum of heating. The yield is 7 g., m.p. 91° (63% of theory). (Insert the melting point tube into the melting point apparatus when the temperature reaches 82–83°.)

(b) Rearrangement of N-Chloroacetanilide

Dissolve *N*-chloroacetanilide (3 g.) in the minimum quantity of hot 50% aqueous ethanol and add 5N hydrochloric acid [concentrated acid (3 ml.) and water (3 ml.)]. Allow the solution to gradually cool to room temperature; then cool in an ice-bath, and filter off the product at the pump. The yield of *p*-chloroacetanilide is 1·5 g.; m.p. 175–178° (50% of theory). (If necessary the product may be recrystallized from boiling water.)

Perkin Reaction

This is the base-catalysed condensation of an aromatic aldehyde with an acid anhydride, containing at least two reactive α-hydrogen atoms, yielding a β-substituted acrylic acid. The base is generally the alkali salt of the acid corresponding to the anhydride, though other bases may be employed, e.g. potassium carbonate, triethylamine, or pyridine:

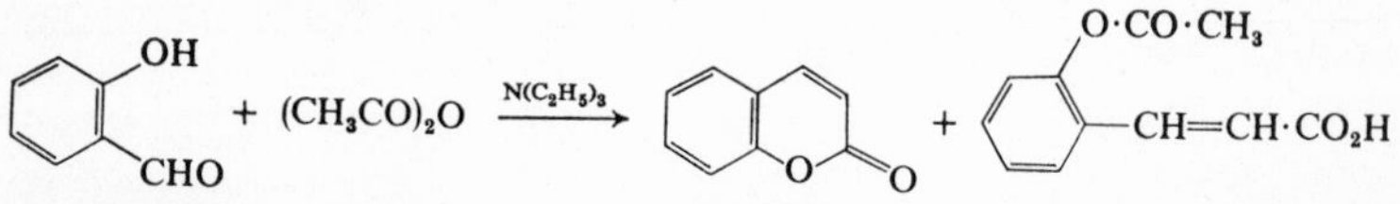

| Salicylaldehyde (o-Hydroxybenzaldehyde) | Acetic anhydride | Coumarin (mainly) | o-Acetoxycinnamic acid |

Generally

$$Ar \cdot CHO + (RCH_2 \cdot CO)_2O \xrightarrow{\text{Base}} \underset{\beta}{Ar \cdot CH} = \underset{\alpha}{\overset{\overset{\displaystyle R}{|}}{C}} \cdot CO_2H + H_2O$$

The Perkin reaction is an important method for the synthesis of αβ-unsaturated aromatic acids; the best known example is the preparation of cinnamic acid:

$$C_6H_5 \cdot CHO + (CH_3CO)_2O \xrightarrow[170-180°]{CH_3CO_2Na}$$

Benzaldehyde   Acetic anhydride

$$C_6H_5 \cdot CH = CH \cdot CO_2H + CH_3CO_2H.$$

Cinnamic acid   Acetic acid

The reaction is an aldol-type condensation, though the intermediate aldol is not normally isolated, and the probable mechanism is as follows:

$$CH_3 \cdot CO \cdot O \cdot COCH_3 + CH_3CO\bar{O} \rightarrow$$

$$\bar{C}H_2CO \cdot O \cdot COCH_3 + CH_3COOH$$

$$Ph-\overset{\overset{\displaystyle O}{\|}}{\underset{\underset{\displaystyle H}{|}}{C}} + \bar{C}H_2CO \cdot O \cdot COCH_3 \longrightarrow Ph-\overset{\overset{\displaystyle O^-}{|}}{\underset{\underset{\displaystyle H}{|}}{C}}-CH_2CO \cdot O \cdot COCH_3$$

$$\big\downarrow H^+$$

$$Ph \cdot CH = CHCO \cdot O \cdot COCH_3 \xleftarrow{-H_2O} Ph-\overset{\overset{\displaystyle OH}{|}}{\underset{\underset{\displaystyle H}{|}}{C}}-CH_2CO \cdot O \cdot COCH_3$$

$$\big\downarrow H_2O$$

$$PhCH = CHCO_2H + CH_3COOH$$

The fact that the anhydride and not sodium acetate is the active entity is demonstrated by the effectiveness of other bases (like sodium carbonate or pyridine) in the reaction.

In the first stage the carboxylate ion acts as a base, abstracting a proton from the reactive α-position of the anhydride, yielding the carbanion which subsequently attacks the carbonyl group of the aldehyde. The initially produced acid then catalyses the dehydration stage, regenerating the carboxylate anion. Evidence for the aldol-type condensation is afforded by the reaction between benzaldehyde and succinic acid, which due to cyclization stops at the 'aldol' stage.

$$C_6H_5 \cdot CHO + \overset{\displaystyle CH_2 \cdot COOH}{\underset{\displaystyle CH_2 \cdot COOH}{|}} \xrightarrow{\text{Base}} C_6H_5 \cdot \overset{\overset{}{\underset{\underset{\displaystyle OH}{|}}{C}H}}{-}\overset{\overset{}{\underset{\underset{\displaystyle CH_2}{|}}{C}H}}{-}COOH$$

Benzaldehyde   Succinic acid

$$HO-\overset{\overset{\displaystyle }{\underset{\underset{\displaystyle O}{\|}}{C}}}{}$$

$$\big\downarrow -H_2O$$

$$C_6H_5-\overset{\overset{\displaystyle }{\underset{\underset{\displaystyle O}{|}}{C}H}}{}\overset{}{-----}\overset{\overset{\displaystyle }{\underset{\underset{\displaystyle CH_2}{|}}{C}H}}{}-COOH$$

$$\overset{\displaystyle }{\underset{\underset{\displaystyle O}{\|}}{C}}$$

Phenylparaconic acid ('The aldol')

Generally it is found that the Perkin reaction is facilitated by the presence of electron-attracting substituents (e.g. halogen or nitro groups) in the aromatic nucleus.

Example 1. Preparation of Cinnamic Acid

Add acetic anhydride (3 ml.) to powdered fused potassium acetate (1 g.) contained in a boiling tube. Warm to dissolve most of the solid, then add pure redistilled benzaldehyde (2 ml.) (free from benzoic acid). Boil gently under reflux for 4 hours. If this cannot be performed in one continuous operation, the tube must be protected from moisture in the interval. Finally cool, and pour into water (20 ml.) in a 150 ml. beaker. Neutralize the product carefully with a concentrated aqueous solution of sodium carbonate, until the solution is just alkaline to litmus paper. Add boiling stone and then boil the solution (in a fume cupboard) to remove any residual benzaldehyde. Cool, and filter the solution through a fluted filter paper into a beaker, and then acidify carefully with hydrochloric acid. Cool, and filter off the cinnamic acid at the pump; wash the crude product with water and finally recrystallize it from a 30% ethanol–water mixture. Dry the product in an oven at 100°. The yield is 1·7 g. (colourless crystals), m.p. 133° (58% of theory based on benzaldehyde).

Example 2. Preparation of α-Phenylcinnamic Acid

$$C_6H_5 \cdot CH{=}O \ + \ \underset{\underset{HO_2C}{|}}{H_2C{-}C_6H_5} \xrightarrow{N(C_2H_5)_3}$$

Benzaldehyde   Phenylacetic acid

$$\underset{\beta \qquad \alpha}{C_6H_5 \cdot CH{=}\underset{\underset{CO_2H}{|}}{\overset{\overset{C_6H_5}{|}}{C}}} + H_2O$$

α-Phenylcinnamic acid

Place benzaldehyde (8·5 g.), phenylacetic acid (10·9 g.), anhydrous triethylamine (8 ml.), and acetic anhydride (16 ml.) in a round-bottomed flask equipped with a reflux condenser. Boil the mixture under reflux for 5 hours, and then steam distil, until all the volatile material has distilled over. Decant the water from the residue in the flask, dissolve it in ethanol (100 ml.) and add water (100 ml.) using the water from the flask as the main bulk. Heat to boiling with the addition of decolourizing charcoal (0·4 g.), then filter and acidify the filtrate to Congo red with hydrochloric acid. Cool, filter, and finally recrystallize from aqueous ethanol, yielding α-phenylcinnamic acid 10 g., m.p. 172–173° (58% of theory based on benzaldehyde).

Pschorr Synthesis

This generally refers to the preparation of a phenanthrene-9-carboxylic acid by cyclization of a diazotized o-amino-α-phenylcinnamic acid on treatment with copper powder:

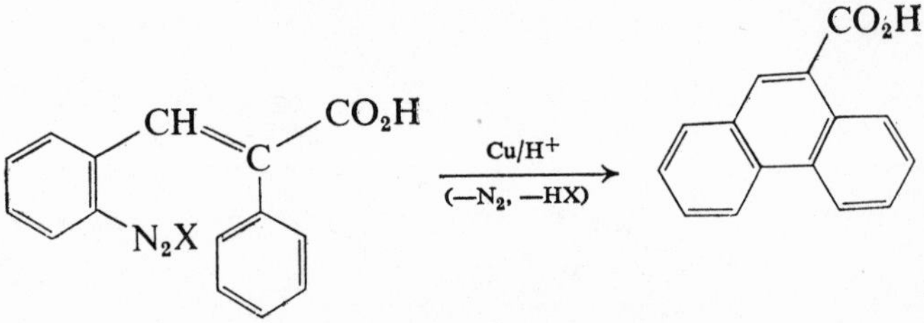

It is a very important method for the synthesis of substituted phenanthrenes, and is capable of considerable variation. Thus an o-amino-N-alkylbenzanilide yields a N-methylphenanthridone; and o-aminobenzophenones give fluorenones:

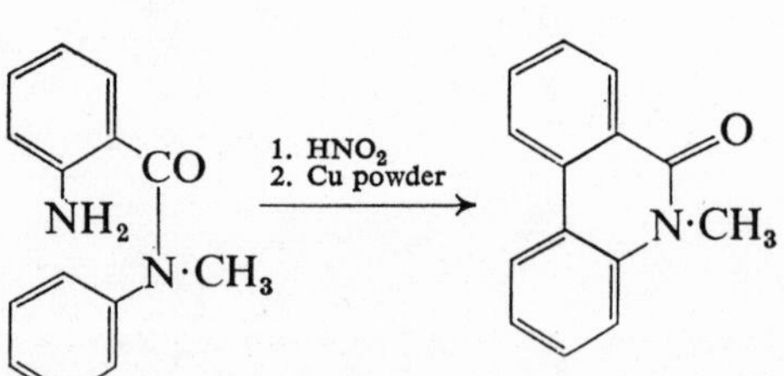

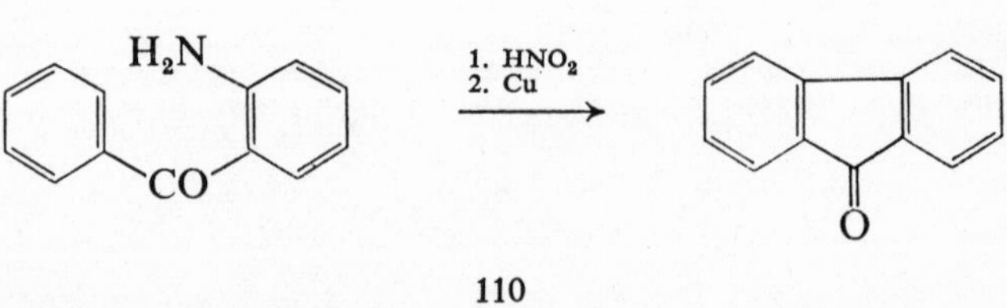

There are two possible mechanisms for the Pschorr reaction:

(a) *A Homolytic (free-radical chain) mechanism*

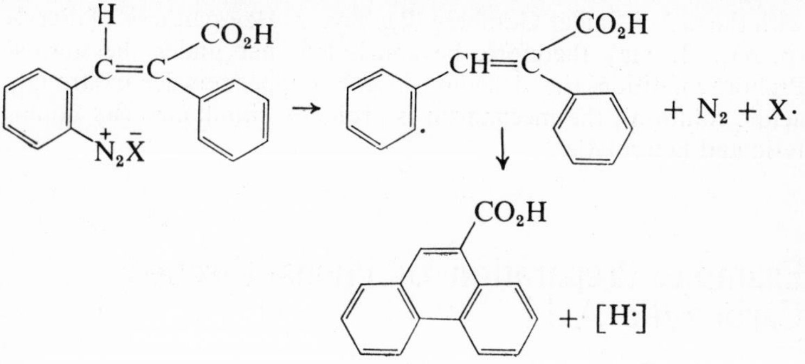

or

(b) *A Heterolytic (ionic) mechanism*

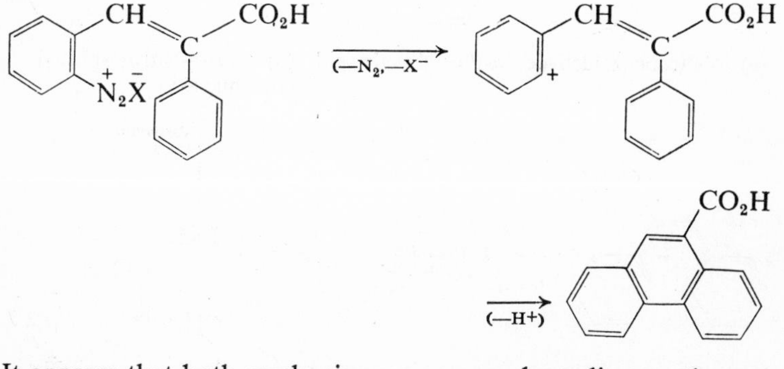

It appears that both mechanisms can occur depending on the conditions; thus when dry diazonium salts are decomposed in the presence of a copper catalyst there is considerable evidence in favour of the homolytic reaction (e.g. electron-attracting groups in the α-phenyl nucleus do not interfere with cyclization). On the other hand, when the diazonium salt is decomposed in strongly acidic solution *without a copper catalyst*, the reaction appears to be heterolytic. When copper powder is added to the acid solution both the yield of the product and the rate of decomposition are considerably increased, suggesting that the copper facilitates the formation of a reactive intermediate, probably an aryl free radical.

The idea that the presence of copper promotes the homolytic reaction is supported by a study of the reduction of diazonium salts with hypophosphorous acid in the presence of copper powder as this is known to be a free-radical chain reaction initiated by the copper. The homolytic mechanism is also supported by analogy with the rather similar Gomberg–Bachmann–Hey synthesis of diaryls (p. 63). It may therefore, be concluded that under the normal Pschorr conditions (i.e. decomposition by copper powder in strongly acidic solution), the mechanism is probably simultaneously homolytic and heterolytic.

Example. Preparation of Phenanthrene-9-Carboxylic Acid

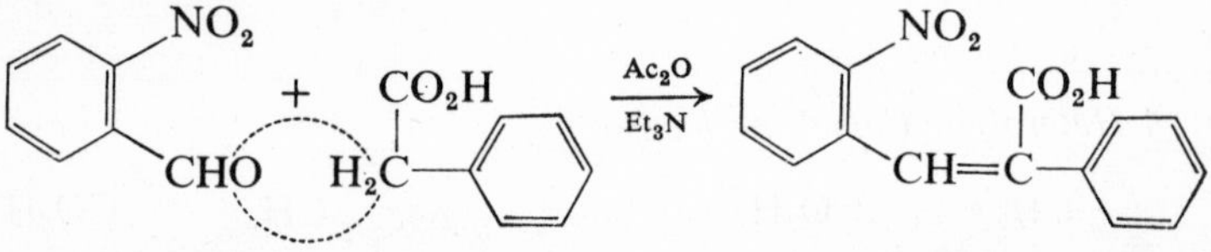

(a) o-Nitrobenzaldehyde   α-Phenylacetic acid   (b) trans-o-Nitro-α-phenyl-cinnamic acid

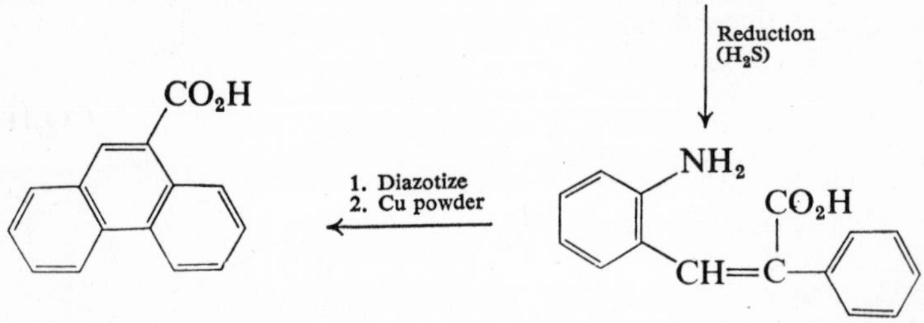

Reduction (H₂S)

(d) Phenanthrene-9-carboxylic acid   (c) trans-o-Amino-α-phenylcinnamic acid

(a) *Preparation of o-nitrobenzaldehyde*

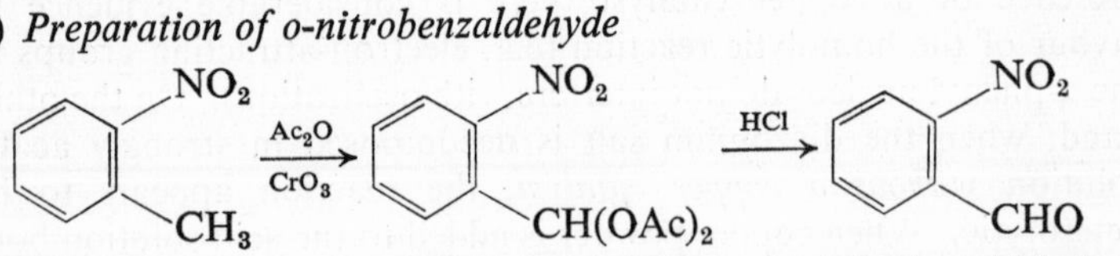

o-Nitrotoluene   o-Nitrobenzalacetate   o-Nitrobenzaldehyde

o-Nitrobenzalacetate (o-Nitrobenzylideneacetate). Place glacial acetic acid (570 ml.), acetic anhydride (565 ml.) and o-nitrotoluene (50 g.) in a 2 litre three-necked round-bottomed flask fitted with a mechanical stirrer, and thermometer. Surround the flask by an ice-bath, and slowly add concentrated sulphuric acid (85 ml.), to the cold stirred solution. When the temperature of the mixture is down to 5°, add chromium trioxide (100 g.) portionwise, so that the temperature does not exceed 10° (addition takes ≏ 2 hours). Continue stirring for 5 hours after all the chromium trioxide has been added. Pour the reaction mixture into a large beaker containing crushed ice and water (total volume ≏ 6 litres), and vigorously stir the mixture to solidify the oily layer. Filter off the oily solid at the pump, wash it with cold water, and then stir mechanically with cold 2% aqueous sodium carbonate solution (500 ml.). Filter off the solid at the pump, wash it with cold water, and air-dry on filter paper. Warm the solid with petroleum ether b.p. 60–80° (150 ml.) for half an hour (this removes unreacted o-nitrotoluene), then cool, filter, and dry the solid in a vacuum desiccator giving o-nitrobenzalacetate 21 g., m.p. 87–88° (24% of theory).

o-Nitrobenzaldehyde. Boil a suspension of the diacetate (20 g.) in concentrated hydrochloric acid (110 ml.), water (170 ml.), and ethanol (30 ml.) under reflux for 45 minutes, with mechanical stirring. Cool the mixture to 0°, filter off the solid product at the pump and wash it with water. Dry the crude aldehyde in a vacuum desiccator,† and then purify it by distillation under reduced pressure, giving o-nitrobenzaldehyde 10 g., b.p. 120–144° 3–6 mm. The distillate solidifies to a pale yellow solid, m.p. 44–45°.

(b) Preparation of trans-o-nitro-α-phenylcinnamic acid
In a 150 ml. round-bottomed flask, place o-nitrobenzaldehyde (7·5 g.), phenylacetic acid (10 g.), acetic anhydride (25 ml.), and triethylamine (5 g.). Boil the mixture under reflux for 15 minutes, then cool the solution to 90° and introduce cold water (25 ml.) at such a rate that the temperature of the solution is kept >90° (addition takes ≏ 5 minutes). Filter the hot solution (temperature ≏ 95°), then cool the filtrate to 20°; filter off the orange precipitate at the pump, wash the crystals with 50% aqueous acetic acid (15 ml.), and water. Dry in a vacuum desiccator, giving *trans-o*-nitro-α-phenylcinnamic acid, 10 g., m.p. 195–198° (75% of theory). It may

† The solid may also be purified by recrystallization. Dissolve 11 g. of the dry crude solid in toluene (≏ 2 ml./g.) at room temperature, then dilute the solution with petroleum ether (b.p. 30–60°, 7 ml. per ml. of solution) and cool the resultant solution to −10° or below with scratching. Leave it for half an hour at −10°, then filter off the solid at the pump, giving o-nitrobenzaldehyde as pale yellow needles 9 g., m.p. 44–45°.

be purified by recrystallization from toluene (125 ml.) (*Care: very inflammable solvent*), giving the pure acid as yellow prisms 9 g., m.p. 198° (70% of theory).

(c) Preparation of o-amino-α-phenylcinnamic acid

Pass hydrogen sulphide gas† into a solution of *o*-nitro-α-phenylcinnamic acid (8 g.) in 0·88 aqueous ammonia (40 ml.) and water (80 ml.) for 6 hours at 0°. Heat the reaction mixture (to expel the excess of ammonia and hydrogen sulphide), then filter it to remove precipitated sulphur. Just acidify the filtrate with dilute acetic acid; filter off the yellow precipitate and dissolve it in boiling dilute hydrochloric acid, then filter the hot solution. Add dilute aqueous ammonia to the filtrate until it is just alkaline, and then re-acidify the solution with dilute acetic acid and filter off the precipitated amino-acid at the pump. Recrystallize it from toluene (*care*), giving pure *o*-amino-α-phenylcinnamic acid as yellow needles 7 g., m.p. 184–185° (95% of theory).

(d) Preparation of phenanthrene-9-carboxylic acid

Dissolve *o*-amino-α-phenylcinnamic acid (6·0 g.) in concentrated hydrochloric acid (13·2 g.) and water (400 ml.) with warming. Cool the solution to 0° and add dropwise a solution of sodium nitrite (2·8 g.) in water (40 ml.). Add copper powder (7 g.) to the diazonium solution with stirring, when nitrogen is evolved. Leave the suspension for 1 hour at room temperature with occasional shaking, and then warm the mixture on a water-bath to complete reaction (as is shown by the absence of a red colour on coupling with alkaline *β*-naphthol). Filter off the precipitated solid at the pump, dissolve it in dilute aqueous ammonia and filter the solution (to remove copper powder). Acidify the filtrate with concentrated hydrochloric acid, and filter off the precipitated solid with suction. Recrystallize it from glacial acetic acid giving phenanthrene-9-carboxylic acid as colourless needles, 5 g., m.p. 250–252° (90% of theory).

† Hydrogen sulphide is very poisonous and this operation must be performed in an efficient fume-cupboard.

Reformatsky Reaction

This reaction is the condensation of a carbonyl compound with an α- or β-halogeno-ester in the presence of zinc to give a β- or γ-hydroxy-ester respectively. The reaction may be performed in an inert solvent; usually ether, benzene, or toluene. The reaction is of wide application, thus the carbonyl compound may be an aliphatic or aromatic aldehyde, ketone, or ester. Aldehydes usually react under milder conditions than ketones. α-Bromoesters are favoured, because the relative reactivity is: $ICH_2COOR > BrCH_2COOR > ClCH_2COOR$, and the bromo compounds are often more readily accessible. Under normal conditions chloroesters do not appear to react, but they will do so if a mixture of *copper powder and zinc* is employed.

The mechanism of the Reformatsky reaction resembles the addition of organo-magnesium halides (Grignard reagents) to carbonyl compounds, and may be illustrated by considering the formation of ethyl-β-hydroxy-β,β-diphenylpropionate from benzophenone and α-bromoacetic ester (ethyl bromoacetate):

$$(C_6H_5)_2CO + BrCH_2CO_2Et + Zn \rightarrow (C_6H_5)_2C(OH) \cdot CH_2CO_2Et$$

Mechanism

$$Zn + BrCH_2CO_2Et \rightarrow Br\overset{\delta+}{Zn} \cdot \overset{\delta-}{C}H_2CO_2Et$$

$$(C_6H_5)_2\overset{\delta+}{C}{=}\overset{\delta-}{O} + Br\overset{\delta+}{Z}n\overset{\delta-}{C}H_2CO_2Et \rightarrow (C_6H_5)_2C\overset{\displaystyle OZnBr}{\underset{}{-}}CH_2CO_2Et$$

$$\xrightarrow[\text{H}_2\text{O/H}^+]{\text{Hydrolysis}}$$

$$(C_6H_5)_2\underset{\beta}{C}\overset{\displaystyle OH}{\underset{}{-}}\underset{\alpha}{CH_2}CO_2Et$$

Like the analogous reactions with Grignard reagents, strictly anhydrous conditions must be employed.

Example 1. Preparation of Ethyl-β-hydroxy-β, β-diphenylpropionate

Place a mixture of benzophenone (3·6 g.), α-bromoacetic ester† (4 g.), dry clean zinc turnings (1·6 g.), and anhydrous benzene (20 ml.), in a round-bottomed flask equipped with an efficient reflux condenser. Heat cautiously until reaction commences and then moderate the reaction by cooling in ice-water; so that the reaction proceeds briskly without becoming violent. Complete the reaction by boiling the mixture under reflux for three-quarters of an hour. Then cool and treat the product with ice-cold dilute sulphuric acid. Transfer the mixture to a separatory funnel and separate the upper benzene layer. Wash it twice with water and then dry over anhydrous sodium sulphate. Remove the desiccant by filtration, and distil off the benzene yielding an oily residue which solidifies on standing. Recrystallize the crude solid from aqueous alcohol, giving ethyl-β-hydroxy-β,β-diphenylpropionate 3 g., m.p. 87° (60% of theory based on benzophenone).

Example 2. Preparation of Ethyl β-Hydroxy-β-phenyl-β-Methylpropionate

$$\begin{array}{c} C_6H_5 \\ \diagdown \\ C{=}O + Zn + Br{\cdot}CH_2{\cdot}CO_2Et \rightarrow \\ \diagup \\ CH_3 \end{array}$$

Acetophenone   α-Bromoacetic ester

$$\begin{array}{c} C_6H_5 \quad OZnBr \\ \diagdown \diagup \\ C \\ \diagup \diagdown \\ CH_3 \quad CH_2CO_2Et \end{array} \downarrow {}_{H_2O/H^+}$$

$$\begin{array}{c} C_6H_5 \quad OH \\ \diagdown \diagup {}_\beta \\ C \\ \diagup \diagdown {}_\alpha \\ CH_3 \quad CH_2CO_2Et \end{array}$$

Ethyl β-hydroxy-β-phenyl-β-methylpropionate

In a 500 ml. round-bottomed flask fitted with a reflux condenser, place acetophenone (12 g.), α-bromoacetic ester† (20 g.), zinc turnings (8 g.), and anhydrous benzene (75 ml.). Heat the mixture

† α-Bromoacetic ester must be handled carefully *in the fume cupboard*, since it is lachrymatory.

on a water-bath with occasional shaking until the reaction begins. Then remove flask from the bath until the reaction slackens, and afterwards boil for three quarters of an hour with frequent shaking. Decant the liquid from any unreacted zinc, cool, and add an equal volume of ice-cold dilute sulphuric acid. Remove the upper benzene layer, and extract the aqueous layer with ether. Then combine the extracts, wash with water, and dry over anhydrous sodium sulphate. Remove the solvents by distillation (*care*), and finally distil the residue under reduced pressure, yielding ethyl β-hydroxy-β-phenyl-β-methylpropionate as a colourless liquid 16 g., b.p. 145–147°/15 mm. (76% of theory based on acetophenone).

Reimer-Tiemann Reaction

This reaction is the conversion of a phenol into the corresponding hydroxy-aldehyde. The conversion is generally effected by heating the phenol with chloroform in an aqueous solution of sodium hydroxide; however other bases, e.g. alkali carbonates or pyridine, may be employed together with bromoform, iodoform, or trichloro-acetic acid. (If carbon tetrachloride is used in place of chloroform the hydroxy-acid is formed.)

The reaction produces a mixture of the *o*- and the *p*-hydroxy-aldehydes the former generally predominating; the precise ratio is dependent upon the nature of the substituents and the solvent: thus when pyridine is used only the *o*-aldehyde is obtained. The yields are normally approximately 20–40%. The scope of the Reimer–Tiemann reaction is rather limited; for instance, it is generally inhibited by the presence of electron-attracting substituents which deactivate the aromatic nucleus, and it only proceeds with compounds containing phenolic hydroxyl groups whose *o*- and *p*-positions are activated by phenoxide ion formation. Aryl ethers do not react but pyrrole and indole will yield the corresponding *o*-aldehydes.

The most probable reaction mechanism involves the bivalent carbon intermediate, dichlorocarbene $:CCl_2$, which is known to be formed in the alkaline hydrolysis of chloroform:

$$CHCl_3 + OH^- \underset{\text{Fast}}{\overset{(-H_2O)}{\rightleftharpoons}} :CCl_3^- \xrightarrow[\text{Slow}]{-Cl^-} :CCl_2$$

This highly reactive electrophile then reacts with the carbanion formed by π-delocalization of the phenoxide ion:

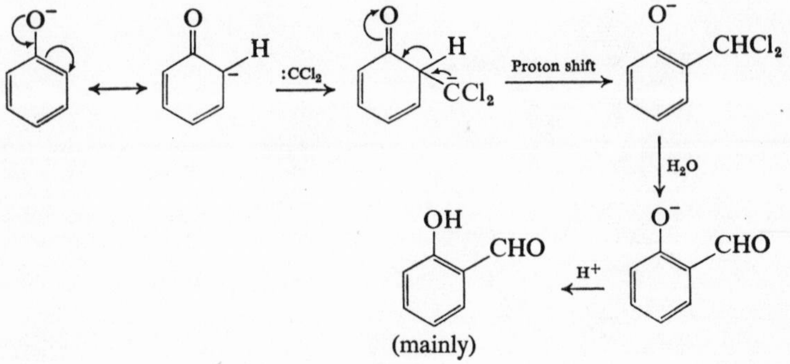

(mainly)

118

The main evidence for such a mechanism arises from the following observations:

1. From *p*-cresol the ketone (I) has been isolated:

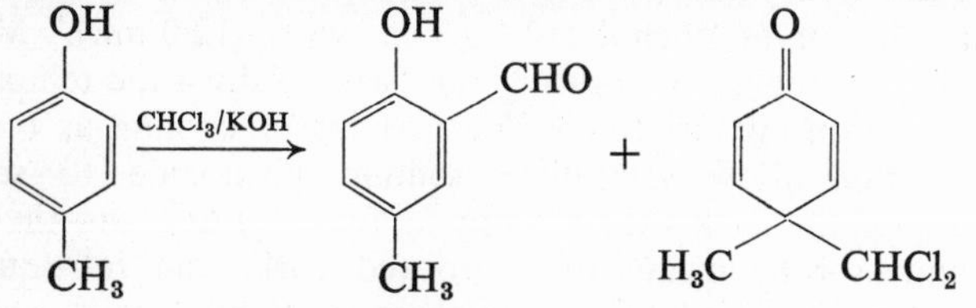

(mainly)   (I)

Similar dichloromethylketones have also been obtained as by-products in other Reimer–Tiemann reactions.

2. The rate of reaction of chloroform with hydroxide ion is much faster than the analogous reaction with phenoxide ion; this makes the alternative mechanism involving the latter reaction unlikely.

3. When chloroform is treated with a base in the presence of cyclohexene the bicyclic dichloride (II) is formed

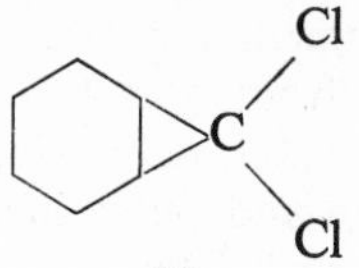

(II)

This is powerful evidence for the formation of dichlorocarbene, since it is well known that this compound will add across olefinic double bonds yielding 1:1-dichlorocyclopropanes.

Example 1. Preparation of Salicylaldehyde (O-Hydroxybenzaldehyde)

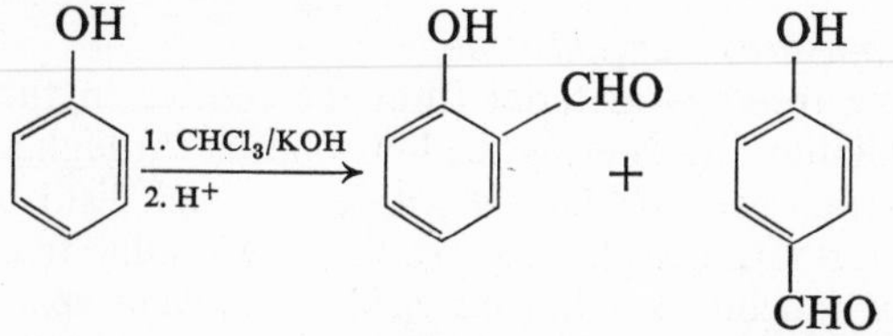

Phenol   Salicylaldehyde   *p*-Hydroxybenz-
                                    aldehyde

Equip a 500 ml. round-bottomed flask with an efficient reflux condenser and a thermometer, and arrange the thermometer bulb to be within 1 cm. of the bottom of the flask. Place a warm solution of sodium hydroxide (40 g.) in water (40 ml.) in the flask, and add a solution of phenol (12·5 g.) in water (12·0 ml.). Mix the contents thoroughly by swirling the flask. Adjust the temperature of the reaction mixture to 60–65°, warming or cooling as required, but do not allow crystalline sodium phenoxide to separate out. Equip the flask with a dropping funnel, fitted into the top of the condenser by means of a grooved cork, and introduce the chloroform (30 g. ≡ 20·5 ml.) in three portions over a period of ten minutes. Maintain the temperature at 65–70° by warming or cooling, and then complete the reaction by heating on a boiling water-bath for 30 minutes. Steam distil the mixture to remove the excess of chloroform; allow the residue in the flask to cool and acidify the orange solution cautiously with dilute sulphuric acid. Steam distil the acidified residue until no further oily droplets are present in the distillate. (Retain the residue in the flask to isolate the p-hydroxybenzaldehyde also formed in the reaction.)

Extract the distillate immediately with ether, and remove most of the ether by distillation from a water-bath (care). Transfer the residue to a separatory funnel, add twice the volume of saturated sodium bisulphite solution and shake mechanically for 30 minutes, and then allow the mixture to stand at room temperature for one hour. Filter off the bisulphite derivative at the pump, wash it with a little ethanol and finally with a little ether (to remove phenol). Decompose the bisulphite derivative by warming it on a water-bath with dilute sulphuric acid in a round-bottomed flask, allow to cool, extract with ether, and dry the extract with anhydrous sodium sulphate. Filter and distil off the ether (care) and finally distil the residue from an air-bath, collecting salicylaldehyde, (a colourless liquid), at 195–197°. The yield is ≃ 4·9 g. (31% of theory).

To isolate p-hydroxybenzaldehyde
Remove the resinous material from the residue in the flask after steam distillation, by filtering the hot solution through a fluted filter paper. Extract the *cold* filtrate with ether, and distil off the ether from a water-bath (care). Recrystallize the residue from hot water containing aqueous sulphurous acid to prevent oxidation. The yield of p-hydroxybenzaldehyde (colourless crystals) is 1·2 g., m.p. 116°.

Example 2. Preparation of β-Hydroxynaphthaldehyde

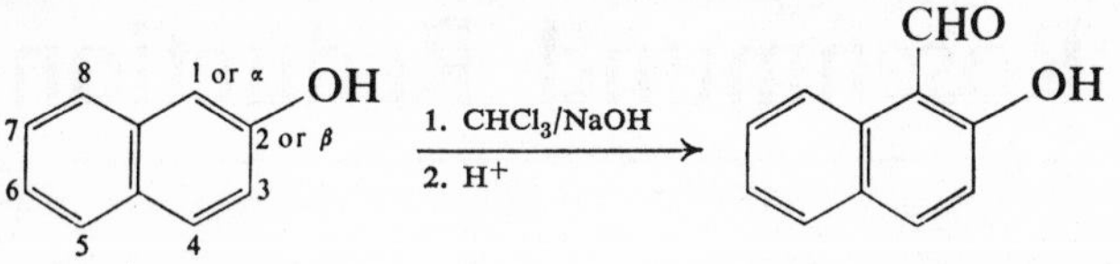

β-Naphthol
(2-Hydroxynaphthalene)

β-Hydroxynaphthaldehyde

Equip a 500 ml. round-bottomed flask with a reflux condenser. Place β-naphthol (10 g.) and sodium hydroxide (20 g.) in a mixture of water (40 ml.) and ethanol (40 ml.) in the flask. Add chloroform (10 g.) dropwise over 10 minutes, from a dropping funnel fitted to the top of the condenser by means of a grooved cork. The start of the reaction will be indicated by a blue colouration. During the reaction heating will not be needed as it is sufficiently exothermic to maintain the reaction. The reaction time is approximately 30 minutes; completion of reaction is indicated by the development of a light red colour, unaltered by the addition of either chloroform or more alkali. Distil off the ethanol and acidify the residue with hydrochloric acid. The crude hydroxy-aldehyde will separate as an oil; extract it with ether, and dry the ethereal extract over anhydrous sodium sulphate. Remove the desiccant by filtration, and distil off the ether (*care*). Distil† the residue under reduced pressure giving β-hydroxynaphthaldehyde 9 g., b.p. 177–180°/20 mm., m.p. 80° (80% of theory).

† Purification may also be effected by recrystallization from ethanol.

Rosenmund Reduction

This is the selective hydrogenation of an acid chloride to the corresponding aldehyde in the presence of a suitable catalyst, e.g. palladium partially poisoned by addition of sulphur or thiourea:

$$R{\cdot}CO{\cdot}Cl + H_2 \xrightarrow{Pd/BaSO_4} R{\cdot}CHO + HCl$$

The catalyst activity is reduced, in order to prevent further reduction of the aldehyde to the alcohol.

Example. Preparation of β-Naphthaldehyde

(a)

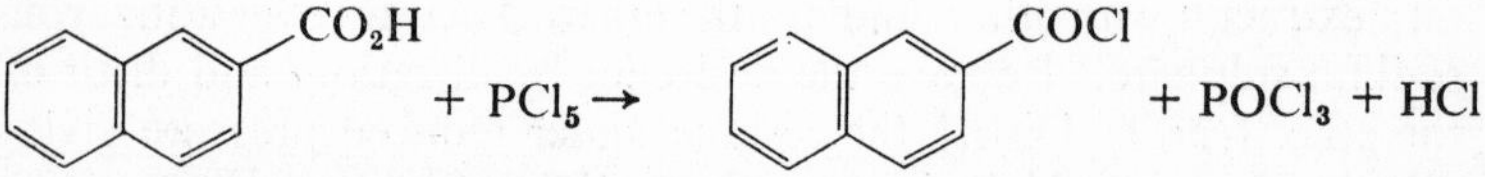

β-Naphthoic acid
(Naphthalene-2-carboxylic acid)

β-Naphthoyl chloride

(b)

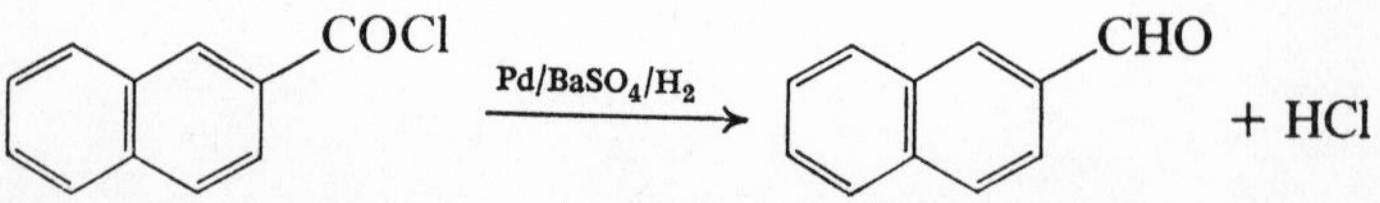

β-Naphthoyl chloride

β-Naphthaldehyde

(a) *β-Naphthoyl chloride*
Place β-naphthoic acid (29 g.), and phosphorus pentachloride (35 g.) in a 150 ml. round-bottomed flask in a fume cupboard. Warm the mixture on a water-bath with occasional stirring, and when a vigorous reaction starts remove the flask from the water-bath until the rapid evolution of hydrogen chloride has ceased. Finally heat on

the water-bath for half an hour, and distil the mixture under reduced pressure collecting β-naphthoyl chloride at 160–162°/11 mm. On cooling the distillate solidifies giving a white solid 30 g., m.p. 50–52°.

Palladium-Barium Sulphate Catalyst

Add a solution of palladium chloride (0·9 g.) in water (25 ml.) and formalin (1 g.) to a suspension of barium sulphate (10 g.) (which has been precipitated from a hot solution) in hot water (200 ml.). Make the suspension slightly alkaline to litmus by addition of sodium hydroxide solution, and boil for a few minutes.

When the supernatant liquid is clear, filter off the grey precipitate, and wash it with hot water until the washings are neutral. Finally dry the catalyst in a vacuum desiccator over sodium hydroxide pellets; powder in a glass mortar, and keep in a well-stoppered bottle.

Quinoline–Sulphur Poison

Boil sulphur (1 g.) with quinoline (6 g.) for 5 hours, and then dilute the brown liquid with xylene (70 ml.) (which has been distilled from anhydrous aluminium chloride).

(b) β-Naphthaldehyde

Equip a 250 ml. three-necked round-bottomed flask with a reflux condenser, a mercury-sealed stirrer, and a gas inlet tube, (see Figure 4). In the flask, place β-naphthoyl chloride (29 g.), dry xylene (100 ml.), palladium–barium sulphate catalyst (3 g.), and quinoline–sulphur poison (0·3 ml.). Attach a rubber tube from the top of the condenser to a short length of glass tube dipping to the bottom of a 250 ml. conical flask containing distilled water (200 ml.) and a few drops of phenolphthalein indicator. Arrange a burette filled with approximately 1N sodium hydroxide solution, so that it can be run into the conical flask; this flask must be at least 3 feet away from any flame. First displace the air in the reaction flask by hydrogen, and then heat the flask in an oil-bath at 140–150° while vigorously stirring the reaction mixture. The course of the reduction is followed by the rate of hydrogen chloride evolution: the first 25 ml. of alkali should be neutralized in approximately 15 minutes, and reaction should be complete in 2 hours, as indicated by hydrogen chloride evolution which will cease. (Approximately 90% of the calculated amount of HCl $\equiv$ 142 ml. of 1N NaOH solution is measured.) Cool

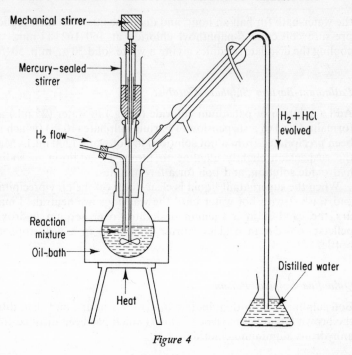

Figure 4

the reaction flask, add activated charcoal (1 g.) while stirring, and filter the solution at the pump (place the precipitate in a bottle kept for palladium residues). Distil off the xylene, and then distil the residual β-naphthaldehyde under reduced pressure. Collect the fraction b.p. 147–149°/11 mm. (oil-bath temperature 160–170°), which solidifies to a white solid, 19 g., m.p. 58–60° (85% of theory).

Sandmeyer Reaction

This is the decomposition of aromatic diazonium salts by warming with cuprous halide, cyanide, or thiocyanide; resulting in replacement of the diazonium group by the halogeno, cyano, or thiocyano group respectively:

$$ArNH_2 \xrightarrow[0°]{NaNO_2/HCl} Ar\overset{+}{N_2}\overset{-}{Cl} \xrightarrow[(X=Hal,\,CN,\,or\,SCN)]{CuX} ArX + N_2$$

A modification is the formation of aryl iodides, by merely warming the diazonium compound with potassium iodide solution:

$$Ar\cdot\overset{+}{N_2}\overset{-}{Cl} \xrightarrow{KI} ArI + KCl + N_2$$

The reaction mechanism in the case of the conversion of aromatic diazonium compounds to aryl halides appears to proceed through aryl radicals since the reaction mixture may be used to initiate the polymerization of acrylonitrile. Kinetic studies show that the reaction is first order with respect to both diazonium ion and dissolved 'cuprous chloride' (actually $CuCl_2^-$ produced by dissolution of cuprous chloride in the chloride solution; $CuCl + Cl^- \rightarrow CuCl_2^-$), indicating the following rate-determining step:

$$Ar\cdot N_2^+ + CuCl_2^- \xrightarrow{Slow} Ar\cdot + CuCl_2 + N_2$$

The reaction is hindered by a large excess of hydrochloric acid, indicating that the complex $CuCl_4^{3-}$ ion is less effective in converting the diazonium ion to an aryl radical. The final stage is a radical displacement reaction by the aryl radical on the chlorine atom of the cupric chloride:

$$Ar\cdot + Cl\!-\!Cu\!-\!Cl \xrightarrow{Fast} Ar\!-\!Cl + CuCl$$

Preparation of the Cuprous Chloride Solution

Dissolve hydrated copper sulphate (12 g.) and pure sodium chloride (3·1 g.) in water (42 ml.), warming if required. Add sodium bisulphite (2·8 g.) (assuming a purity of 90%) dissolved in water

(30 ml.) to the hot solution during approximately 5 minutes with constant shaking. Cool the solution to room temperature, but preferably in an ice-bath, and then decant the supernatant liquor from the colourless cuprous chloride. Wash the precipitate twice with a small volume of water containing a little sulphurous acid. Dissolve the cuprous chloride in concentrated hydrochloric acid (60 ml.). Stopper the flask loosely (to prevent oxidation) and cool in an ice salt-bath while the diazotization is performed.

Example 1. Preparation of *p*-Chlorotoluene

$$CH_3-\langle\ \rangle-NH_2 \xrightarrow[0-5°]{NaNO_2/HCl}$$

p-Toluidine

$$CH_3-\langle\ \rangle-\overset{+}{N_2}\overset{-}{Cl} \xrightarrow[2.\ Warm]{1.\ CuCl/HCl} CH_3-\langle\ \rangle-Cl$$

p-Chlorotoluene

Dissolve pure *p*-toluidine (4 g.) in concentrated hydrochloric acid (10 ml.) and water (10 ml.) in a 100 ml. conical flask. Cool the solution to 0° in an ice salt-bath with vigorous shaking and the addition of a little crushed ice (the base hydrochloride will separate out). Add, during 10 minutes, a solution of sodium nitrite (3 g.) in water (7 ml.) dropwise from a dropping funnel. Shake or stir the solution well during this addition and do not allow the temperature to exceed 5°. At the end of the addition, the mixture should give a blue colouration to starch–iodide paper indicating the presence of an excess of nitrous acid. Pour this cold solution slowly with shaking into the cold cuprous chloride solution (previously prepared). (The diazonium solution decomposes on standing so mixing should occur without delay.) The mixture will become viscous, the copper complex separating from solution (CuCl, *p*-CH$_3$·C$_6$H$_4$N$_2$$^+Cl^-$). Allow the mixture to warm up to room temperature without external heating and occasionally shake it. When the temperature reaches 15° the complex begins to decompose; evolution of nitrogen occurs and an oily layer of *p*-chlorotoluene will form. Warm the mixture on a water-bath to about 60° to complete the reaction, and shake it occasionally. When the evolution of nitrogen ceases, steam distil the mixture until no more oily drops are present in the distillate. Transfer the distillate to a separatory funnel and remove the upper *p*-chlorotoluene layer. Wash it with 10% aqueous sodium hydroxied solution (5 ml.) (to remove any *p*-cresol), water, and then concentrated sulphuric acid (5 ml.) (to remove any azo compound), followed again by water (to remove the acid). Finally dry the product over anhydrous magnesium sulphate (0·5 g.), and filter it into a 10 ml. distillation flask bearing an air condenser. Distil the liquid using an air-bath, collecting *p*-chlorotoluene 3·5 g., at 158–162° (m.p. 6–7°) (74% of theory).

Example 2. Preparation of *p*-Iodonitrobenzene

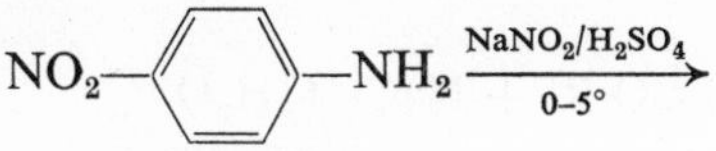

$$NO_2 \underset{\text{\textit{p}-Nitroaniline}}{-\!\!\!\bigcirc\!\!\!-} NH_2 \xrightarrow[\text{0–5°}]{\text{NaNO}_2/\text{H}_2\text{SO}_4}$$

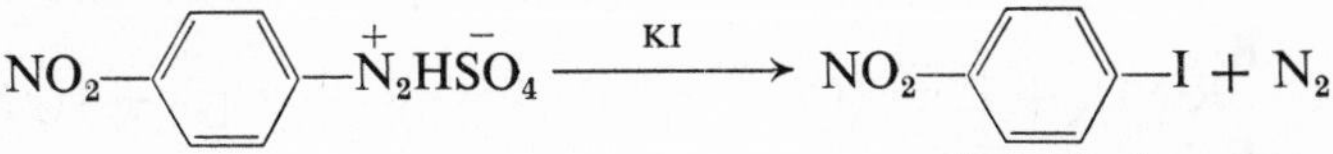

$$NO_2 -\!\!\!\bigcirc\!\!\!- \overset{+}{N_2}\overset{-}{HSO_4} \xrightarrow{\text{KI}} NO_2 \underset{\text{\textit{p}-Iodonitrobenzene}}{-\!\!\!\bigcirc\!\!\!-} I + N_2$$

Stir a mixture of *p*-nitroaniline (1·0 g.), concentrated sulphuric acid (1·5 g. ≡ 0·9 ml.) and water (6 ml.) in a 50 ml. beaker for 15 minutes. Cool the mixture to 0–5°, and diazotize with a solution of sodium nitrite (0·5 g.) in water (2 ml.). Filter the cold solution, and add the filtrate, with stirring, to a solution of potassium iodide (2 g.) in water (6 ml.). Collect the precipitated solid by filtration using suction, and then shake it with sodium thiosulphate solution to remove the excess of iodine. Filter off the product, dry by suction, and then recrystallize it from ethanol. The yield of *p*-iodonitrobenzene is 1·0 g., m.p. 171° (64% of theory based on *p*-nitroaniline).

Schotten-Baumann Reaction

This is the acylation of hydroxyl or amino groups by treatment with an acid chloride in the presence of dilute alkali. Sulphonyl chlorides may also be used in this reaction:

$$R \cdot OH + R' \cdot CO \cdot Cl \xrightarrow{\text{NaOH}} R \cdot O \cdot CO \cdot R' + NaCl + H_2O$$

$$R \cdot NH_2 + R' \cdot CO \cdot Cl \xrightarrow{\text{NaOH}} R \cdot NH \cdot CO \cdot R' + NaCl + H_2O$$

$$R \cdot NH_2 + R' \cdot SO_2Cl \xrightarrow{\text{NaOH}} R \cdot NH \cdot SO_2R' + NaCl + H_2O$$

The reaction is usually carried out in 10% aqueous sodium hydroxide solution using an excess of the acylating agent.

The Schotten–Baumann reaction is important for the characterization of hydroxy and amino compounds. Using benzene or p-toluenesulphonyl chloride, the reaction forms the basis of the Hinsberg separation of primary, secondary, and tertiary amines:

1. $R_3N + CH_3$—⟨benzene ring⟩—$SO_2Cl \xrightarrow{\text{NaOH}}$ No reaction; so R_3N can be distilled off.
   Tertiary

2. $R_2NH + CH_3$—⟨benzene ring⟩—$SO_2Cl \xrightarrow{\text{NaOH}} R_2NSO_2$—⟨benzene ring⟩—$CH_3 \downarrow$
   Secondary   insoluble product

3. $RNH_2 + CH_3$—⟨benzene ring⟩—$SO_2Cl \xrightarrow{\text{NaOH}} RN(Na)SO_2$—⟨benzene ring⟩—$CH_3$
   Primary   soluble in alkali; but precipitated on acidification

$$\downarrow H^+$$

$$R \cdot NH \cdot SO_2\text{—⟨benzene ring⟩—}CH_3$$

The p-toluenesulphonyl derivatives of the primary and secondary amines (from reactions 3 and 2 respectively) are finally hydrolysed to the corresponding amines by boiling dilute acid.

Example 1. Preparation of Phenyl Benzoate

$$C_6H_5{\cdot}OH + C_6H_5{\cdot}COCl \xrightarrow{\text{NaOH}} C_6H_5{\cdot}COOC_6H_5 + NaCl + H_2O$$

Phenol   Benzoyl chloride   Phenyl benzoate

Dissolve phenol (1 g.) in 10% aqueous sodium hydroxide solution (15 ml.) in a 50 ml. conical flask. Add benzoyl chloride (2·2 g. ≡ 2 ml.) (*carry out this operation in a fume cupboard*). Securely cork the flask and vigorously shake the mixture for 15 minutes. (Release the cork from time to time to prevent the build up of pressure.) At the end of this period the reaction should be complete and a solid product will have separated out. Filter off the solid at the pump, breaking up any lumps with a spatula, and afterwards wash it with water, and then dry by suction. Recrystallize the crude product from ethanol, giving phenyl benzoate as colourless crystals. The yield is 1·6 g., m.p. 69° (80% of theory).

Example 2. Preparation of Benzanilide (*N*-Benzoylaniline)

$$C_6H_5{\cdot}NH_2 + C_6H_5{\cdot}COCl \xrightarrow{\text{NaOH}}$$
$$C_6H_5{\cdot}NH{\cdot}CO{\cdot}C_6H_5 + NaCl + H_2O$$

Aniline   Benzoyl chloride   Benzanilide

Add aniline (1 ml. ≡ 1·04 g.) to 10% aqueous sodium hydroxide solution (17 ml.) contained in a 50 ml. conical flask. Add benzoyl chloride (1·7 g. ≡ 1·4 ml.) and shake vigorously for 15 minutes as above. Filter off the solid benzoyl derivative at the pump, break up any lumps and wash thoroughly with water and then dry by suction. Recrystallize from ethanol giving benzanilide as colourless crystals. The yield is 1·8 g., m.p. 163° (79% of theory).

Example 3. Preparation of *N*-Phenyl *p*-Toluenesulphonamide

$$C_6H_5NH_2 + p\text{-}CH_3{\cdot}C_6H_4SO_2Cl \xrightarrow{\text{NaOH}}$$

Aniline   *p*-Toluenesulphonyl chloride

$$C_6H_5NH{\cdot}SO_2C_6H_4{\cdot}CH_3\text{-}p + NaCl + H_2O$$
N-Phenyl *p*-toluenesulphonamide

Suspend aniline (2 g. $\equiv$ 1·9 ml.) in 10 % aqueous sodium hydroxide solution (30 ml.) in a small conical flask. Dissolve p-toluenesulphonyl chloride (5 g.) in the minimum volume of acetone (filtering if necessary), and add the resultant solution gradually with shaking to the aniline suspension. Stopper the flask and shake vigorously; cool if necessary, in water. Test the mixture and make sure it is alkaline during this process. Acidify the mixture with dilute hydrochloric acid and filter off the sulphonamide at the pump. Recrystallize the crude solid from ethanol or aqueous ethanol. The yield is 4·2 g., m.p. 103° (80 % of theory based on aniline).

Skraup Quinoline Synthesis

The reaction is a valuable preparative method for quinolines and involves heating together a primary aromatic amine, anhydrous glycerol, and concentrated sulphuric acid in the presence of a suitable oxidizing agent, such as nitrobenzene or arsenic acid. Moderators, e.g. ferrous sulphate, or water, are also sometimes added. Very satisfactory results are often obtained using iodine as the oxidizing agent, because then there is little danger of a violent reaction, and consequently no moderators are necessary. Unsaturated aldehydes may be sometimes substituted for the glycerol in the reaction.

Some examples to illustrate the scope of the Skraup synthesis are:

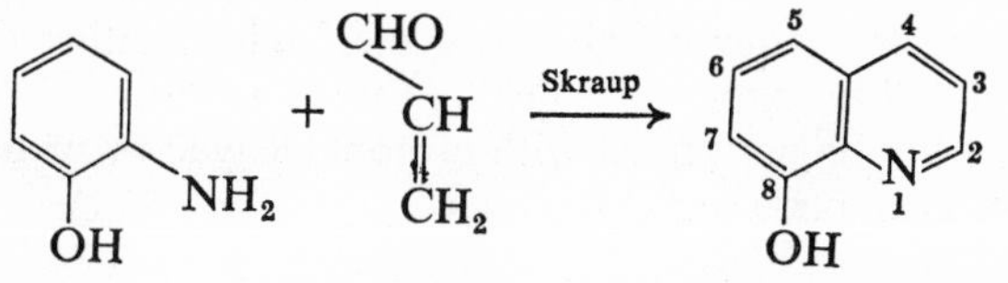

| o-Aminophenol | Acraldehyde (from glycerol) | 8-Hydroxyquinoline (or oxine) |

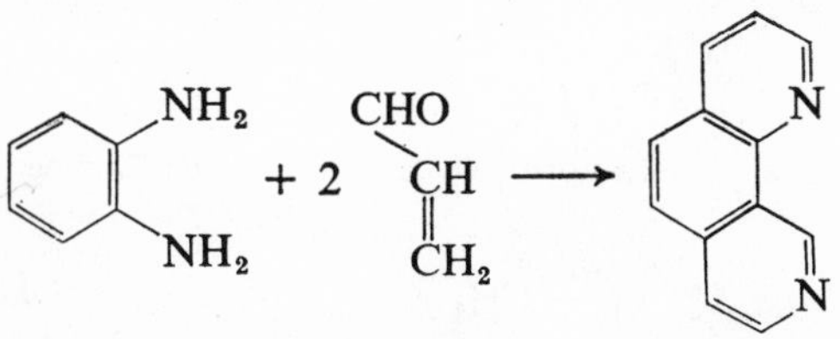

o-Phenylenediamine   Acraldehyde   o-Phenanthroline

Considering the formation of quinoline, the probable reaction sequence is as follows: glycerol is first dehydrated to acraldehyde, to which aniline adds in the 1,2 positions. Then cyclization with loss of water yields 1,2-dihydroquinoline, which is finally oxidized to

131

quinoline by the added oxidant:

1.

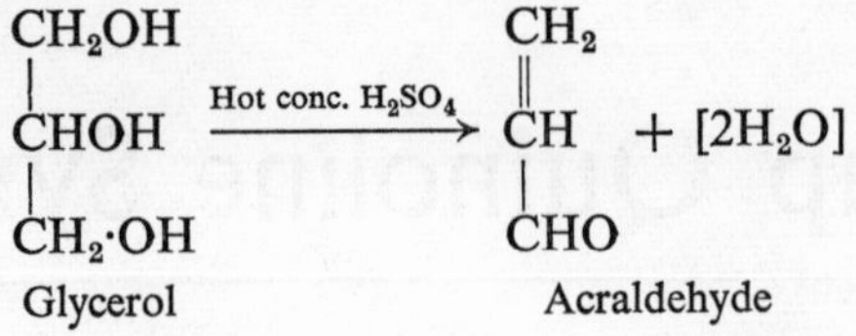

$$
\begin{array}{c}
CH_2OH \\
| \\
CHOH \\
| \\
CH_2 \cdot OH
\end{array}
\xrightarrow{\text{Hot conc. } H_2SO_4}
\begin{array}{c}
CH_2 \\
\| \\
CH \\
| \\
CHO
\end{array}
+ [2H_2O]
$$

Glycerol   Acraldehyde

2.

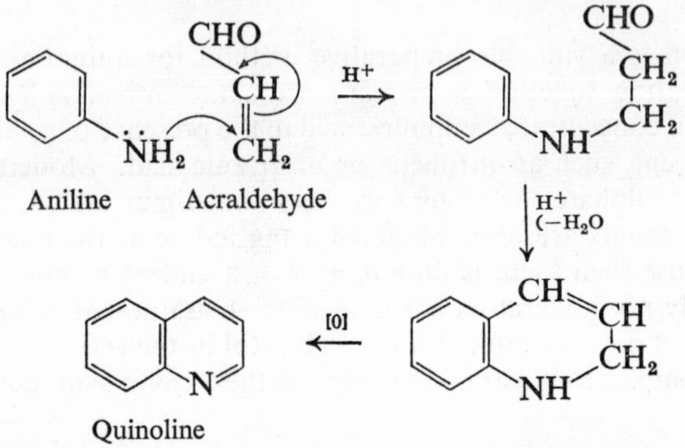

Aniline   Acraldehyde

Quinoline

The evidence in favour of the above mechanism, rather than one based on initial formation of a Schiffs base is as follows. When the Skraup reaction is performed with crotonaldehyde or methyl vinyl ketone, for example, the products are:

1.

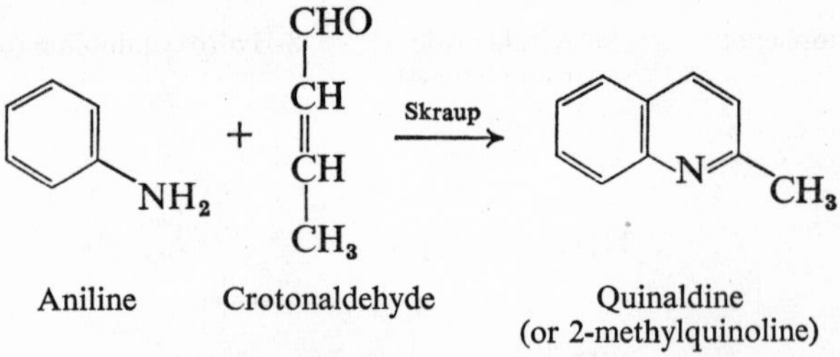

Aniline   Crotonaldehyde   Quinaldine
(or 2-methylquinoline)

2.

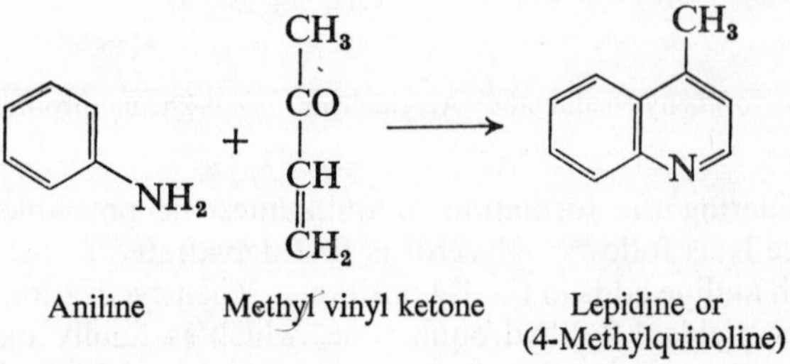

Aniline   Methyl vinyl ketone   Lepidine or
(4-Methylquinoline)

If the reactions had involved the Schiffs base, subsequent cyclization should have yielded 4-methylquinoline and 2-methylquinoline respectively.

Example 1. Preparation of Quinoline

Equip a 250 ml. three-necked flask with a thermometer, a mercury-sealed stirrer, and a condenser. Place redistilled aniline (10·0 g. ≡ 9·8 ml.), laboratory grade glycerol (15·0 g.) and iodine (0·5 g.) in the flask. Set up the apparatus in a fume cupboard, because sulphur dioxide will be liberated during the reaction. Stir the reaction mixture and add concentrated sulphuric acid (30·0 g. ≡ 16·4 ml.) down the condenser. Reaction will soon occur and the temperature will rise to 100–105°. Heat the flask gradually with stirring in an air-bath to 140°, the main reaction will now take place and sulphur dioxide and a little iodine vapour will be evolved and the liquid boils. Heat at 170° for one hour and then allow the flask to cool. Add cautiously, with stirring, sufficient 5N sodium hydroxide (≃ 85 ml.) to make the solution alkaline. Arrange the apparatus for steam distillation, and distil until the distillate is free from quinoline and unreacted aniline; this will be shown by the disappearance of oily droplets in the distillate. Extract the distillate with ether (2 × 25 ml.), and combine the extracts. Distil off the ether from a water-bath (*care*). Dissolve the crude material in 2·5 N-hydrochloric acid (100 ml.) in a 250 ml. beaker and warm to 60°, and then add with stirring a solution of zinc chloride (13 g.) in 2·5 N-hydrochloric acid (22 ml.). Cool the solution thoroughly in ice-water whilst stirring, and filter at the pump when crystallization is complete. Wash the product with dilute hydrochloric acid (2 × 10 ml.) and drain well. Transfer the solid to a 250 ml. beaker, add water, and 10% aqueous sodium hydroxide solution so that the precipitated zinc hydroxide dissolves. Transfer to a separatory funnel and extract with ether (2 × 25 ml.), combine the extracts and dry over anhydrous magnesium sulphate (1 g.).

Filter off the desiccant and distil off the ether from a water-bath (*care*). Finally distil the residue from a 10 ml. distillation flask using an air-bath. The yield of quinoline is 6·9 g., b.p. 238–239° (49% of theory).

NOTES

(i) The preparation of anhydrous glycerol is unnecessary when iodine is employed as the oxidizing agent.

(ii) Quinoline forms a chlorozincate $[(C_9H_7N)_2ZnCl_4]H_2$ with zinc chloride which is practically insoluble in water, whereas the chlorozincate from aniline $[(C_6H_7N)_2ZnCl_4]H_2$ remains in solution under the experimental conditions, thereby leading to a good method of separation of the desired product.

Example 2. Preparation of 6-Nitroquinoline

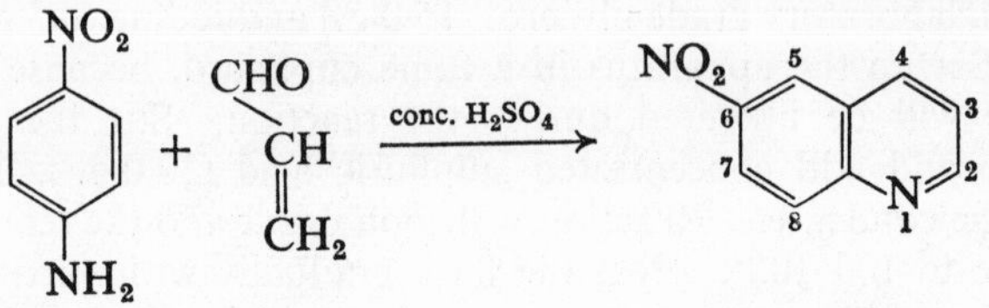

p-Nitroaniline	Acraldehyde	6-Nitroquinoline

Carefully heat a mixture of arsenic acid (11·6 g.), p-nitroaniline (11·2 g.), glycerol (24 g.), and concentrated sulphuric acid (22 g.) under a reflux condenser, until the exothermic reaction is observed, then remove the flame. When the rate of boiling has considerably decreased, heat again, so as to maintain boiling for a further 3 hours. Then dilute the mixture with water, and allow to stand overnight. Filter and make the filtrate alkaline with aqueous sodium hydroxide solution. Filter off the precipitated solid at the pump; dissolve it in hot dilute hydrochloric acid, and treat the solution with activated charcoal. Filter and saturate the filtrate with ammonia gas, collect the precipitated solid at the pump, and recrystallize it from aqueous ethanol yielding 6-nitroquinoline 9·8 g., m.p. 148–149° (70% of theory).

Stephen Reaction

This is the conversion of a nitrile (or cyanide) into an aldehyde by treatment with an ethereal solution of anhydrous stannous chloride and hydrogen chloride. The aldimine hydrochloride is obtained as the initial product, which is subsequently hydrolysed to the aldehyde.

Addition of the dry nitrile to stannous chloride dissolved in ether saturated with hydrogen chloride gives a white crystalline solid (the aldimine-stannichloride, formed by reduction of the imino-chloride) which is converted into the aldehyde by hydrolysis with warm water. The yields from both aliphatic and aromatic nitriles are usually quantitative except for aromatic nitriles containing o-substituents.

The Stephen synthesis may, therefore, be represented as follows:

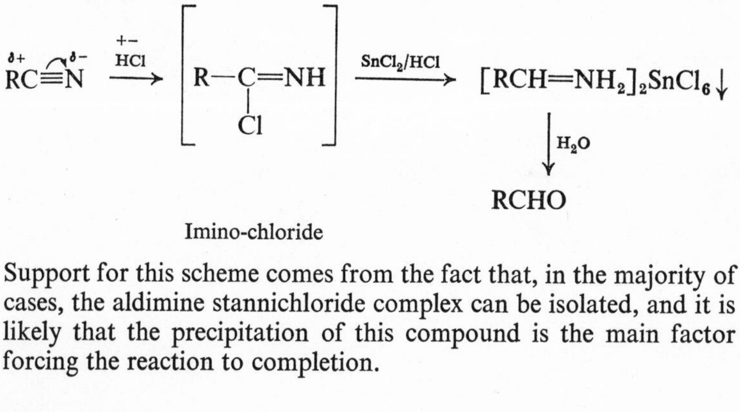

$$\overset{\delta+}{R}\overset{\delta-}{C \equiv N} \xrightarrow{\overset{+-}{HCl}} \left[\underset{\underset{Cl}{|}}{R-C=NH} \right] \xrightarrow{SnCl_2/HCl} [RCH=NH_2]_2SnCl_6 \downarrow$$

$$\downarrow{H_2O}$$

$$RCHO$$

Imino-chloride

Support for this scheme comes from the fact that, in the majority of cases, the aldimine stannichloride complex can be isolated, and it is likely that the precipitation of this compound is the main factor forcing the reaction to completion.

Example Preparation of p-Tolualdehyde (p-Tolylaldehyde)

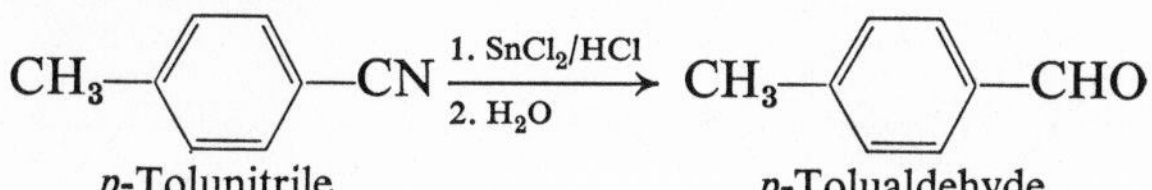

$$CH_3-\!\!\underset{}{\bigcirc}\!\!-CN \xrightarrow[\text{2. } H_2O]{\text{1. } SnCl_2/HCl} CH_3-\!\!\underset{}{\bigcirc}\!\!-CHO$$

p-Tolunitrile p-Tolualdehyde
(p-Tolylcyanide)

Place anhydrous ether (100 ml.) and anhydrous stannous chloride (30 g.) in a three-necked 500 ml. flask equipped with a reflux condenser, a calcium chloride tube, and an inlet-tube leading to the bottom of the flask. Cool the flask in ice-water and pass in dry hydrogen chloride gas, until the stannous salt has formed a heavy oily layer. Add a solution of *p*-tolunitrile (12 g.) in anhydrous ether (30 ml.) over 10 minutes with gentle shaking. Allow to stand at room temperature for one hour, and then remove the aldimine stannichloride by filtration in a fume cupboard. Wash the solid with a little ether and then dissolve it in water (100 ml.) and heat on a steam-bath for 30 minutes. Cool and extract with ether; dry the extract over anhydrous sodium sulphate and then distil off the ether (*care*). Finally distil the residue under reduced pressure, collecting *p*-tolualdehyde 8 g., b.p. 106° at 10 mm. (80% of theory).

Ullmann Reaction

This is the condensation of aryl halides with themselves or with other aromatic halides, by treatment with copper powder at temperatures between 100–300°, to form a biaryl.

The reaction proceeds best with aryl iodides; the order of reactivity being $I > Br > Cl$. The latter two halides only react readily, when they are activated by electron-attracting substituents in the o- or p-positions.

Conversely the synthesis is inhibited by electron-donor groups in these positions. Low yields are often obtained due to side reactions, such as amination, ether formation, or decarboxylation, when the aryl halide possesses the following nuclear substituents: $-NH_2$, $-NHCH_3$, $-COOH$, $-SO_2NH_2$, or $-NHCOCH_3$. The scope of the reaction is wide; both symmetrical and unsymmetrical biaryls and polyaryls may be produced, e.g.

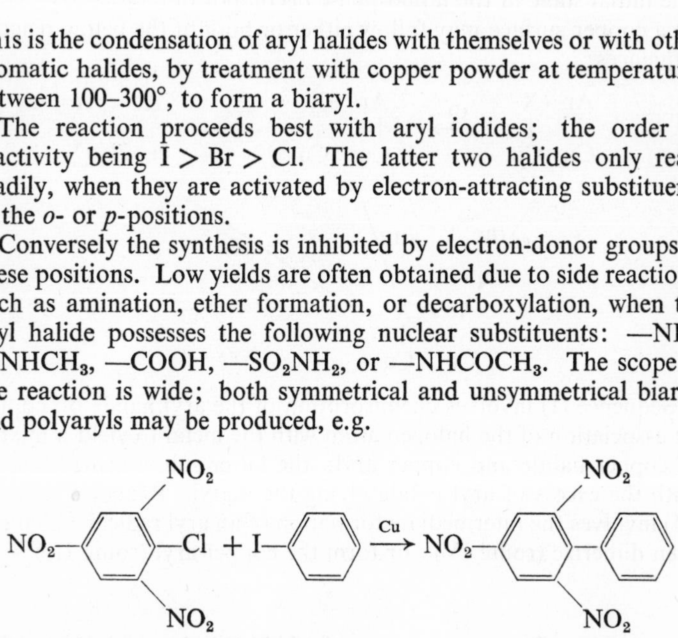

2,4,6-Trinitrochlorobenzene   Iodobenzene   2,4,6-Trinitrobiphenyl

The synthesis may also be intramolecular:

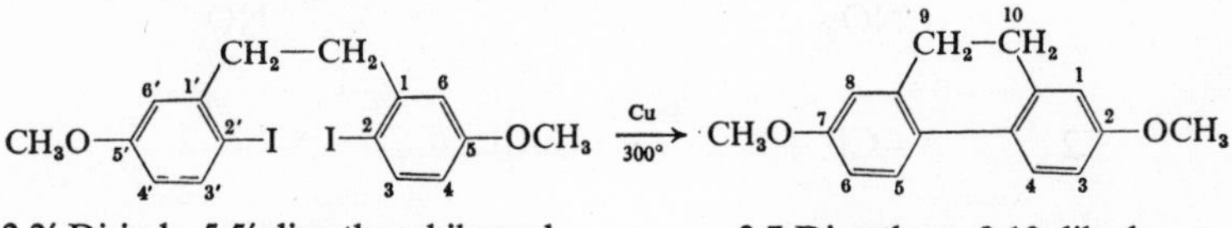

2,2'-Di-iodo-5,5'-dimethoxybibenzyl   2,7-Dimethoxy-9,10-dihydro-phenanthrene

The low yields generally obtained may often be improved by using dimethylformamide, nitrobenzene, toluene, or naphthalene as solvent. The mechanism of the reaction is not fully resolved; it may be a homolytic or a heterolytic process. The latter is thought to be more usual, and the free-radical mechanism is probably restricted to specific cases. The synthesis is now considered to proceed *via* the intermediate formation of the organometallic copper aryl, a thermally unstable species, which can give both ions or radicals:

$$Ar\cdot + Cu \rightleftharpoons Ar\text{-}Cu \rightleftharpoons \overset{-}{Ar}\text{-}\overset{+}{Cu}$$

The initial stage in the liquid-phase decomposition of an aryl halide on a copper surface may follow either or both of the below reaction sequences:

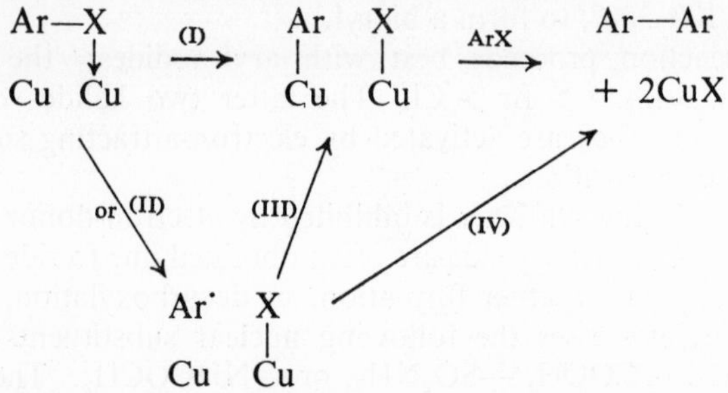

Sequence (I) involves chemisorption of the aryl halide on copper, by association of the halogen atom with the metal to yield a mixture of copper halide and copper aryl; the latter subsequently reacting with the excess of aryl halide giving the diaryl. Reaction sequence (II) involves the intermediate formation of an aryl radical which may then dimerize (route IV); or form the copper aryl (route III).

Example. Preparation of 2,2'-Dinitrobiphenyl

Method I

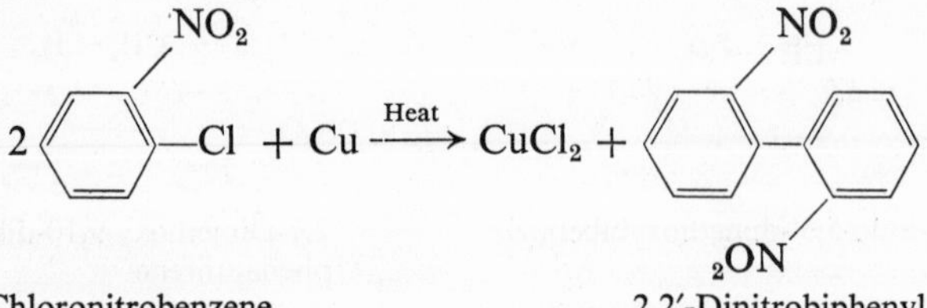

o-Chloronitrobenzene   2,2'-Dinitrobiphenyl

Place *o*-chloronitrobenzene (5 g.) in a 50 ml. flask, equipped with a mechanical stirrer, and heat it in an oil or fusable metal bath to

215–225°. Add, over a period of 10 minutes, copper bronze (5 g.) (or activated copper bronze). Then keep the temperature at 215–225° for one hour with mechanical stirring. Allow the mixture to cool, and extract with ethanol (2 × 50 ml.), by boiling the residue with the solvent for 10 minutes at each extraction, followed by filtration. Cool the filtrates at 0° and filter off the crude product at the pump. Do not discard the filtrates; combine them, and reduce the volume to half by distillation. Cool the solution and obtain a further crop of crystals. (The total yield of crude solid should be 2·4 g., if it is less than this weight, a third extraction should be made.) Recrystallize the product from hot ethanol (≃ 40 ml.) with added decolourizing charcoal; boil the solution for 5 minutes, and then filter and cool in ice. Finally recrystallize again from hot ethanol. The yield of pure 2,2'-dinitrobiphenyl is 2 g., m.p. 123–124° (51% of theory).

Method II

Place o-bromonitrobenzene (5 g.) in a tube and heat it to 200°. Add copper bronze (3 g.) gradually to the hand stirred solution, using a thermometer as the stirring rod. The copper will lose its lustre and the mass becomes viscous. Heat the reaction mixture at 210–220° for 30 minutes, and then cool. Extract the residue with benzene (3 × 25 ml.), as described in method I. Finally reduce its volume to one half by distillation and cool giving 2:2'-dinitrobiphenyl 4·5 g., m.p. 123–124° (76% of theory).

Ullmann Condensation

This is the condensation of aryl halides with nucleophilic reagents in the presence of a copper catalyst, e.g.

$$C_6H_5Br + C_6H_5ONa \xrightarrow{Cu} NaBr + (C_6H_5)_2O$$

Bromobenzene　　　Sodium phenoxide　　　Diphenyl ether

The reaction is particularly important for the synthesis of *N*-phenylanthranilic acid derivatives, which are intermediates in the preparation of 9-chloroacridines, e.g.

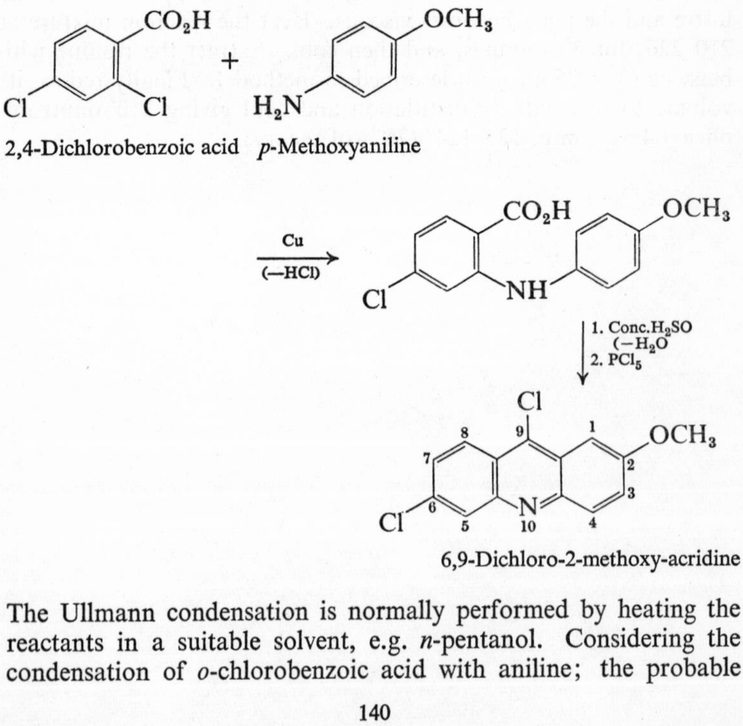

2,4-Dichlorobenzoic acid　　*p*-Methoxyaniline

6,9-Dichloro-2-methoxy-acridine

The Ullmann condensation is normally performed by heating the reactants in a suitable solvent, e.g. *n*-pentanol. Considering the condensation of *o*-chlorobenzoic acid with aniline; the probable mechanism involves attack by the nucleophile on the carbon atom attached to the chlorine:

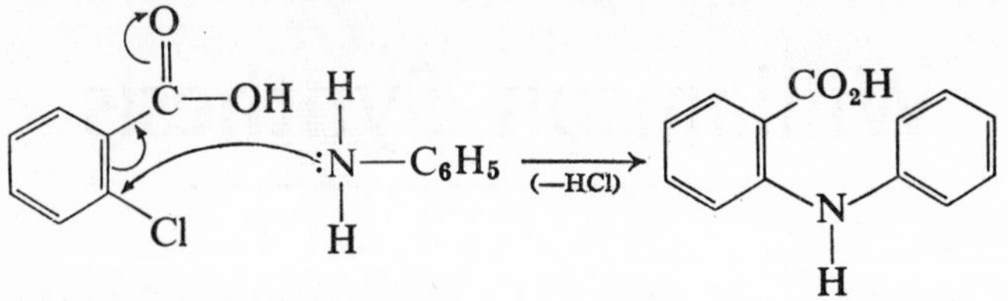

In support of this general scheme, it has been shown that electron-attracting substituents *o* or *p* to the chlorine atom facilitate the reaction; also the reactivity of the nitrogen atom depends on the basic strength of the amine.

Example. Preparation of N-Phenylanthranilic Acid

| o-Chlorobenzoic acid | Aniline | N-Phenylanthranilic acid |

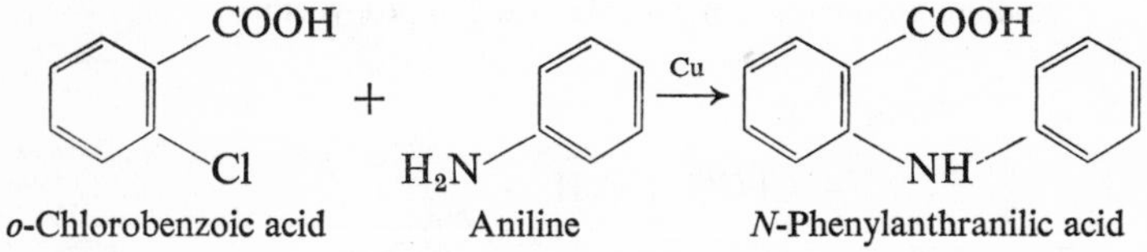

Place together in a 500 ml. round-bottomed flask aniline (21 ml.), o-chlorobenzoic acid (6 g.), anhydrous potassium carbonate (6 g.) and copper oxide (0·5 g.). Equip the flask with an air condenser and boil the mixture under reflux for one hour; the mixture will foam during the early part of the reaction and thus a large flask *must* be used. After one hour arrange the flask for steam distillation, and distil until all the excess aniline has been removed, as shown by the disappearance of oily droplets in the distillate. The residual solution contains the potassium salt of the acid; add activated charcoal (≃ 2 g.) and boil for five minutes, followed by filtration. Acidify the filtrate with dilute hydrochloric acid, until no further precipitation occurs, and then cool in ice water with stirring. Filter off the precipitated acid at the pump, wash it with water, and dry by suction. Recrystallize the solid from aqueous ethanol, giving N-phenyl-anthranilic acid 6 g., m.p. 179–181° (85% of theory).

Williamson Synthesis

This is the production of ethers by treatment of an alkyl halide or dialkyl sulphate with an alkali metal alkoxide:

$$ROM + X-R' \rightarrow R \cdot O \cdot R' + MX \ (M = \text{alkali metal})$$

The reaction is of wide application and can be used to obtain both simple and mixed ethers. The following are some illustrative examples:

$$n\text{-}C_3H_7 \cdot ONa + C_2H_5I \rightarrow C_2H_5 \cdot O \cdot C_3H_7\text{-}n + NaI$$
Sodium propoxide Ethyl iodide Ethyl n-propyl ether

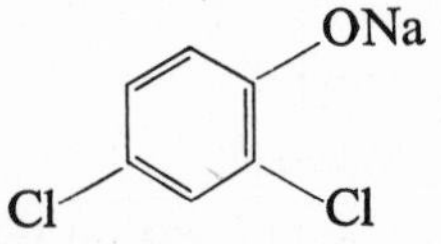

$$+ \ Cl \cdot CH_2 \cdot CO_2H \rightarrow$$
$$(-NaCl)$$

Sodium-2,4-dichlorophenoxide   Chloroacetic acid

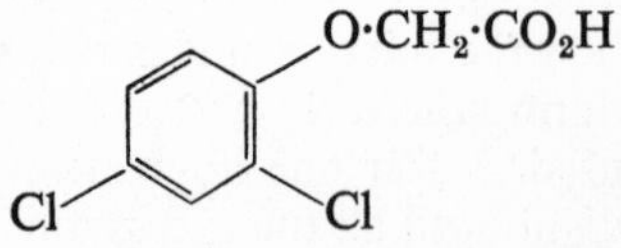

2,4-Dichlorophenoxyacetic acid

$$C_6H_5 \cdot ONa + (CH_3)_2SO_4 \xrightarrow{\text{Heat}} C_6H_5 \cdot O \cdot CH_3 + CH_3NaSO_4$$
Sodium phenoxide Dimethyl sulphate Anisole (Methyl phenyl ether)

Mechanistically the reaction consists of a bimolecular nucleophilic substitution ($S_N:2$) of the halogen atom by the alkoxide ion; and considering the example:

$$R \cdot CH_2 \cdot X + R'OK \rightarrow R \cdot CH_2 \cdot OR' + KX$$

142

The reaction may be formulated as follows:

$$R'O^- \; ^\curvearrowright CH_2 {-} X \;^\curvearrowright \rightarrow \left[R'O {\cdots} \overset{R}{\underset{H \quad H}{C_\alpha}} {\cdots} X \right] \rightarrow R'O{-}\overset{R}{CH_2} + X^-$$

Linear transition state (R'O, C_α and X are collinear)

Such $S_N:2$ reactions are one-stage processes and the rate V is dependant on the concentration of both reactants, i.e. $V = k[R'O^-][R{\cdot}CH_2X]$ (where k is a constant); kinetic studies show that this equation is valid for the Williamson synthesis.

Using primary alkyl halides $R{\cdot}CH_2X$ good yields of ethers are generally obtained; but with secondary or tertiary halides the reaction is unsatisfactory, because now the main product is the olefin arising from the operation of an elimination reaction: for instance with tert.-butyl bromide and sodium ethoxide the major product is isobutylene, and not tert.-butyl ethyl ether:

$$\underset{CH_3}{\overset{CH_3}{CH_3{\to}C{-}Br}} \xrightarrow{(-Br^-)} \underset{CH_3}{\overset{CH_3}{CH_3{-}C^+}} \xrightarrow[\substack{-H^+ \text{ (Abstracted by} \\ OH^- \text{ behaving as} \\ \text{a base)}}]{} CH_2{=}C(CH_3)_2$$

isoButylene

However secondary and tertiary alkyl ethers can be prepared using the Williamson Synthesis, by employing the potassium alkoxides of the corresponding secondary or tertiary alcohols, thus:

$$(CH_3)_3C{\cdot}OK + C_2H_5Br \rightarrow (CH_3)_3C{\cdot}O{\cdot}C_2H_5 + KBr$$

Potassium tert.-butoxide   Ethyl iodide   tert.-Butyl ethyl ether

Under these conditions, the normal $S_N:2$ process occurs yielding the required ether.

Example 1. Preparation of n-Butyl Ethyl Ether

$$n{-}C_4H_9Br + C_2H_5ONa \rightarrow C_2H_5{\cdot}O{\cdot}C_4H_9{-}n + NaBr$$

n-Butyl bromide   Sodium ethoxide   n-Butyl ethyl ether

Place clean sodium (3 g.) in a 150 ml. round-bottomed flask fitted with a double-surface reflux condenser. Add absolute ethanol (60 ml.) down the condenser and allow the reaction to proceed until all the sodium has dissolved. (If the reaction becomes too vigorous cool by immersing *momentarily* in a beaker of cold water.) Then add n-butyl bromide (10·7 g. $\equiv$ 8·3 ml.) down the condenser; fit a cotton wool plug into the top of the condenser, and boil the mixture under reflux on a water-bath for one hour. During this process sodium bromide will be precipitated. Cool the product, add water (30–50 ml.), and transfer the mixture to a separatory funnel. Remove the upper ether layer and wash it with water (20 ml.), and then dry over anhydrous calcium chloride. Remove the desiccant by filtration, and distil the butyl ethyl ether from a 10 ml. distillation flask containing a few boiling granules, collect the fraction boiling at 90–92°. The yield is 7·0 g. (87 % of theory based on butyl bromide).

Example 2. Preparation of Phenetole (Ethylphenyl ether)

$$\text{ONa} \qquad\qquad \text{O}-\text{C}_2\text{H}_5$$

$$+ \ \text{C}_2\text{H}_5\text{Br} \rightarrow \qquad\qquad + \ \text{NaBr.}$$

Sodium phenoxide　Ethyl bromide　Phenetole

Dissolve sodium (3·8 g.) (cut into small pieces) in absolute ethanol (75 ml.), contained in a 250 ml. flask fitted with a double-surface condenser. When all the sodium has dissolved, cool the solution in ice-water, and add phenol (15 g.), which will quickly dissolve forming sodium phenoxide when the mixture is gently shaken. Add ethyl bromide (19·1 g. $\equiv$ 13·2 ml.), some boiling chips, and boil the solution gently under reflux on a water-bath for one hour. Distil off the excess ethanol as completely as possible, and pour the residual liquid in the flask into water (100 ml.) in a separatory funnel. Extract the phenetole by shaking with ether (50 ml.). Run off the lower aqueous layer and shake the ethereal extract with an equal volume of 10 % aqueous sodium hydroxide solution (this will remove any unreacted phenol). Run off the lower sodium hydroxide layer, and then wash the ethereal layer with water (to remove traces of sodium hydroxide). Dry the ethereal layer with anhydrous calcium chloride; remove the desiccant then distil off the ether in a 50 ml. distilling flask (*care*). When all the ether has been removed, replace the water-condenser by an air-condenser, and distil the residual phenetole, collecting the fraction boiling at 168–172°. The yield is 14 g. (61 % of theory based on ethyl bromide).

Wolff-Kishner Reduction

This resembles the Clemmensen reduction, in that it converts the carbonyl group of aldehydes or ketones into a methylene group. The reduction is effected by heating the hydrazone or semicarbazone of the carbonyl compound at 150–200° in the presence of an alkaline catalyst, e.g. potassium hydroxide or sodium ethoxide. In the Huang–Minlon modification the hydrazone is not isolated, it being formed *in situ* and subsequently decomposed by reaction of the carbonyl compound with hydrazine hydrate and sodium hydroxide in a suitable high boiling solvent such as di- or tri-ethylene glycol. This procedure greatly reduces the reaction time.

Advantages, as compared with the Clemmensen reduction, are that both acid sensitive and high molecular weight compounds may be reduced, and the yields do not decrease in large-scale preparations. Considering the general reduction:

$$\diagdown_{\diagup}C=O \xrightarrow{N_2H_4} \diagdown_{\diagup}C=N-NH_2 \xrightarrow{OH^-} \diagdown_{\diagup}CH_2 + N_2$$

The mechanism probably involves the initial removal of a proton from the weakly acidic hydrazone by the base, giving the stabilized anion as shown below:

$$\diagdown_{\diagup}C=N-NH_2 \underset{H^+}{\overset{OH^-}{\rightleftharpoons}} \left(\diagdown_{\diagup}C=N-\ddot{\underset{..}{N}}-H \right) + H_2O$$

$$\updownarrow$$

$$\left(\diagdown_{\diagup}\ddot{\underset{..}{C}}-N=N-H \right)$$

Subsequent addition of a proton to the carbanion (I) yields the unstable compound (II) which loses nitrogen at high temperatures, possibly by a free-radical mechanism, yielding the final product:

$$\underset{(I)}{\overset{..}{\underset{/}{\overset{\backslash}{C}}}-N=N-H} \underset{-H^+}{\overset{H^+}{\rightleftharpoons}} \underset{(II)}{\overset{\backslash}{\underset{/}{C}}\overset{\overset{H}{\diagup}}{\underset{N=NH}{\diagdown}}} \longrightarrow \overset{\backslash}{\underset{/}{C}}H_2 + N_2$$

Example 1. Preparation of Ethylbenzene

$$\underset{\text{Acetophenone}}{C_6H_5COCH_3} \longrightarrow \underset{\text{Ethylbenzene}}{C_6H_5C_2H_5}$$

Place redistilled acetophenone (9 g.), diethylene glycol (75 ml.), hydrazine hydrate (7·5 ml. of 90%) and potassium hydroxide pellets (10 g.) in a 150 ml. Claisen flask equipped with a reflux condenser and a thermometer dipping into the liquid. Warm the mixture on a boiling water-bath, until most of the potassium hydroxide has dissolved, then boil under reflux for one hour. Arrange the apparatus for distillation and distil until the temperature rises to 175° retaining the distillate (≃15 ml.). Separate the upper hydrocarbon layer from the distillate, and extract the aqueous layer with ether (2 × 20 ml.). Dry the combined hydrocarbon layer and the ethereal extracts with anhydrous sodium sulphate. Filter and distil off the ether (care). Distil the residue from a 50 ml. distillation flask, collecting ethylbenzene 5·6 g., b.p. 135–136° (70% of theory).

Example 2. Preparation of p-Ethyltoluene

p-Methylacetophenone hydrazone   p-Ethyltoluene

Boil p-methylacetophenone (6 g.) under reflux with 85% hydrazine hydrate (12 g.) for one hour. Cool the solution and extract it with ether; wash the ethereal extract with a little water and dry it over potassium hydroxide pellets. Decant, and remove the ether by distillation from a water-bath, and finally distil the residual liquid under reduced pressure. Collect p-methylacetophenone hydrazone at

166–168°/16 mm.; it solidifies in the receiver (m.p. 34°). Mix the hydrazone (5 g.) with powdered potassium hydroxide (2 g.) in a small flask fitted with a reflux condenser, the top of which is connected to a gas burette. Gently heat the mixture in the flask to 90–100°, and maintain this temperature until most of the calculated volume of nitrogen has been collected. Then heat the flask to 150°, and afterwards cool, and add water to the contents of the flask. Extract with ether; dry the ethereal extract over anhydrous sodium sulphate, filter off the desiccant, and distil off the ether from a water-bath (care). Finally distil the residual liquid giving p-ethyltoluene 3·2 g., b.p. 157–160° (80 % of theory).

Wöhler Synthesis

This refers to the formation of urea by the isomerization of ammonium cyanate (structurally this compound is probably an isocyanate):

$$NH_4 \cdot N{=}C{=}O \xrightarrow{\text{Heat}} NH_2 \cdot CO \cdot NH_2$$

Ammonium cyanate   Urea (Carbamide)

This process was first carried out by Wöhler in 1828 and is of considerable historic interest, since it led to the breakdown of the theory of vital force. Ammonium cyanate is an unstable compound, and is accordingly prepared *in situ* from ammonium sulphate and potassium cyanate:

$$(NH_4)_2SO_4 + 2K \cdot NCO = 2NH_4NCO + K_2SO_4$$

The generally accepted mechanism of the Wöhler synthesis possibly involves the following stages:

1. $NH_4 \cdot NCO \xrightarrow{\text{Dissociation}} NH_3 + H \cdot N{=}C{=}O$

2.

$$H_3N{:}\ C{=}O \longrightarrow H_2N{-}\underset{NH}{\overset{\|}{C}}{-}OH \xrightarrow{\text{Rearrangement}} H_2N{-}\underset{O}{\overset{\|}{C}}{-}NH_2$$

In the second step, the liberated nucleophilic ammonia attacks the electrophilic carbonyl carbon atom.

The Wöhler reaction may be extended to the synthesis of substituted ureas, by treatment of cyanic acid or an alkyl/aryl isocyanate with the appropriate primary or secondary amine. Analogous reactions using isothiocyanates yield thioureas:

$$R \cdot NH_2 + \begin{cases} H \cdot N{=}C{=}O \xrightarrow{\text{Warm}} R \cdot NH \cdot CO \cdot NH_2 \\ H \cdot N{=}C{=}S \longrightarrow R \cdot NH \cdot CS \cdot NH_2 \\ R' \cdot N{=}C{=}O \longrightarrow R \cdot NH \cdot CO \cdot NH \cdot R' \\ R' \cdot N{=}C{=}S \longrightarrow R \cdot NH \cdot CS \cdot NH \cdot R' \end{cases}$$

and: $NH_4 \cdot N{=}C{=}S \xrightarrow{\text{Heat}} NH_2 \cdot CS \cdot NH_2$

Ammonium thiocyanate   Thiourea

These reactions provide support for the suggested mechanism of the Wöhler synthesis:

$$RR'\overset{..}{N}H + \overset{\frown}{C}\overset{\frown}{=}O \rightarrow RR'N-\underset{\underset{R''N}{\|}}{C}-OH \rightarrow RR'N-\underset{\underset{R''NH}{|}}{C}=O$$

Example 1. Preparation of Urea (or Carbamide)

In a porcelain basin dissolve potassium cyanate (12 g.), and ammonium sulphate (10 g.) in water (80 ml.). Evaporate the solution to dryness on a steam-bath (takes 4–5 hours). The crust of solid potassium sulphate which forms on the surface of the liquid must be continually broken up, and heating maintained until the residue is quite dry. Place the solid residue in a 100 ml. round-bottomed flask fitted with a reflux condenser, add ethanol (40 ml.), and gently boil for 10 minutes. Filter, and cool the filtrate in ice-water, when urea crystallizes out as white needles 4 g., m.p. 132° (45% of theory). Some further product may be obtained by concentration of the filtrate.

Example 2. Preparation of Phenylurea

$$\underset{\text{Aniline}}{PhNH_2} \cdot \xrightarrow{\text{HOAc}} Ph\overset{+}{N}H_3\overset{-}{O}Ac \xrightarrow{\text{NaCNO}} [Ph\overset{+}{N}H_3 \cdot \overset{-}{C}NO] \longrightarrow \underset{\text{Phenylurea}}{PhNH \cdot CONH_2}$$

Dissolve aniline (1·9 g. ≡ 1·8 ml.) in glacial acetic acid (2 ml.) diluted with water to 20 ml., contained in a 50 ml. beaker or conical flask. Add with shaking a solution of sodium cyanate (1·3 g.) in warm water (10 ml.). Leave the mixture for 30 minutes at room temperature, then filter off the precipitate with suction, wash it with water, and dry at 100°. The product is generally a pure, colourless, solid, and melts at 148°. (If not, recrystallize from boiling water in the presence of a little activated charcoal.) The yield of phenylurea is 2 g., m.p. 148° (72% of theory).

Wurtz and Wurtz-Fittig Synthesis

Wurtz Synthesis

This is the reaction between an alkyl halide and metallic sodium in ether yielding a hydrocarbon:

$$2RX + 2Na \rightarrow 2NaX + R\text{---}R$$

Alkyl bromides and iodides are favoured and high yields are obtained with primary halides; but with tertiary halides the olefin is formed. With two different alkyl halides a mixture of products results:

$$R\text{---}X + 2Na + R'\text{---}X \rightarrow R\text{---}R' + R'\text{---}R' + R\text{---}R + 2NaX$$

It is difficult to separate the individual hydrocarbons, and so the method is only effective for the preparation of symmetrical hydrocarbons.

Wurtz–Fittig Synthesis

This is the analogous reaction between alkyl and aryl halides:

$$ArX + 2Na + RX \rightarrow Ar\cdot R + 2NaX$$

Ar—Ar and R—R are also formed as by-products; however separation can be effected by fractional distillation.

The mechanism of the Wurtz synthesis may be either ionic or free radical, though the former appears more likely, i.e.

$$RX + 2Na \rightarrow \overset{-}{R}\overset{+}{Na} + NaX$$

$$\overset{-}{R}\overset{+}{Na} + \overset{\delta^+\delta^-}{RX} \rightarrow R\text{---}R + NaX$$

This ionic mechanism is supported by the isolation of organo-sodium intermediates under special conditions. Also some optically active halides, e.g.

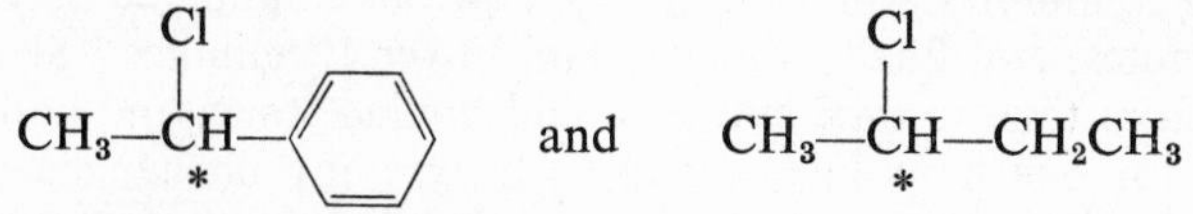

(* = An asymmetric carbon atom)

yield hydrocarbons with inversion of configuration, suggesting a bimolecular nucleophilic displacement reaction ($S_N:2$) involving the organosodium compound:

$$RX + 2Na \rightarrow \bar{R} \overset{+}{Na} + NaX$$

Then:

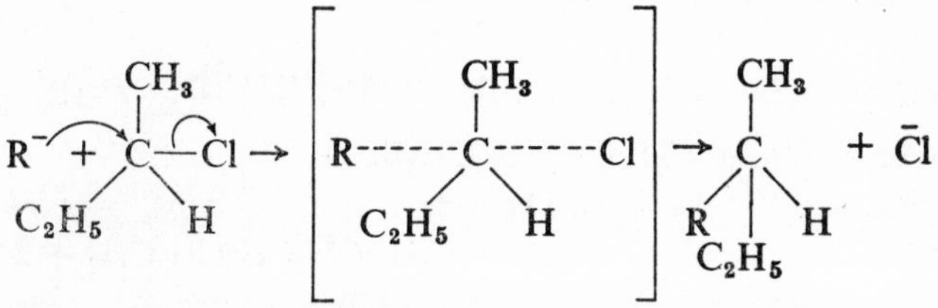

Linear transition state   Inversion

Wurtz Reaction

Example. Preparation of n-Octane

$$2CH_3CH_2CH_2CH_2Br + 2Na \rightarrow C_8H_{18} + 2NaBr$$
n-Butyl bromide   n-Octane

Place clean sodium† (8 g.) (cut in small pieces) in a 250 ml. round-bottomed flask, and equip it with a double-surface reflux condenser. Arrange the apparatus so that the flask may be heated over a wire-gauze. Weigh out n-butyl bromide (24 g.≡18 ml.) and add (2 ml.) down the condenser. If no reaction occurs, warm the flask with a small luminous flame, removing the flame as soon as reaction begins (the sodium will become blue in colour). When the reaction subsides, shake the flask vigorously, this will often cause further reaction and some of the sodium will melt. Add n-butyl bromide (2 ml.) and shake the flask, and when the reaction has subsided repeat the process until all the n-butyl bromide has been added (about 30 minutes).

Allow the reaction mixture to stand for one hour with occasional shaking. After this time add, by means of a dropping funnel fitted to the top of the condenser by a slotted cork, ethanol (30 ml.), dropwise during 30 minutes, followed by 50% aqueous ethanol (20 ml.) during 15 minutes, and finally water (20 ml.) over 10 minutes. Shake the flask from time to time and then add boiling stone, and boil under reflux for one hour in order to hydrolyse any unchanged n-butyl bromide. Pour the reaction mixture into a large excess of water (250 ml.) and separate the upper octane layer (6 g.). Wash it with water (an equal volume), and dry over anhydrous sodium sulphate. Filter the octane from the desiccant, collecting the filtrate in a Claisen flask fitted with a short fractionating column. The yield of n-octane is 5 g., b.p. 123–126° (48% of theory).

Wurtz–Fittig Reaction

Example 1. Preparation of n-Butylbenzene

$C_6H_5Br + 2Na + CH_3 \cdot CH_2CH_2CH_2Br \rightarrow$

Bromobenzene   n-Butyl bromide

$$C_6H_5 \cdot CH_2CH_2CH_2CH_3 + 2NaBr.$$

n-Butylbenzene

Place clean sodium† (11·2 g.) (cut in small pieces or preferably as wire) in a 250 ml. round-bottomed flask. Equip the flask with a double-surface condenser, stand it on an asbestos centred wire-gauze, and cover the sodium with dry ether (50 ml.). Mix together bromo-benzene (26·0 g.≡17·6 ml.) and n-butyl bromide (24·6 g.≡20 ml.) and add this mixture cautiously down the condenser with shaking. Set the flask aside overnight, decant the liquid, and wash the blue solid with dry ether (2 × 10 ml.). Combine and distil off the ether from a water-bath. (*care*). Destroy the excess of sodium present by carefully treating the blue solid with ethanol (30 ml.), and then 50% aqueous ethanol (25 ml.), and finally water (25 ml.). Separate the n-butylbenzene layer, dilute it with ether (10 ml.), and dry over anhydrous magnesium sulphate; then filter and distil off the ether.

† *Treatment of sodium*
Sodium metal is stored in bottles under toluene or xylene, remove 2 or 3 lumps of the metal, place on dry filter paper and dry with filter paper. Then carefully remove any tarnished surfaces with a knife. placing these under toluene or xylene in a bottle reserved for sodium residues. Finally cut the clean, dry metal into small pieces and immediately place the correct weight of it in the reaction flask (see experimental detail.).

(*care*). Finally distil the residue from a 20 ml. Claisen flask using an air-bath, collecting n-butylbenzene at 180–184°. The yield is 9·6 g. (40% of theory based on n-butyl bromide).

Example 2. Preparation of Bibenzyl

$$2C_6H_5CH_2Cl + 2Na \rightarrow C_6H_5CH_2 \cdot CH_2C_6H_5 + 2NaCl$$

Benzyl chloride   Bibenzyl

Add sodium wire (6 g.) to benzyl chloride (25 g.) in a round-bottomed flask equipped with a reflux condenser. Boil the mixture under reflux on a water-bath, until no further change occurs. Cool and extract the mixture with ether, dry the ethereal extract over anhydrous sodium sulphate, filter, and distil off the ether (*care!*). Fractionally distil the residue, collecting the fraction boiling at 244–254° which solidifies on cooling. Recrystallize the product from ethanol giving bibenzyl, as colourless needles, 12 g.; m.p. 51–52°, b.p. 248°. (40% of theory).

6

MISCELLANEOUS
REACTIONS

Benzidine Rearrangement

This is the conversion of a hydrazobenzene into a 4,4'-diamino-biphenyl by treatment with an acid, e.g.

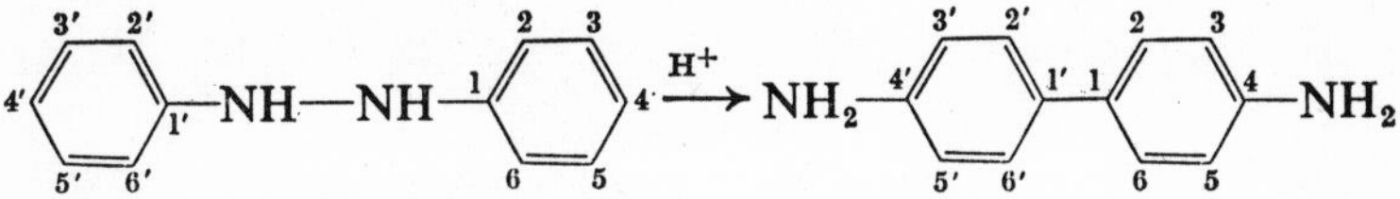

Hydrazobenzene (N,N'-Diphenylhydrazine) Benzidine (4,4'-Diaminobiphenyl)

The process has been proved to be intramolecular, because the rearrangement of an unsymmetrical hydrazobenzene never gives any of the symmetrical benzidines, i.e.

$$\text{Ar—NH—NH—Ar'} \xrightarrow{H^+} \text{H}_2\text{N—Ar—Ar'—NH}_2 \text{ with none of the}$$

products $\text{H}_2\text{N—Ar—Ar—NH}_2$ or $\text{H}_2\text{N—Ar'—Ar'—NH}_2$

e.g.

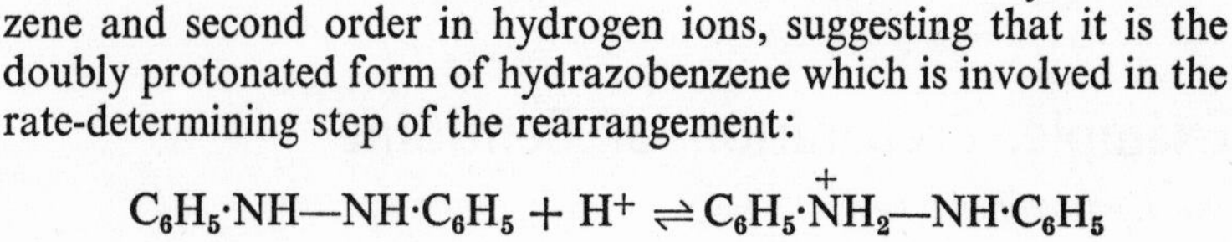

3-Methylhydrazobenzene   2-Methylbenzidine

The reaction rate has been found to be first order in hydrazobenzene and second order in hydrogen ions, suggesting that it is the doubly protonated form of hydrazobenzene which is involved in the rate-determining step of the rearrangement:

$$\text{C}_6\text{H}_5\text{·NH—NH·C}_6\text{H}_5 + \text{H}^+ \rightleftharpoons \text{C}_6\text{H}_5\text{·}\overset{+}{\text{N}}\text{H}_2\text{—NH·C}_6\text{H}_5$$

$$\text{C}_6\text{H}_5\text{·}\overset{+}{\text{N}}\text{H}_2\text{—NH·C}_6\text{H}_5 + \text{H}^+ \rightleftharpoons \text{C}_6\text{H}_5\text{·}\overset{+}{\text{N}}\text{H}_2\text{—}\overset{+}{\text{N}}\text{H}_2\text{·C}_6\text{H}_5$$

$$\text{C}_6\text{H}_5\overset{+}{\text{N}}\text{H}_2\text{—}\overset{+}{\text{N}}\text{H}_2\text{·C}_6\text{H}_5 \rightarrow \text{H}_2\text{N—C}_6\text{H}_4\text{—C}_6\text{H}_4\text{—NH}_2 + 2\text{H}^+$$

In the last step the electrostatic repulsion between the two positive charges probably weakens the nitrogen–nitrogen bond, causing the development of opposite charges in the two *p*-positions, leading eventually to rupture of the original nitrogen-nitrogen bond and simultaneous formation of a new carbon–carbon link between the 4 and 4′-positions. So the probable mechanism may be formulated as follows:

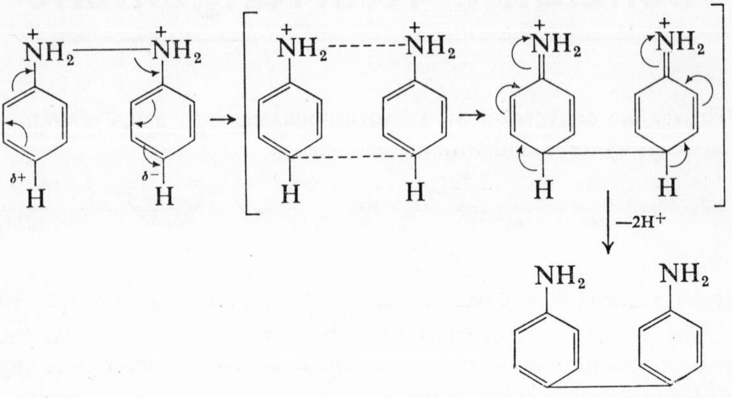

The benzidine rearrangement also occurs easily with substituted hydrazobenzenes, *provided the p-positions to the imino groups are vacant.*

E.g.,

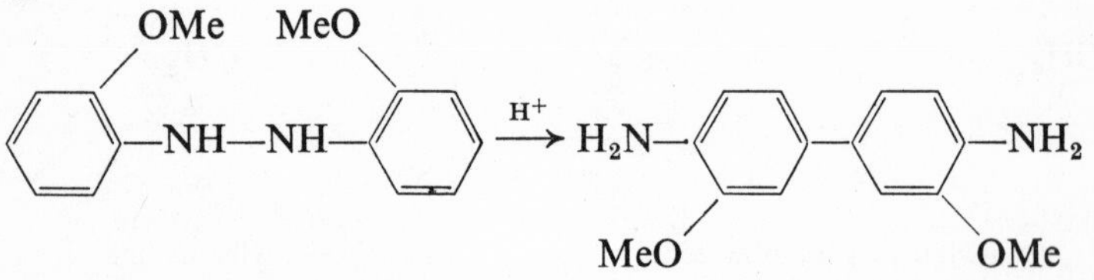

2,2′-Dimethoxyhydrazobenzene   3,3′-Dimethoxybenzidine

Example. Preparation of Benzidine

(*a*) *Hydrazobenzene*

$$2C_6H_5 \cdot NO_2 + 5Zn + 10\,NaOH \rightarrow C_6H_5NH—NH \cdot C_6H_5 +$$

Nitrobenzene   Hydrazobenzene

$$5Na_2ZnO_2 + 4H_2O$$

Place nitrobenzene (15 ml.), ethanol (120 ml.), and a solution of sodium hydroxide (10 g.) in water (20 ml.) in a 500 ml. round-bottomed flask. Attach an efficient reflux condenser, and heat the mixture to 70° on a steam-bath. Then take the flask off the bath, wrap it in a cloth, and shake vigorously. Weigh out zinc dust (40 g.) and add a portion of the zinc (5 g.) to the reaction mixture with further vigorous shaking until the reaction begins; if the reaction becomes violent, moderate it by cooling the flask in cold water. After the reaction subsides, reheat the flask on the steam-bath, remove it, and add another portion of zinc dust (5 g.) as previously and shake vigorously. Continue this process, adding all the zinc dust portion-wise, until the colour of the solution changes from red to pale yellow. Now add ethanol (35 ml.), boil, and filter quickly using a preheated Buchner funnel, and extract the residue of zinc oxide with a little hot ethanol. Place the filtrate (and washings) in a conical flask and cool rapidly by immersion in an ice-bath. Filter off the hydrazobenzene at the pump (work as fast as possible, and do not suck air through the crystals to avoid oxidation of the product), and wash the solid with a little cold ethanol. The yield of hydrazobenzene, as colourless plates, is 12 g., m.p. 125° (45% of theory).

(b) Rearrangement of Hydrazobenzene into Benzidine
Dissolve crude hydrazobenzene (6 g.) in ether (50 ml.) and add the solution portionwise into a 250 ml. conical flask containing con-centrated hydrochloric acid (25 ml.), water (25 ml.), and a few lumps of ice, and surround it by a beaker filled with crushed ice and water. After each addition of the ethereal solution, stopper the flask, and shake it thoroughly. The reaction is accompanied by the gradual precipitation of benzidine hydrochloride. When all the hydrazo-benzene solution has been added, more concentrated hydrochloric acid (35 ml.) is run into the mixture which is left in the ice-bath for half an hour. Filter off the benzidine hydrochloride with suction; wash it with 20% aqueous hydrochloric acid (15 ml.), and finally with ether (three portions of 10 ml. each). (This will remove any unreacted hydrazobenzene.) Dissolve the benzidine hydrochloride (approximately 7 g.) in warm water (100 ml.), filter the solution, and quickly cool it to 15°. Add the solution to a mixture of 10% aqueous sodium hydroxide solution (35 ml.) and crushed ice (100 g.) in a 250 ml. beaker. Stir well during the addition. Filter off the product at the pump, and thoroughly wash the solid with water. Recrystallize it from aqueous ethanol giving benzidine monohydrate as colourless plates, m.p. 100–105° with decomp. Dry in a vacuum desiccator giving anhydrous benzidine 3 g., m.p. 127–128° (50% of theory).

Benzilic Acid Rearrangement

This is the base-catalyzed conversion of aromatic-1,2-diketones into salts of α-hydroxycarboxylic acids:

$$Ar \cdot CO \cdot CO \cdot Ar \xrightarrow{OH^-} Ar_2C(OH) \cdot CO_2^-$$

The best known example is the conversion of benzil into benzilic acid:

$$C_6H_5 \cdot CO \cdot CO \cdot C_6H_5 \xrightarrow{OH^-} (C_6H_5)_2C(OH) \cdot CO_2^-$$

Benzil   Benzilic acid (anion)
(Diphenylglyoxal)   (α-Hydroxy-α,α-diphenylacetic acid)

The probable mechanism for the rearrangement is as follows:

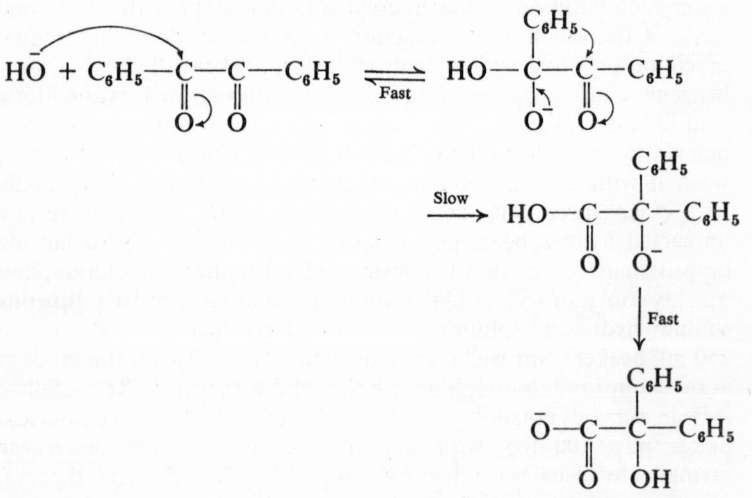

Kinetic measurements show that the overall rate of the reaction is second order (first order with respect to both hydroxide ion and benzil), i.e. $V = k[\text{Ph·CO·CO·Ph}][\text{OH}^-]$. Further, it has been found that benzil undergoes O^{18} exchange on treatment with a solution of potassium hydroxide in labelled water (enriched with H_2O^{18}) much more rapidly than it rearranges. This indicates that the initial addition of hydroxide ion is rapid and reversible; and it is the subsequent rearrangement, the migration of the phenyl group with its electron pair to the weakly positive carbon atom of the adjacent carbonyl group, which is the rate-determining step.

Example Preparation of Benzilic Acid

(a) *Preparation of Benzil.*

$$C_6H_5CO\cdot CHOH\cdot C_6H_5 \xrightarrow[(HNO_3)]{\text{Oxidation}} C_6H_5COCOC_6H_5$$

Benzoin   Benzil

Place benzoin (10 g.) and concentrated nitric acid (30 ml.) in a 150 ml. round-bottomed flask. Heat the mixture in a fume cupboard on a steam-bath with occasional shaking, for about 2 hours (until the evolution of brown fumes stops). Pour into a stirred mixture of crushed ice and water, filter off the crystalline precipitate with suction, and wash it with water to remove acid. Recrystallize the solid from boiling ethanol ($\simeq$20 ml.), yielding benzil as yellow prisms 8 g., m.p. 95° (80% of theory).

(b) *Rearrangement of Benzil to Benzilic acid*

Place a solution of potassium hydroxide (5 g.) in water (10 ml.), in a 100 ml. round-bottomed flask and add ethanol (15 ml.) with swirling. Now introduce pure benzil (5 g.) which dissolves giving a bluish-black solution, and then boil under reflux on a water-bath for a quarter of an hour. Pour the contents into a conical flask and cool in ice with swirling. Filter off the crystals of potassium benzilate at the pump, and wash them with a little ice-cold ethanol. Dissolve the salt in water ($\simeq$50 ml.), add concentrated hydrochloric acid (3 drops) with stirring, and filter off the reddish-brown precipitate. Gradually acidify the filtrate, which should be colourless, with more concentrated hydrochloric acid ($\simeq$8 ml.) until the liquid is acid to Congo-red paper. Filter off the precipitate of benzilic acid at the pump; wash it thoroughly with water (to remove chlorides), and recrystallize from boiling water in the presence of activated charcoal. The yield of pure benzilic acid is 4 g., m.p. 149–150° (78% of theory).

Benzoin Condensation

This reaction involves two molecules of an aromatic aldehyde joining together to form an aromatic α-hydroxyketone (a benzoin). The reaction is specifically catalysed by cyanide ion, and the probable mechanism is as follows:

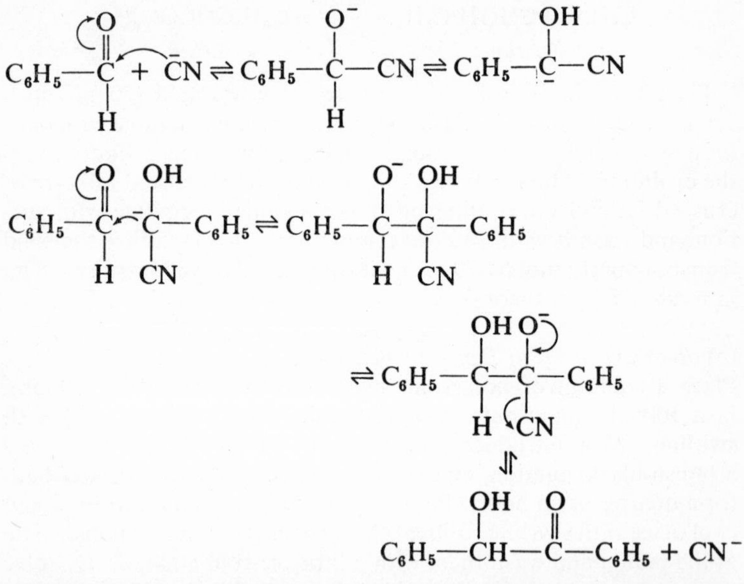

$$C_6H_5-\underset{\underset{H}{|}}{\overset{O}{\overset{\|}{C}}} + \bar{C}N \rightleftharpoons C_6H_5-\underset{\underset{H}{|}}{\overset{O^-}{\overset{|}{C}}}-CN \rightleftharpoons C_6H_5-\underset{\underset{|}{\cdot}}{\overset{OH}{\overset{|}{C}}}-CN$$

$$C_6H_5-\underset{\underset{H}{|}}{\overset{O}{\overset{\|}{C}}}\overset{}{\underset{\underset{CN}{|}}{C}}-C_6H_5 \rightleftharpoons C_6H_5-\underset{\underset{H}{|}}{\overset{O^-}{\overset{|}{C}}}-\underset{\underset{CN}{|}}{\overset{OH}{\overset{|}{C}}}-C_6H_5$$

$$\rightleftharpoons C_6H_5-\underset{\underset{H}{|}}{\overset{OH}{\overset{|}{C}}}-\underset{\underset{CN}{|}}{\overset{O^-}{\overset{|}{C}}}-C_6H_5$$

$$C_6H_5-\underset{\underset{}{}}{\overset{OH}{\overset{|}{C}}}H-\overset{O}{\overset{\|}{C}}-C_6H_5 + CN^-$$

Nucleophilic attack by the cyanide ion at the carbonyl carbon atom makes the attached hydrogen atom reactive (acidic); this is then abstracted by the base yielding a carbanion, which attacks the carbonyl group of a second molecule of benzaldehyde. Finally the adduct gives benzoin by ejection of a cyanide anion.

In this scheme the last step is probably the rate-determining one, which is supported by kinetic studies showing that the benzoin condensation is first order in cyanide ion and second order in benzaldehyde, i.e. $V = k[\text{Ph·CHO}]^2[\text{CN}^-]$. Substituted benzaldehydes similarly yield the corresponding symmetrical benzoins. With two different aldehydes the reaction often produces a single mixed benzoin, as the main product:

$$\text{ArCHO} + \text{Ar'CHO} \xrightarrow{\text{CN}^-} \text{Ar·CO·CHOH·Ar'} + \text{ArCHOH·COAr'}$$

(mainly)

The benzoin condensation is inhibited by powerful electron-attracting groups, e.g. *p*-bromo and nitro groups; it also fails when the strongly electron-donating dimethylamino group, is substituted *p*- to the aldehyde group.

Example 1. Preparation of Benzoin (α-Hydroxybenzyl Phenyl Ketone)

$$2\text{C}_6\text{H}_5\text{CHO} \xrightarrow{\text{CN}^-} \text{C}_6\text{H}_5·\text{CH(OH)·CO·C}_6\text{H}_5$$

Benzaldehyde   Benzoin

In a fume cupboard dissolve sodium cyanide† (1·5 g.) in water (15 ml.) in 200 ml. round-bottomed flask, and add ethanol (25 ml.) followed by pure benzaldehyde (15 ml.). Attach a reflux condenser, introduce a few boiling chips and gently boil the mixture under reflux on a steam-bath for half an hour. Cool the flask in an ice-bath with swirling, and filter off the product at the pump. Wash it with cold water, and a little cold 50% aqueous ethanol. Finally air-dry the material on filter paper. The yield of benzoin is 12 g., m.p. 134–136° (75% of theory). Recrystallize a small portion of the product (1 g.) from boiling ethanol (≃10 ml.); on cooling pure benzoin separates out as white needles 0·8 g., m.p. 137°.

Example 2. Preparation of αα-Furoin

Furfural (Furfuraldehyde)   α,α-Furoin

† Sodium cyanide is very poisonous and *must be treated with extreme care.* Wash the hands well after weighing it out; the filtrate, which contains cyanide must be poured down the drain at *the back of the fume cupboard* and well flushed down with water.

This may be similarly obtained from sodium cyanide (1 g.), water (15 ml.), ethanol (10 ml.) and furfuraldehyde (8 g.). After heating, make the reaction mixture slightly acid by addition of acetic acid, then cool and filter as before. Purify by recrystallization from ethanol in the presence of activated charcoal (to remove coloured impurities). The yield of α,α-furoin is 4 g., m.p. 135° (50% of theory).

Diazoaminobenzene Rearrangement

When diazoaminobenzene is warmed with a weakly acid catalyst, e.g. aniline hydrochloride, an intermolecular rearrangement occurs yielding p-aminoazobenzene.

The mechanism is probably as follows:

1. Protonation of the diazoaminobenzene followed by breakdown of the protonated species to yield the diazonium cation and aniline

$$C_6H_5 \overset{\overset{\displaystyle \cdot\cdot}{}}{\underset{\underset{\displaystyle H}{|}}{N}} - N{=}N - C_6H_5 + C_6H_5NH_3^+ \rightleftharpoons$$

$$\left[C_6H_5\underset{\underset{\displaystyle H}{|}}{\overset{\overset{\displaystyle H}{|}}{N}} - N{=}N - C_6H_5 \right]^+ + C_6H_5NH_2$$

$$\downarrow$$

$$C_6H_5NH_2 + [C_6H_5\overset{+}{N}{\equiv}N]$$

2. Electrophilic attack by the diazonum cation on the aniline then occurs:

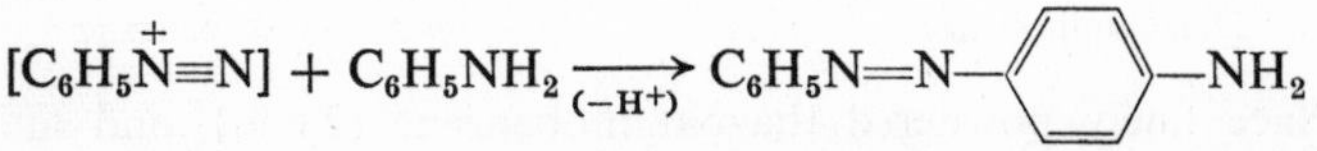

$$[C_6H_5\overset{+}{N}{\equiv}N] + C_6H_5NH_2 \xrightarrow[(-H^+)]{} C_6H_5N{=}N{-}\langle\ \rangle{-}NH_2$$

The rearrangement has been shown to be intermolecular, because if it is conducted in the presence of added NN-dimethylaniline, the chief product is p-dimethylaminoazobenzene,

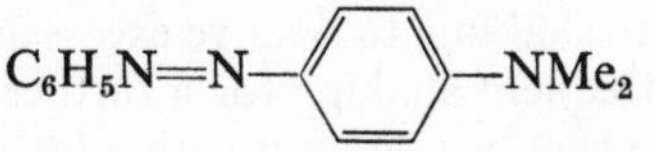

$$C_6H_5N{=}N{-}\langle\ \rangle{-}NMe_2$$

This would be expected, if the above mechanism is valid, because N,N-dimethylaniline is more reactive toward electrophilic reagents than aniline.

Preparation of Diazoaminobenzene

$$\langle \rangle\!\!-\!\overset{+}{N}_2\bar{C}l + \langle \rangle\!\!-\!NH_2 \rightarrow$$

Benzenediazonium chloride Aniline

$$\langle \rangle\!\!-\!N\!=\!N\!-\!NH\!-\!\langle \rangle + HCl$$

Diazoaminobenzene

Place water (20 ml.), concentrated hydrochloric acid (5 ml.) and redistilled aniline (3·5 ml.) in a 50 ml. conical flask. Shake the mixture vigorously and then add crushed ice (13 g.); now run in a solution of sodium nitrite (1·3 g.) in water (4 ml.) with constant shaking during 5 minutes. Continue shaking the mixture for a further 5 minutes, and then gradually add a solution of hydrated sodium acetate (5·3 g.) in water (10 ml.) over 5 minutes. A yellow precipitate of diazoaminobenzene starts to form at once, allow the suspension to stand with frequent shaking for half an hour, keeping the temperature <20° by the addition of ice if necessary. Filter off the diazoaminobenzene with suction, wash it with cold water (50 ml.), dry by suction, and finally air-dry on filter paper. The yield of the crude product is 3·9 g. Recrystallize 0·5 g. from petroleum ether (b.p. 60–80°) giving pure diazoaminobenzene, m.p. 97°.

Preparation of p-Aminoazobenzene

$$C_6H_5\!\cdot\!N\!=\!N\!-\!NH\!\cdot\!C_6H_5 \xrightarrow{H^+} NH_2\!-\!\langle \rangle\!\!-\!N\!=\!N\!-\!\langle \rangle$$

Diazoaminobenzene   p-Aminoazobenzene

Place finely powdered diazoaminobenzene (2·6 g.), and aniline (7·0 ml.) in a 50 ml. conical flask. Add finely powdered aniline hydrochloride (1·3 g.), and warm the mixture, with frequent shaking, on a water-bath at 40–50° for half an hour. Allow it to stand at room temperature for 15 minutes then add 1:1-glacial acetic acid water mixture (15 ml.) with shaking, to remove excess aniline as the soluble acetate; continue frequent shaking for a further 10 minutes. Filter off the product with suction; wash it with a little water, and air-dry on filter paper. Recrystallize the crude material from aqueous ethanol, giving yellow crystals of pure p-aminoazobenzene 1·5 g., m.p. 124–125° (60% of theory).

Electrophilic Substitution Reactions

Nitration

This has been studied more extensively than any other electrophilic aromatic substitution reaction. In normal nitration in concentrated sulphuric acid, it is considered that the sulphuric acid assists in the production of nitronium ions:

$$HNO_3 + 2H_2SO_4 \rightleftharpoons NO_2^+ + H_3O^+ + 2HSO_4^-$$

This equation is supported by spectral and cryoscopic data and by the isolation of nitronium salts, such as the perchlorate $NO_2^+ClO_4^-$. It is considered that the nitronium ion is the active nitrating species, since the directing effects of different groups in the benzene nucleus show that the attacking entity must be an electrophile. The actual attack of the nitronium ion on an aromatic nucleus is probably not a concerted process, but proceeds via a definite intermediate (σ-complex) as shown below:

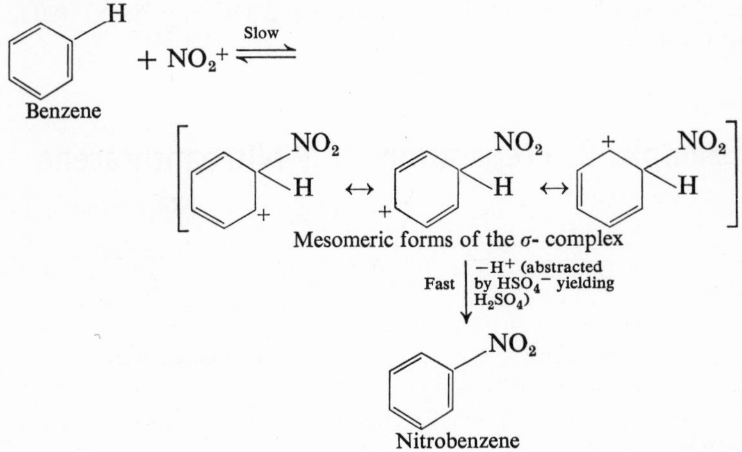

Benzene

Mesomeric forms of the σ- complex

Fast | $-H^+$ (abstracted by HSO_4^- yielding H_2SO_4)

Nitrobenzene

There is strong evidence for such σ-complex intermediates from conductimetric measurements in liquid hydrogen fluoride, and from the isolation of such derivatives together with their nuclear magnetic resonance (n.m.r.) spectra in liquid sulphur dioxide at low temperatures. It is thought that in normal nitration media such as nitric–sulphuric, or nitric–acetic acid mixtures, the active electrophile is the nitronium ion whilst nitration by dilute nitric acid may involve the nitrosonium ion, NO^+.

Example 1. Preparation of α-Nitronaphthalene

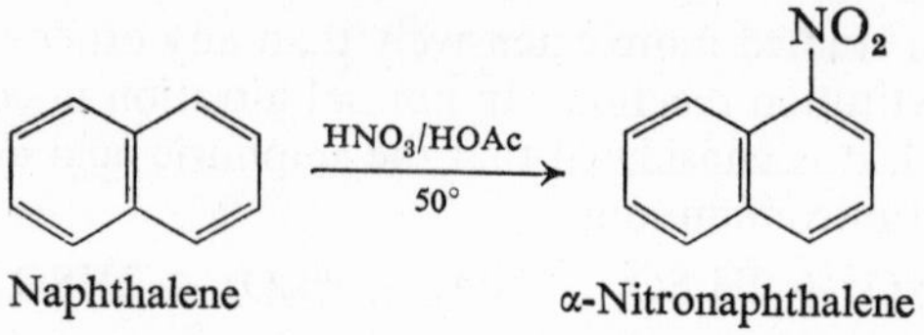

Naphthalene   α-Nitronaphthalene

Dissolve naphthalene (2 g.) in glacial acetic acid (10 ml.) by gentle warming. Cool the solution and add concentrated nitric acid (2 ml.) dropwise, keeping the temperature of the reaction mixture <40°. Then heat the mixture on a water-bath at 50°† for 10 minutes, and pour the solution onto crushed ice (20 g.) with stirring. When the ice has melted, filter off the crystals with suction, and thoroughly wash them with water. Recrystallize the crude product from ethanol giving α-nitronaphthalene as pale yellow needles, 2·3 g., m.p. 58–59° (90% of theory).

Example 2. Preparation of 9-Nitroanthracene

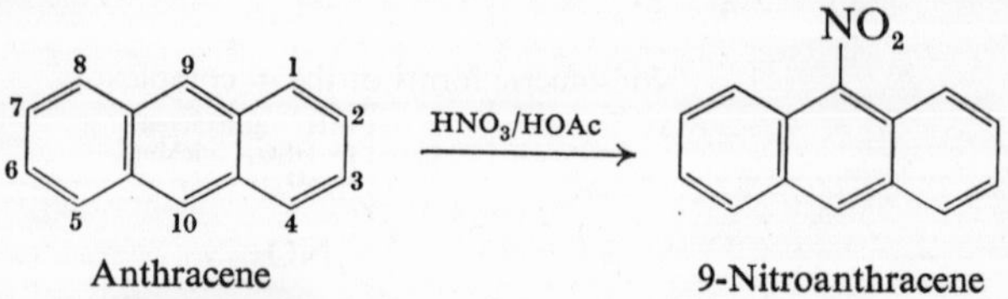

Anthracene   9-Nitroanthracene

† The temperature of the solution must not exceed 50° otherwise dinitration occurs.

Add concentrated nitric acid (4 ml.) dropwise to a suspension of finely powdered anthracene (10 g.) in glacial acetic acid (40 ml.), keeping the temperature of the mixture at 20–30°. Allow it to stand at room temperature for half an hour with occasional shaking, and then filter. Add to the filtrate a mixture of glacial acetic acid (30 ml.) and concentrated hydrochloric acid (30 ml.). Collect the percipitate of 9-chloro-10-nitro-9,10-dihydroanthracene; wash it with acetic acid and with water. Then heat with 2N sodium hydroxide solution (250 ml.) on the steam-bath for 1 hour. Filter off the product, wash it with water, and finally crystallize from boiling glacial acetic acid. Dry the yellow needles of 9-nitroanthracene in air on filter paper yielding 6 g., m.p. 146° (55 % of theory).

Electrophilic nitration occurs more readily in the aliphatic series with compounds containing a tertiary hydrogen atom, e.g.

$$(CH_3)_3C \cdot H \xrightarrow[\text{120° in a sealed tube}]{\text{Heat with conc. HNO}_3 \text{ at}} (CH_3)_3C \cdot NO_2$$

tert.-Butane   Nitro tert.-butane

Normally aliphatic nitro-compounds are obtained by vapour phase nitration of paraffins. This is an important commercial process, as many nitro-paraffins are useful industrial solvents, e.g.

$$CH_3 \cdot CH_2 \cdot CH_3 \xrightarrow[\text{350–400°}]{\text{HNO}_3}$$

$$CH_3 \cdot NO_2 + CH_3 \cdot CH_2NO_2 + CH_3 \cdot \overset{\overset{\displaystyle NO_2}{|}}{C}H \cdot CH_3 + CH_3CH_2CH_2NO_2$$

Separated by fractional distillation

Vapour phase nitration is a free-radical reaction, and may proceed as follows:

1. $$HO \cdot NO_2 \xrightarrow[\text{temperature}]{\text{High}} HO \cdot + \cdot NO_2$$

2. $$R \cdot H + HO \cdot \longrightarrow R \cdot + H_2O$$

3. $$R \cdot + \cdot NO_2 \longrightarrow R \cdot NO_2$$

Nitromethane can, however, be easily prepared in the laboratory from chloroacetic acid:

$$Cl \cdot CH_2 \cdot CO_2 H \xrightarrow[\substack{\text{nitrite} \\ (-NaCl)}]{\text{Sodium}} [NO_2 \cdot CH_2 \cdot COOH] \xrightarrow[(-CO_2)]{\text{Heat}} CH_3 \cdot NO_2$$

Chloroacetic acid   Nitromethane

This is an interesting reaction since at some stage rearrangement of

the nitrite ($-O \cdot N{=}O$) into the nitro group $\left(-N \overset{+}{\underset{\underset{O}{-}}{\diagup}}^{\overset{O}{\diagdown}} \right)$ takes place.

Example. Preparation of Nitromethane

Place chloroacetic acid (50 g.) in a 500 ml. round-bottomed flask, and dissolve it in water (100 ml.). Neutralize the solution by careful introduction of powdered anhydrous sodium carbonate (30 g.). Make the addition portionwise (approximately 1 g. portions), gently shaking the mixture after each addition, to assist the evolution of carbon dioxide, keeping a clear solution during the neutralisation. Dissolve sodium nitrite (36·5 g.) in warm water (50 ml.), then cool it in an ice-bath and add the cold nitrite solution to the solution of sodium chloroacetate with shaking. Add a few boiling chips to the flask, and attach a water condenser arranged for distillation. Place the flask on a wire-gauze, and heat it with small Bunsen flame. The solution first turns yellow, then greenish, and eventually yellowish-brown and vigorous effervescence begins. At this stage, remove the flame and allow the spontaneous evolution of carbon dioxide to continue. When the reaction ceases, maintain gentle boiling by further heating. Nitromethane distils over with the steam, separating as a colourless oil at the bottom of the distillate. Discontinue distillation when drops of nitromethane are no longer detected in the distillate leaving the condenser. Place the distillate in a separatory funnel; run off the lower nitromethane layer, and dry it with anhydrous sodium sulphate for half an hour. Then filter it into a 30 ml. distillation flask, attach a water condenser, and distil collecting the fraction of b.p. 100–102°. The yield of nitromethane, as a colourless liquid, is 10 g. (33% of theory).

Sulphonation

The mechanism of sulphonation, by analogy with other aromatic substitution reactions, is assumed to be a two-step process. The precise details are not definitely known, but when concentrated or fuming sulphuric acid is used, it is probable that the active electrophilic species is free sulphur trioxide rather than the bisulphonium ion, SO_3H^+:

$$2H_2SO_4 \rightleftharpoons H_3O^+ + HSO_4^- + SO_3$$

Although sulphur trioxide is a neutral molecule, it possesses a strongly electron-deficient sulphur atom, and so the mechanism of sulphonation may be written as below:

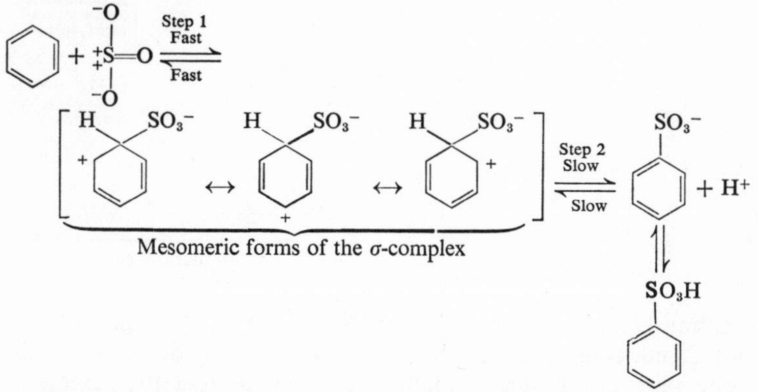

Mesomeric forms of the σ-complex

Sulphonation is a reversible process (cf. nitration), in which it is considered that the intermediate σ-complex must revert to the reactants at a comparable rate to its conversion into the products. Also it is found that sulphonation shows an isotope effect—when the hydrogen atoms of benzene are replaced by tritium, the rate of sulphonation is reduced. This observation indicates that removal of the proton from the σ-complex (step 2) is the rate-determining stage in sulphonation. A practical application, based on the reversibility of sulphonation, is the replacement of the sulphonic acid group by hydrogen on treatment with superheated steam, e.g.

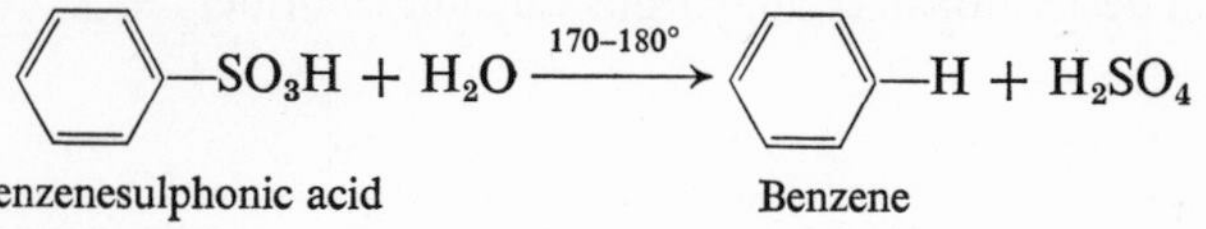

Benzenesulphonic acid   Benzene

Example 1. Preparation of Sulphanilic Acid (*p*-Aminobenzenesulphonic Acid)

By heating aniline sulphate with concentrated sulphuric acid at 180° ('The Baking Process'), the final isolated product is sulphanilic acid which may be formed by the following steps:

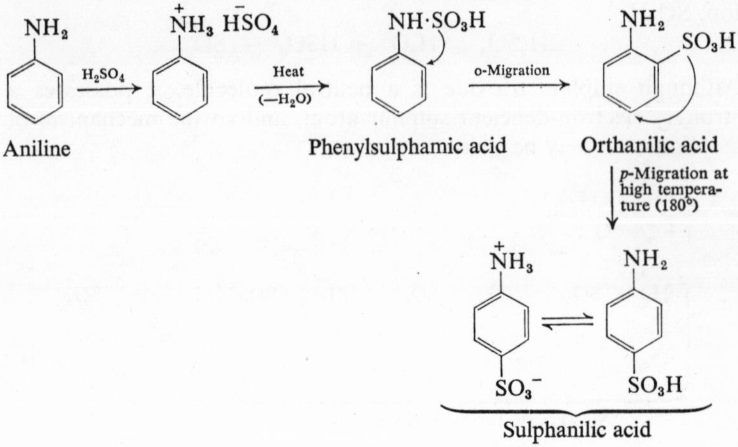

Cautiously add concentrated sulphuric acid (8 ml.) to aniline (4 ml.) in a 25 ml. conical flask, with shaking and cooling during the addition. Now add fuming sulphuric acid containing a 10% excess of sulphur trioxide (8 ml.) and heat the mixture in an oil-bath, so that the actual *temperature of the reaction mixture* is kept at 180–190° for 1 hour. (The temperature must not rise above 190° otherwise extensive decomposition of the product occurs.) Cool, and gradually pour the mixture onto crushed ice (80 g.) in a 250 ml. beaker with stirring. When the ice has melted, filter off the product with suction, and wash it with a little cold water. Recrystallize the solid from hot water (if the solution is coloured, add activated charcoal) giving sulphanilic acid dihydrate as colourless plates 3·8 g., without a definite m.p. (41% of theory). The anhydrous acid can be obtained by drying in a vacuum desiccator over anhydrous calcium chloride.

Example 2. Preparation of Naphthalene-β-Sulphonic Acid

The orientation of the monosulphonation of polynuclear aromatic hydrocarbons, like naphthalene, is temperature dependent. Thus at temperatures $< 40°$, the sulphonic acid group mainly enters the more reactive α-position; whereas at 160° the more thermodynamically stable β-acid is almost the sole product:

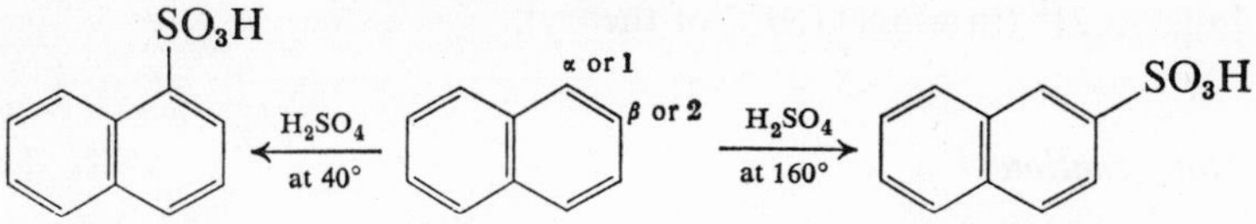

Naphthalene-α-   Naphthalene   Naphthalene-β-
sulphonic acid   sulphonic acid

Place naphthalene (5 g.) in a boiling tube and add concentrated sulphuric acid (5 ml.). Heat the mixture with stirring, and gradually increase the temperature to 160°. Keep the stirred mixture at this temperature for a quarter of an hour. Cool, and pour the solution slowly into water (6 ml.), and then allow to stand at 0°. Filter off the crystals of naphthalene-β-sulphonic acid trihydrate 6 g.; m.p. 124° with suction. Recrystallize the solid from water (3 ml.) containing concentrated hydrochloric acid (1 ml.) yielding pure naphthalene-β-sulphonic acid 4 g., m.p. 92° (70% of theory).

Example 3. Preparation of dextro-Camphor-10-Sulphonic Acid

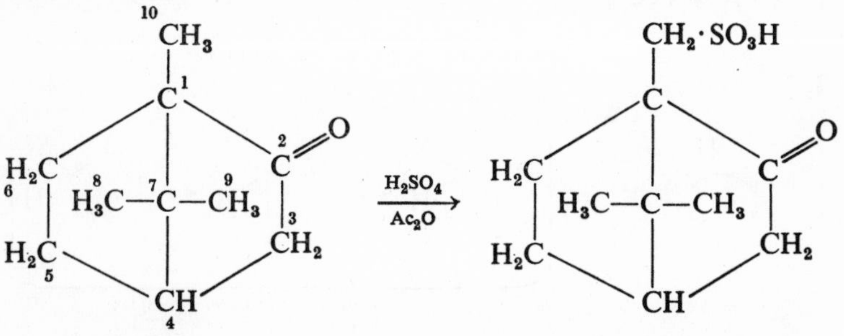

dextro-Camphor   dextro-Camphor-10-sulphonic acid

Carefully mix concentrated sulphuric acid (10 g.) and acetic anhydride (20 g.) and cool the mixture in an ice-bath. Then gradually add powdered dextro-camphor (15 g.) to the cold mixture, shaking well after each addition. The camphor easily dissolves giving a pale yellow solution. Set it aside at room temperature for 2–3 days, when crystals of dextro-camphor-10-sulphonic acid are deposited. Filter off the product at the pump, and wash the crystals with ether. Recrystallize it from ethyl acetate giving colourless prisms of

dextro-camphor-10-sulphonic acid 8 g., m.p. 190–193° (with decomp.)
$[\alpha]_D^{15°} + 21°$ (in water) (50% of theory).

Halogenation

Benzene homologues may undergo two distinct types of halogenation:

A. *Nuclear* is effected by treatment of the hydrocarbon with halogen in the presence of a suitable catalyst ('halogen carrier'), e.g. $FeCl_3$ or $AlCl_3$. The active species is X^+ and the catalyst probably functions by facilitating its production (cf. the Friedel–Crafts reaction). Support for the effective electrophilic reagent being either a halonium ion or a positively polarized complex is shown by the effect of interhalogen compounds in aromatic substitution. Iodine chloride and bromine chloride lead to iodination and bromination, respectively, which indicates that it is the less electronegative halogen which is introduced due to an induced polarization, i.e.

$$\overset{\delta^+}{Br}—\overset{\delta^-}{Cl} \qquad \overset{\delta^+}{I}—\overset{\delta^-}{Cl}$$

The mechanism for the nuclear halogenation of benzene may then be written as below:

1. $X—X + FeCl_3 \rightleftharpoons X^+ + [FeCl_3X]^-$

$$\text{or } \overset{\delta^+}{X}—\overset{\delta^-}{X}FeCl_3 \text{ a polarized complex}$$

2.

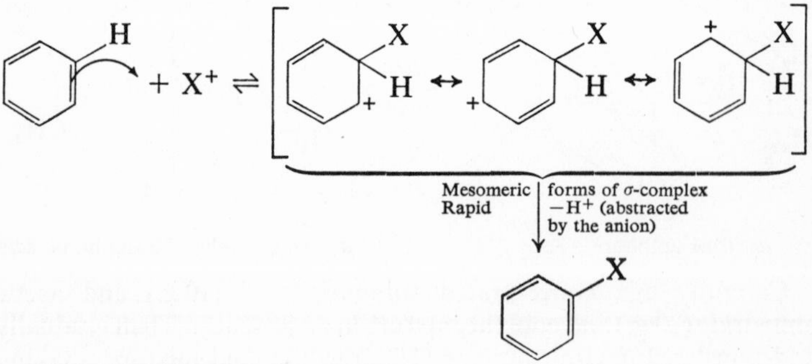

Mesomeric | forms of σ-complex
Rapid | −H⁺ (abstracted
          | by the anion)

3. $H^+ + [FeCl_3X]^- \rightarrow HX + FeCl_3$
(where X = Cl or Br)

Nuclear iodo compounds are generally best prepared indirectly, by the Sandmeyer reaction (p. 125). When nucleophilic groups, such as —OH, —NHAc, —NH₂, are attached to the benzene ring, nuclear halogenation occurs easily without the need for a 'halogen carrier', as in example 1.

B. *Side chain halogenation* is favoured by high temperature and the absence of a 'halogen carrier'. By passing chlorine (or bromine) into boiling toluene, stepwise replacement of the hydrogen atoms of the methyl group occurs:

$$C_6H_5 \cdot CH_3 \xrightarrow[+\ Cl_2]{\text{Heat}} C_6H_5CH_2Cl \xrightarrow[+\ Cl_2]{\text{Heat}}$$

Toluene   Benzyl chloride

$$C_6H_5CHCl_2 \xrightarrow[+\ Cl_2]{\text{Heat}} C_6H_5 \cdot CCl_3$$

Benzylidene chloride   Benzotrichloride

The substitution may be stopped at any desired stage. Similar side chain halogenation may be effected at lower temperatures in the presence of ultra-violet radiation; it is a free-radical chain reaction:

1. $Cl_2 \xrightarrow{h\nu} 2Cl\cdot$ (initiation)

2. $C_6H_5 \cdot CH_3 + Cl\cdot \rightarrow C_6H_5 - \dot{C}H_2 + HCl$

3. $C_6H_5\dot{C}H_2 + Cl_2 \rightarrow C_6H_5 \cdot CH_2Cl + Cl\cdot$

4. $C_6H_5 \cdot CH_2Cl + Cl\cdot \rightarrow C_6H_5\dot{C}HCl + HCl$

5. $C_6H_5\dot{C}HCl + Cl_2 \rightarrow C_6H_5CHCl_2 + Cl\cdot$

The chlorine radical can then continue the chain reaction.

Example 1. Preparation of 2,4,6-Tribromophenol

Phenol   2,4,6-Tribromophenol

Dissolve phenol (2·5 g.) in warm water (50 ml.), and then cool the solution. Slowly add bromine† (4·2 ml.) to the cold solution with stirring. Filter off the precipitate at the pump. Wash it well with water, and recrystallize from aqueous ethanol giving 2,4,6-tribromophenol, as colourless needles, 8·5 g., m.p. 95° (96% of theory).

† Bromine requires careful handling, and operations with it must be performed in the fume cupboard.

Example 2. Preparation of α-Bromonaphthalene

Naphthalene   α-Bromonaphthalene

In an efficient fume cupboard, place naphthalene (17 g.) and carbon tetrachloride (20 ml.) in a 100 ml. three-necked round-bottomed flask fitted with a mechanical stirrer, double-surface reflux condenser, and a 25 ml. dropping funnel. Pour bromine (8 ml., *care.*) into the funnel and heat the flask on a steam-bath, until the solvent is boiling gently; then drop in bromine with stirring, so that gentle boiling is maintained (addition takes about half an hour). Continue heating, until the evolution of hydrogen bromide ceases (about 15 minutes). Evaporate the carbon tetrachloride using a water-bath and slightly reduced pressure; stir the residue with powdered sodium hydroxide (1 g.) at 90–100° for 4 hours. Transfer the liquid to a distillation flask and fractionally distil it under reduced pressure,† collecting α-bromonaphthalene, 20 g. as a colourless liquid, boiling at 144–148°/20 mm. (72% of theory).

Example 3. Preparation of *p*-Iodoaniline

Aniline   *p*-Iodoaniline

Nuclear iodo compounds are generally best obtained indirectly by the Sandmeyer reaction. However, in certain cases direct iodination

† The first fractions contain some unchanged naphthalene, which may be removed by cooling, followed by filtration. Further α-bromonaphthalene can be obtained by redistillation of these filtrates; the fractions boiling above 148°/20 mm. contain 1,5- and 1,8-dibromonaphthalene.

in the presence of a suitable base (e.g. sodium hydrogen carbonate), to remove the hydriodic acid formed, is satisfactory.

Place aniline (6 ml.), sodium hydrogen carbonate (9 g.) and water (60 ml.) in a 250 ml. beaker. Cool the mixture to 12–15° by addition of a little crushed ice with mechanical stirring. Gradually add powdered iodine (14 g.) in 1 g. portions approximately every 2 minutes, so that the total operation takes about half an hour. By this time, the reaction should be complete and all the colour of the iodine should have disappeared. Filter off the crude product at the pump and air-dry the material on filter paper. Place the dry product in a 250 ml. round-bottomed flask fitted with a reflux condenser; add petroleum ether, b.p. 60–80° (60 ml.), and boil under reflux for approximately a quarter of an hour with frequent shaking. Decant the hot solution into a 250 ml. conical flask surrounded by an ice-salt freezing mixture, with continual stirring. p-Iodoaniline separates out almost immediately as colourless needles. Filter off the product at the pump, and air-dry it on filter paper. The yield of p-iodoaniline is 10 g., m.p. 62–63° (45% of theory).

Example 4. Preparation of Benzyl Chloride (Side-Chain Halogenation)

$$C_6H_5 \cdot CH_3 + Cl_2 \rightarrow C_6H_5 \cdot CH_2Cl + HCl$$

Toluene   Benzyl chloride

In an efficient fume cupboard, place toluene (25 g.) in a weighed 150 ml. two-necked flask fitted with a reflux condenser. Heat the flask on a graphite-bath, so that the toluene boils gently. Now pass a steady stream of dry chlorine gas† (from a cylinder) into the boiling toluene by a tube attached to the side arm of the flask. The reaction mixture slowly turns yellow and hydrogen chloride is evolved. Weigh the flask and its contents from time to time and continue passing in chlorine gas, until the correct increase in weight (9–9·5 g.) has occurred. Now transfer the reaction mixture to a distillation flask and fractionally distil. At first unchanged toluene distils over; collect the fraction boiling at 165–185° (which contains nearly all the benzyl chloride). Redistil this material using a short fractionating column, collecting the fraction b.p. 176–180° which is almost pure benzyl chloride. It is a colourless liquid, b.p. 176°, whose vapour irritates eyes and nose. The yield is 20 g. (60% of theory).

† Chlorine gas is highly poisonous and must be handled with great care, in a good fume cupboard with the hood kept down as much as possible.

Hydrolysis

This generally refers to the addition of the elements of water (H^+, OH^-) to an organic compound; the reaction is catalysed by acids or bases and its scope is illustrated by the following examples:

$$R\text{—}Hal \xrightarrow{OH^-} R\cdot OH$$

$$R\cdot COOR' \xrightarrow{H_2O/H^+ \text{ or } OH^-} R\cdot COOH + R'\cdot OH$$

$$R\cdot CN \xrightarrow{H_2O/H^+ \text{ or } OH^-} R\cdot CO\cdot NH_2 \rightarrow R\cdot COOH + NH_3$$

$$R\cdot CO\cdot Hal \xrightarrow{H_2O/H^+ \text{ or } OH^-} R\cdot COOH + H\cdot Hal$$

$$R\cdot CO\cdot O\cdot COR' \xrightarrow{H_2O/H^+ \text{ or } OH^-} R\cdot CO_2H + R'\cdot CO_2H$$

$$R\cdot SO_2Cl \text{ or } R\cdot SO_2\cdot NH_2 \xrightarrow{H_2O/H^+ \text{ or } OH^-} R\cdot SO_2\cdot OH + HCl \,(\text{or } NH_3)$$

$$Ar\cdot \overset{+}{N_2}\overset{-}{Cl} \xrightarrow{H_2O/H^+} Ar\cdot OH + HCl + N_2$$

$$R\cdot Mg\cdot Hal \xrightarrow{H_2O/H^+} R\cdot H + Mg(OH)\cdot Hal$$

$$R\cdot CH\text{——}CH_2 \xrightarrow{H_2O/H^+} R\cdot CH(OH)\cdot CH_2\cdot OH$$

$$CH_2{=}CH_2 \xrightarrow{conc. \; H_2SO_4} CH_3\cdot CH_2\cdot HSO_4 \xrightarrow{H_2O} CH_3\cdot CH_2\cdot OH$$

Hydrolysis is often a bimolecular nucleophilic reaction ($S_N:2$), and so is subject to steric hindrance; for instance 2,6-dialkylbenzoic acid esters cannot be hydrolysed by normal methods. In such cases, however, hydrolysis can be effected by dissolving the compound in concentrated sulphuric acid, and then pouring the solution into water, because the reaction then proceeds *via* the acylium ion

(S_N:1 process) which is not sensitive to steric factors:

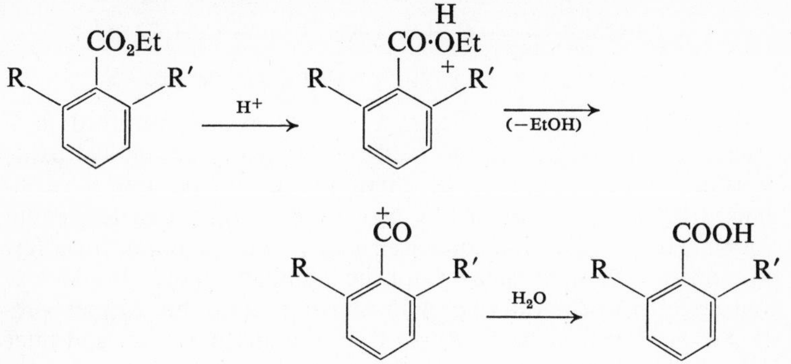

Hydrolysis is also important in the use of acetoacetic ester for the synthesis of ketones and acids, e.g.

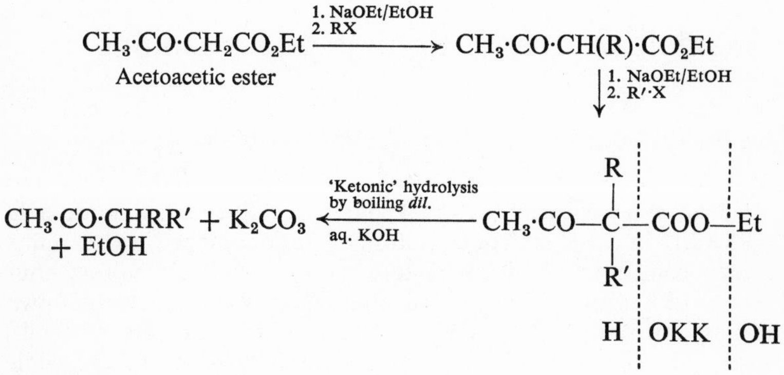

$$CH_3 \cdot CO \cdot CH_2CO_2Et \xrightarrow[\text{2. RX}]{\text{1. NaOEt/EtOH}} CH_3 \cdot CO \cdot CH(R) \cdot CO_2Et$$

Acetoacetic ester

$$\left\downarrow \begin{array}{l}\text{1. NaOEt/EtOH}\\\text{2. R'·X}\end{array}\right.$$

$$CH_3 \cdot CO \cdot CHRR' + K_2CO_3 + EtOH \xleftarrow[\text{aq. KOH}]{\substack{\text{'Ketonic' hydrolysis}\\ \text{by boiling } dil.}} CH_3 \cdot CO \underset{\underset{R'}{|}}{\overset{\overset{R}{|}}{C}} COO \mathbin{\vert} Et$$

H ¦ OKK ¦ OH

Also:

$$CH_3 \cdot CO \mathbin{\vert} CRR' \mathbin{\vert} COO \mathbin{\vert} Et \xrightarrow[\text{alc. KOH}]{\substack{\text{'Acid' hydrolysis}\\ \text{by boiling } conc.}}$$

KO ¦ H   K ¦ OH

$$\underset{R'}{\overset{R}{\diagdown}}CH \cdot CO_2K + CH_3CO_2K + EtOH$$

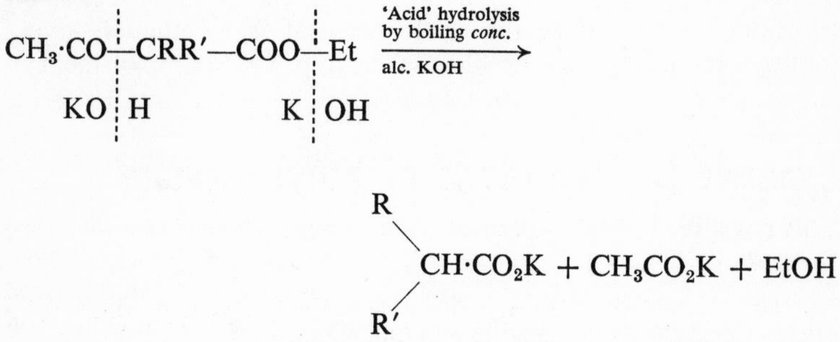

Example 1. Preparation of Benzoic Acid

$$C_6H_5CN \xrightarrow[(-NH_3)]{NaOH} C_6H_5CO_2Na \xrightarrow{H^+} C_6H_5CO_2H$$

Benzonitrile   Benzoic Acid

Place benzonitrile (2·5 ml.) in a 100 ml. round-bottomed flask fitted with a reflux condenser. Add 10% aqueous sodium hydroxide solution (40 ml.), and boil the mixture under reflux, until the condensed liquid is free from oily drops (about three-quarters of an hour). Then remove the condenser and boil the solution for a few minutes to expel ammonia. Cool the liquid and gradually add concentrated hydrochloric acid with shaking, until no further precipitation of benzoic acid occurs. Cool the mixture in ice and filter off the acid at the pump; wash it with a little cold water and air-dry on filter paper. The yield of pure benzoic acid is 2·8 g., m.p. 120–121° (90% of theory).

Example 2. Preparation of *p*-Nitroaniline

$$NO_2-\langle\!\!\!\bigcirc\!\!\!\rangle-NH\cdot CO\cdot CH_3 \xrightarrow[2.\ OH^-]{1.\ H_2SO_4} NO_2-\langle\!\!\!\bigcirc\!\!\!\rangle-NH_2$$

p-Nitroacetanilide   *p*-Nitroaniline

Place *p*-nitroacetanilide (5 g.) and 70% aqueous sulphuric acid (25 ml.)† in a 100 ml. round-bottomed flask equipped with a reflux water condenser. Boil the mixture for approximately half an hour (or until a sample remains clear after dilution with 3 times its own volume of water). Pour the hot solution into cold water (170 ml.) and add an excess of 10% aqueous sodium hydroxide solution, while cooling the mixture in ice. Filter off the yellow crystalline precipitate with suction, wash it thoroughly with water, and dry it by suction on the filter. Recrystallize the crude material from ethanol, giving *p*-nitroaniline as yellow needles 3·0 g., m.p. 148° (90% of theory).

Example 3. Hydrolysis of Ethyl Acetate

This has already been described under Fischer–Speier esterification. (page 46.)

† The 70% sulphuric acid may be obtained by cautiously adding concentrated sulphuric acid (30 ml.) to water (23 ml.) with stirring.

Mercuration

Example 1. Preparation of *o*-Chloromercuriphenol

OH

$+ \text{Hg(OAc)}_2 \xrightarrow[(-\text{HOAc})]{}$

Phenol   Mercuric acetate

OH   HgOAc $\xrightarrow[(-\text{NaOAc})]{\text{NaCl}}$ OH   Hg·Cl

o-Chloromercuriphenol

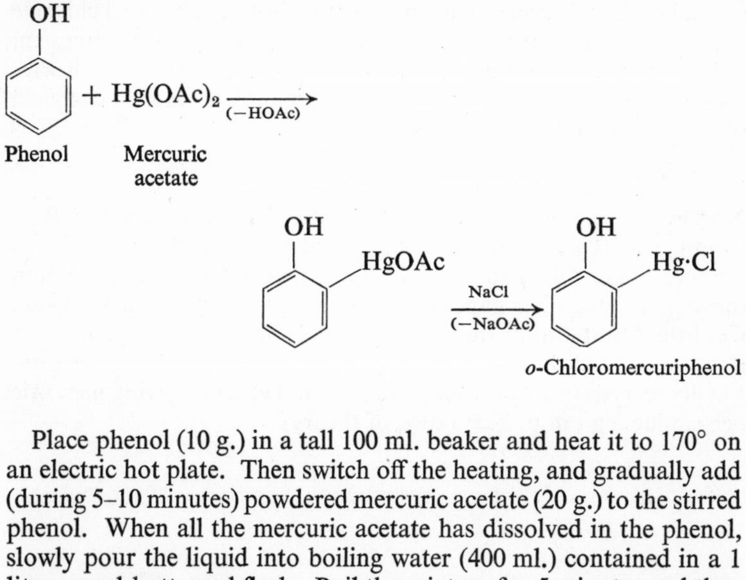

    Place phenol (10 g.) in a tall 100 ml. beaker and heat it to 170° on an electric hot plate. Then switch off the heating, and gradually add (during 5–10 minutes) powdered mercuric acetate (20 g.) to the stirred phenol. When all the mercuric acetate has dissolved in the phenol, slowly pour the liquid into boiling water (400 ml.) contained in a 1 litre round-bottomed flask. Boil the mixture for 5 minutes and then filter it through a preheated Buchner funnel. Transfer the filtrate to a clean flask and again boil it, then add a solution of sodium chloride (4 g.) in boiling water (40 ml.). Boil the mixture and filter it through a preheated Buchner funnel. Cool the filtrate at 0°, preferably overnight, and filter off the product at the pump. Air-dry the solid on filter paper, yielding *o*-chloromercuriphenol, as feathery crystals, 9 g., m.p. 147–150°† (44% of theory).

---

  † If the product is coloured, or melts low, purify it by a further recrystallization from boiling water.

Example 2. Preparation of Mercuric Benzamide

$$2C_6H_5CONH_2 + HgO \rightarrow (C_6H_5CONH)_2Hg + H_2O$$

Benzamide   Mercuric oxide   Mercuric benzamide

(a) Benzamide

$$C_6H_5 \cdot CO \cdot Cl + 2NH_3 \rightarrow C_6H_5 \cdot CO \cdot NH_2 + NH_4Cl$$

Benzoyl chloride   Benzamide

Cool concentrated ammonia solution (d. 0·88, 50 ml.) in a 200 ml. conical flask by immersion in an ice-bath. Now add benzoyl chloride (10 ml.) dropwise from a 25 ml. dropping funnel, with frequent swirling of the flask. Filter off the product at the pump, wash it with a little cold water, and recrystallize it from boiling water. The yield of pure benzamide is 9 g., m.p. 128–129°.

(b) Mercuric benzamide

Add benzamide (8 g.), and finely-powdered mercuric oxide (10 g.) to ethanol (100 ml.) in a 250 ml. round-bottomed flask. Boil the mixture under reflux for half an hour, then filter the hot solution through a fluted filter paper (to remove unchanged mercuric oxide). Cool the filtrate in an ice-bath; filter off the crystalline product at the pump, wash it with a little cold ethanol, and dry by suction. Finally recrystallize the crude solid from hot ethanol, giving mercuric benzamide 3 g., m.p. 223° (20% of theory).

Miscellaneous Heterocyclic Syntheses

Example 1. Preparation of 3-Methyl-1-Phenyl-5-Pyrazolone

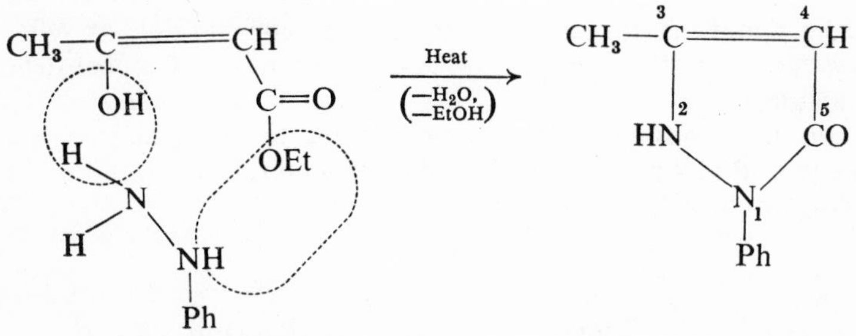

Acetoacetic ester (as enol form)
and phenylhydrazine

3-Methyl-1-phenyl-5-pyrazolone

Place acetoacetic ester (3·1 ml.) and phenylhydrazine† (2·4 ml.) in a boiling tube. Heat the solution on a steam-bath for one hour with occasional stirring. Cool the mixture, and add ether (10 ml.) with stirring; the ether does not dissolve the product but by removing impurities helps to promote solidification. If necessary, decant off the ether, and triturate the red oil at 0° with more ether ($\simeq$ 5 ml.), (it may require to be left for several days in the refrigerator before solidification occurs unless it can be seeded with a few crystals of the pyrazolone). Filter off the solid product at the pump, wash it with ether, and recrystallize from 50% aqueous ethanol. Dry in an oven at 100° giving 3-methyl-1-phenyl-5-pyrazolone, as colourless needles, 2·9 g., m.p. 126–127° (68% of theory based on acetoacetic ester).

† Phenylhydrazine is toxic and must be carefully handled, and must not be allowed to get on the skin.

Example 2. Preparation of Benzimidazole

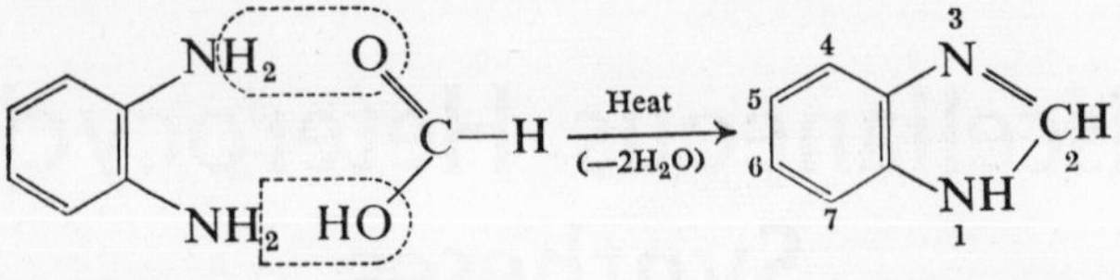

o-Phenylenediamine   Formic acid   Benzimidazole

Place o-phenylenediamine (2·5 g.) and 90% formic acid (2 ml.) in a boiling tube. Heat the mixture on a steam-bath for 2 hours; then cool the solution, and make it alkaline by gradual addition of 10% aqueous sodium hydroxide solution, with swirling. Cool the mixture in ice–water, and filter off the product at the pump. Recrystallize it from boiling water ($\simeq$ 40 ml.), in the presence of activated charcoal (0·3 g.), and dry the solid at 100°, giving benzimidazole as yellow crystals, 2·0 g., m.p. 170–171° (69% of theory based on o-phenylene-diamine).

An analogous experiment, replacing the formic acid by glacial acetic acid (2·4 ml.), gives 2-methylbenzimidazole 1·5 g., m.p. 173° (48% of theory).

Example 3. Preparation of Barbituric Acid (or Malonylurea)

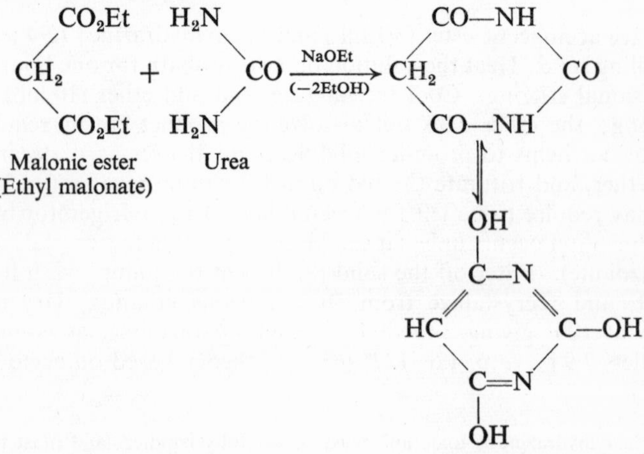

Malonic ester   Urea
(Ethyl malonate)

Barbituric acid

Dissolve sodium (2 g.) in absolute ethanol (50 ml.) contained in 100 ml. round-bottomed flask fitted with a reflux condenser and calcium chloride guard tube. Dry urea (4 g.) in an oven at 100°, and add it to the solution of sodium ethoxide, followed by malonic ester (6·4 ml.). Gently boil the mixture under reflux for two hours (or longer if possible). Pour the suspension into water (50 ml.) in a 250 ml. beaker, and heat to dissolve the solid precipitate. Acidify the solution with concentrated hydrochloric acid, and cool it in an ice-bath with trituration. Filter off the solid at the pump, wash it with cold water, and dry in an oven at 100°, giving barbituric acid 3·7 g., m.p. 245° (decomp. in a sealed tube) (74% of theory based on malonic ester).

7

Oxidation

This may be regarded as the addition of oxygen to, or the removal of hydrogen, from an organic compound. Potassium permanganate, sodium dichromate, chromic acid, and nitric acid are important general oxidizing agents. Their action is illustrated by the following examples:

$$R \cdot CH{=}CH \cdot R' \xrightarrow[35°]{\text{Dil. KMnO}_4}$$

$$R \cdot CH(OH){-}CH(OH) \cdot R' \xrightarrow{\text{Hot KMnO}_4} R \cdot CO_2H + R' \cdot CO_2H$$

$$\downarrow \text{Na}_2\text{Cr}_2\text{O}_7/\text{H}^+; \text{ CrO}_3/\text{H}^+; \text{ or HNO}_3$$

$$R \cdot CH_2 \cdot OH \rightarrow R \cdot CHO \rightarrow R \cdot CO_2H$$

(If the aldehyde is required, it must be removed from the reaction mixture as it is formed.)

$$RR'CH \cdot OH \rightarrow R \cdot CO \cdot R'$$

$$C_6H_5 \cdot R \xrightarrow{\text{Hot Na}_2\text{Cr}_2\text{O}_7/\text{H}^+; \text{ KMnO}_4/\text{H}^+ \text{ or OH}^-} C_6H_5 \cdot CO_2H$$

(R = alkyl group)

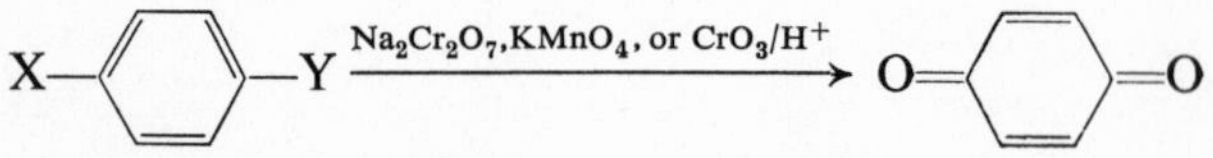

$$\left(\begin{array}{l} X = H, Y = OH \text{ or } NH_2 \\ \text{or} \\ X = NH_2, \text{ or OH}; \ Y = OH, \text{ or } NH_2 \end{array} \right)$$

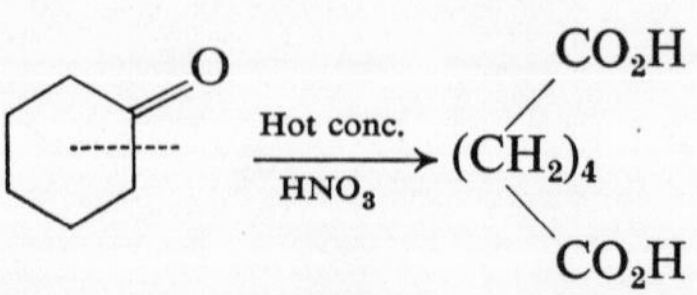

Nitric acid is generally avoided for the oxidation of aromatic compounds, because of the danger of simultaneous nitration. By variation of the experimental conditions, these general oxidants may be employed more specifically, e.g. dilute potassium permanganate at 35°C converts an olefin into the glycol; and a methyl group attached to an aromatic nucleus may be oxidised to an aldehyde group by treatment with chromic anhydride/acetic anhydride mixture:

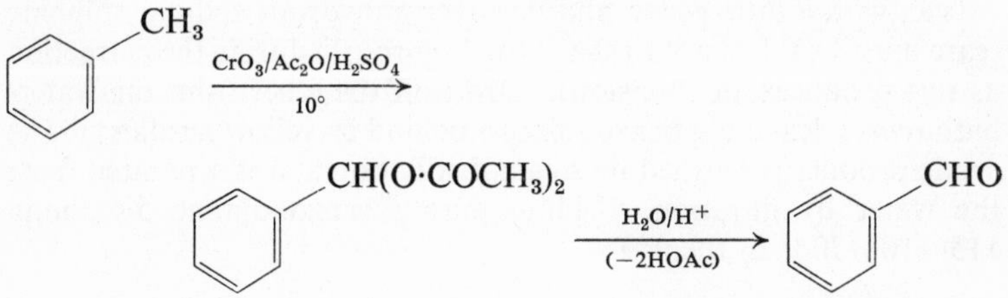

The removal of hydrogen (dehydrogenation) may be achieved by heating the compound with selenium, or palladium/charcoal:

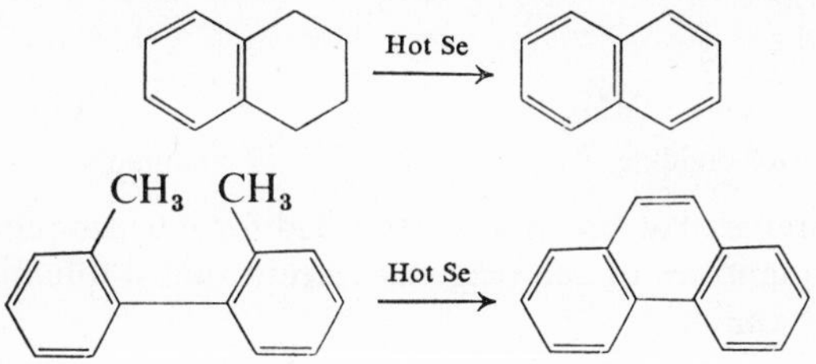

Dichromate Oxidations

Example 1. Preparation of *p*-Benzoquinone

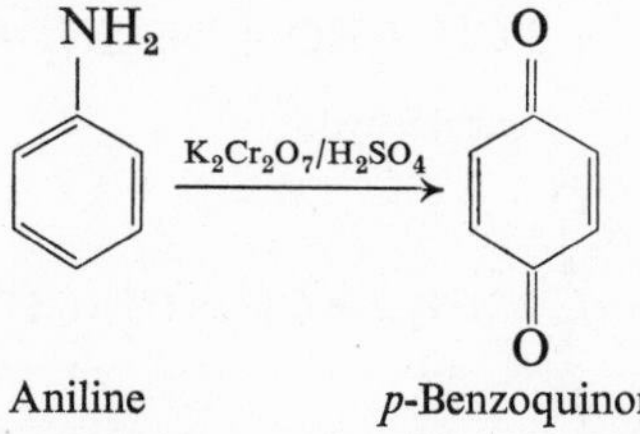

Aniline   *p*-Benzoquinone

Gradually add concentrated sulphuric acid (40 g.) to water (150 ml.) with mechanical stirring, in a 250 ml. beaker surrounded by ice-water. Add aniline (5 g.) to the cold dilute sulphuric acid with cooling and stirring. Add powdered potassium dichromate (5 g.) in 1 g. portions over one hour, taking care that the temperature does not exceed 10°. Allow the mixture to stand overnight, and then add further potassium dichromate (8 g.) under the conditions previously described. Aniline black separates in the first stage of the oxidation, and subsequently this dissolves to yield a dark brown solution. Allow the reaction mixture to stand for 4–5 hours and then extract it three times with ether (100 ml. each time). Wash the combined extract with a little water, and dry over anhydrous sodium sulphate (care must be taken not to shake too vigorously during the extraction as this produces an emulsion). Distil off the ether from the water-bath (*care*), leaving *p*-benzoquinone behind as yellow needles†. The crude product is purified by steam distillation and is separated from the water by filtration, yielding pure *p*-benzoquinone 5 g., m.p. 115–116° (70% of theory).

Preparation of toluquinone

$$\text{o-Toluidine} \xrightarrow{\text{K}_2\text{Cr}_2\text{O}_7/\text{H}_2\text{SO}_4} \text{Toluquinone}$$

This is prepared as previously described for *p*-benzoquinone using the same quantities of the reagents, except that *o*-toluidine is substituted for aniline.

The yield of toluquinone is 5 g., m.p. 67° (70% of theory).

Example 2. Preparation of Acetaldehyde

$$3\text{C}_2\text{H}_5{\cdot}\text{OH} + \text{Na}_2\text{Cr}_2\text{O}_7 + 4\text{H}_2\text{SO}_4$$
$$= 3{\cdot}\text{CH}_3{\cdot}\text{CHO} + \text{Na}_2\text{SO}_4 + \text{Cr}_2(\text{SO}_4)_3 + 7\text{H}_2\text{O}$$

Ethanol   Acetaldehyde

$$\text{CH}_3-\overset{\overset{\text{O}}{\|}}{\underset{\text{H}}{\text{C}}}\,\overset{..}{\text{N}}\text{H}_3 \rightarrow \text{CH}_3 \cdot \text{CH(OH)} \cdot \text{NH}_2$$

Acetaldehyde   Acetaldehyde ammonia

The oxidizing mixture for this preparation is made as follows: add concentrated nitric acid (115 ml., d. 1·42) to a mixture of sodium

† The solid quinone is appreciably volatile and the pungent vapour attacks the eyes.

dichromate (60 g.), water (220 ml.), and concentrated sulphuric acid (20 g.). (In making up the mixture the sulphuric acid must be slowly added to the water.)

Arrange the apparatus as indicated in Figure 5. Place ethanol (25 ml.) in the 500 ml. three-necked flask, and boil it gently over a small flame. Introduce the oxidizing mixture gradually from the

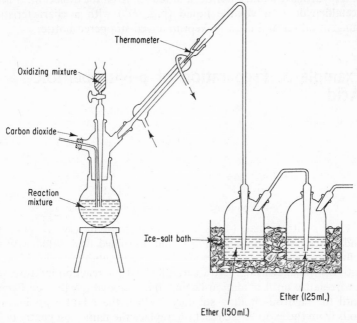

Figure 5

dropping funnel, at such a rate that the thermometer in the top of the condenser reads 20–25°. The addition should take approximately 20 minutes. During this process, a steady stream of carbon dioxide is passed through the apparatus in order to remove the volatile acetaldehyde from the reaction mixture as soon as it is formed, in order to prevent its further oxidation to acetic acid. The product is collected in two wash-bottles containing cold ether. Combine the cold ethereal solutions of the aldehyde in a 500 ml. conical flask. Saturate the solution with dry ammonia gas, and set the mixture aside for 1 hour. Filter off the crystals of acetaldehyde ammonia at the pump, wash them with a little dry ether, and finally dry in a vacuum desiccator. The yield of acetaldehyde-ammonia is 18 g.

(70% of theory). Pure acetaldehyde may be obtained from the aldehyde–ammonia derivative as follows: place the crystals ($\backsimeq 15$ g.) in a small distillation flask and dissolve them in an equal weight of water. Then add a mixture of concentrated sulphuric acid (20 ml.) and water (30 ml.). Distil the mixture from a water-bath, and collect the distillate in a well-cooled receiver. Dry it over an equal weight of anhydrous calcium chloride, and redistil from the desiccant. Pure acetaldehyde is a volatile liquid (b.p. 21°) with a characteristic pungent odour and must be kept in a well-stoppered bottle.

Example 3. Preparation of *p*-Nitrobenzoic Acid

p-Nitrotoluene   p-Nitrobenzoic acid

Place *p*-nitrotoluene (4·5 g.), sodium dichromate crystals (14 g.), and water (30 ml.) in a 250 ml. round-bottomed flask fitted with a reflux condenser. Gradually add concentrated sulphuric acid (20 ml.) with continual swirling. Now carefully heat the reaction mixture on a wire-gauze until oxidation begins, then remove the Bunsen flame until the vigorous boiling subsides. When the mixture no longer boils from the exothermic reaction, replace the flame and gently boil it under reflux for 2 hours. Cool and pour the reaction mixture into cold water (60 ml.) with stirring. Filter off the crude product at the pump, and wash it with water (40 ml.). Powder the crude acid in a mortar, add 1*N*-sulphuric acid (30 ml.), and warm on the steam-bath with stirring (to remove most of the chromium salts from the product). Cool, filter at the pump, and wash the residue with water (40 ml.). Triturate in a mortar with water, and treat the resultant paste with 5% aqueous sodium hydroxide solution (40 ml.). Add activated charcoal (2 g.) and warm to 50° with stirring for approximately 5 minutes. (This dissolves the product, but any unchanged *p*-nitrotoluene and chromium hydroxide remain out of solution.) Filter the alkaline solution with suction, and then pour it into dilute sulphuric acid (concentrated sulphuric acid (4 ml.) in water (40 ml.)) with stirring. Filter off the *p*-nitrobenzoic acid at the pump and recrystallize from ethanol or benzene. The yield is 3·5 g., m.p. 236–238° (65% of theory).

Chromic Anhydride Oxidations

Example 1. Preparation of Anthraquinone

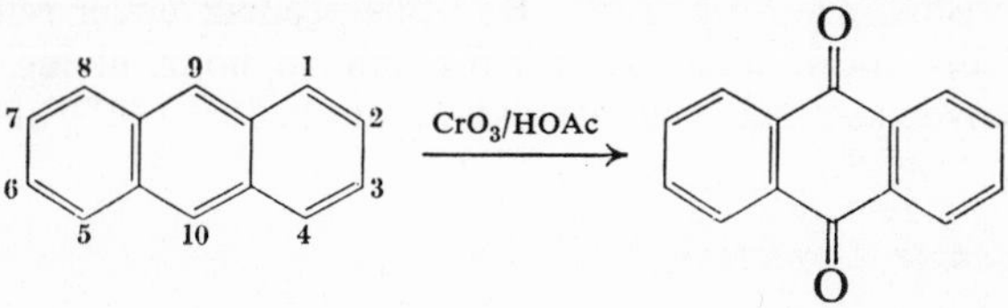

Anthracene   9,10-Anthraquinone

Place anthracene (2·0 g.), in a 100 ml. round-bottomed flask; add glacial acetic acid (25 ml.), and boil under reflux to effect complete solution. Dissolve chromium trioxide (4 g.) in a mixture of water (2 ml.) and glacial acetic acid (15 ml.). Add the oxidizing solution very slowly through a dropping funnel into the boiling solution of anthracene. The addition should take about a quarter of an hour, then boil the mixture under reflux for a further half an hour. Cool, and pour the dark green solution into water (100 ml.), stir it well, and allow the precipitate to settle. Filter off the brown powder with suction, wash it with water, 5% aqueous sodium hydroxide solution, and water. Dry in an oven at 100–110°, and finally recrystallize the anthraquinone from toluene (≃ 40 ml.). (*Take care as toluene is highly inflammable.*) The yield of anthraquinone is 1·8 g., m.p. 285° (in a sealed tube) (75% of theory).

Example 2. Preparation of *p*-Nitrobenzaldehyde

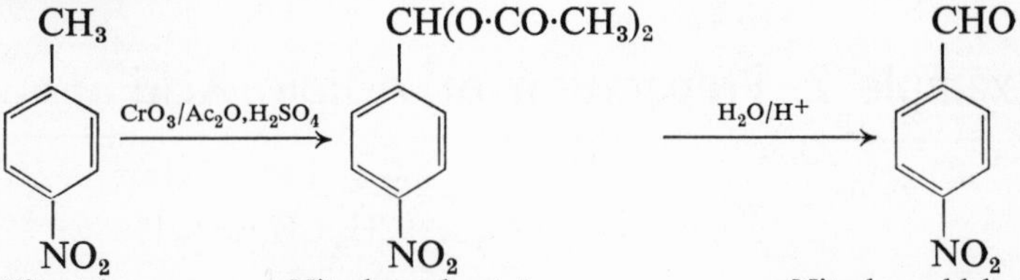

p-Nitrotoluene   *p*-Nitrobenzalacetate   *p*-Nitrobenzaldehyde

Dissolve *p*-nitrotoluene (5 g.) in a mixture of acetic anhydride (40 g.), concentrated sulphuric acid (15 g.) and glacial acetic acid

(40 g.) in a 250 ml. round-bottomed flask. Cool in an ice-bath and gradually add solid chromium trioxide (10 g.) with vigorous mechanical stirring. Keep the temperature of the reaction mixture between 0° and 10° during the addition and then stir for a further half an hour. Pour the mixture onto crushed ice, and when the ice has melted, filter off the precipitate with suction. Wash it with water, and crystallize from ethanol, giving *p*-nitrobenzalacetate as pale yellow prisms, 7 g., m.p. 125°. Boil this product under reflux with dilute hydrochloric acid (30 ml.) for half an hour, giving *p*-nitrobenzaldehyde as a pale yellow solid 4 g., m.p. 106° (70% of theory).

Permanganate Oxidations

Example 1. Preparation of iso-Butyric Acid

$$(CH_3)_2CH \cdot CH_2 \cdot OH \xrightarrow[\text{[O]}]{\text{KMnO}_4} (CH_3)_2 \cdot CH \cdot CO_2H + H_2O$$
iso-Butanol   iso-Butyric acid

Place iso-butanol (25 g.), sodium carbonate (8 g.), and water (750 ml.) in a 2 litre round-bottomed flask. Add finely powdered potassium permanganate (140 g.) in a single operation. The reaction is strongly exothermic, and the flask must be shaken in ice-water for 1 hour. Allow the mixture to warm up gradually to room temperature overnight. Filter off (or better centrifuge) the precipitate of manganese dioxide, and evaporate the filtrate on a steam-bath to a volume of 80 ml. Cool, then cautiously acidify with dilute sulphuric acid, and extract the mixture with three 30 ml. portions of ether. Dry the combined ethereal extract over anhydrous sodium sulphate, filter, and distil off the ether from the water-bath (*care*). Finally fractionally distil the residue, collecting iso-butyric acid at 152–155°. The yield is 22 g. (73% of theory).

Example 2. Preparation of Adipic Acid

Cyclohexanone   the enolate   Adipic acid
(Butane-1,4-dicarboxylic acid)

Place potassium permanganate (15·3 g.) and water (125 ml.) in a 250 ml. round-bottomed flask. Add cyclohexanone (5 g.) with swirling, and then warm the mixture on a water-bath until the internal temperature is 30°. Now add 10% aqueous sodium hydroxide solution (1 ml.); this causes an almost immediate rise in temperature, when the temperature recorded by the thermometer in the mixture reaches 45° (after about 15 minutes), check the oxidation by briefly cooling in an ice-bath, and maintain the reaction temperature at 45° for 20 minutes. Then allow the temperature to rise to 47° and eventually begin decreasing (about 25 minutes). Finally heat the mixture on a wire-gauze over a Bunsen flame to complete the oxidation, and also to coagulate the manganese dioxide precipitate. Test for the presence of unreacted permanganate, by spotting a little of the reaction mixture on to a piece of filter paper: if permanganate is present it will appear as a ring around the spot of manganese dioxide. If permanganate is still present, add small quantities of sodium hydrogen sulphite until the spot test is negative. Filter the reaction mixture at the pump, thoroughly wash the brown precipitate with water, and evaporate the filtrate over a Bunsen flame to a volume of 35 ml. If the solution is coloured, boil it with a little activated charcoal, and filter. Acidify the hot filtrate with concentrated hydrochloric acid until the pH is 1–2, and then add an excess of concentrated hydrochloric acid (5 ml.) and set aside the solution to crystallize. Filter off the crystals at the pump, giving adipic acid 3·4 g., m.p. 152° (50% of theory).

Nitric Acid Oxidations

Example 1. Preparation of Adipic Acid

| Cyclohexanol | | Adipic acid |

In a fume cupboard place 50% aqueous nitric acid (16 ml., d. 1·32), and a few boiling chips in a 100 ml. two-necked round-bottomed flask fitted with a double-surface reflux condenser and a 25 ml. dropping funnel.† Place cyclohexanol (5 g.) in the dropping

† Standard ground glass joint apparatus *must* be employed in this preparation, since corks are rapidly attacked by hot nitric acid.

funnel, and heat the nitric acid in the flask just to the boiling point. Now introduce a *drop or two* of the cyclohexanol, this results in a vigorous reaction with evolution of oxides of nitrogen. Continue dropwise addition of the cyclohexanol, taking care that each drop has completely reacted with the nitric acid before the next one is introduced. Maintain gentle boiling and *on no account allow unreacted cyclohexanol to build up in the reaction flask*, otherwise a very violent reaction will occur. Addition of the cyclohexanol takes approximately 20 minutes; afterwards continue gently boiling the mixture under reflux for a further half an hour to complete the oxidation. Cool the contents of the flask, and filter off the crude product at the pump, wash it with a small quantity of ice-water, and recrystallize from hot water. The yield of adipic acid is 4 g., m.p. 152° (56% of theory).

Example 2. Preparation of Oxalic Acid (Dihydrate)

Sucrose (cane sugar)   Oxalic acid

Owing to the copious evolution of nitrogen oxides during this oxidation the experiment must be conducted in a fume cupboard.

Place sucrose (15 g.) in a 500 ml. round-bottomed flask, and add concentrated nitric acid (80 ml.). Heat the mixture on a steam-bath; as it becomes warm the majority of the sucrose dissolves and a vigorous reaction accompanied by considerable evolution of oxides of nitrogen begins. Immediately remove the flask from the steam-bath and place it on a cork ring, allowing the reaction to subside (which generally takes about a quarter of an hour). Then pour the hot solution into an evaporating basin, wash out the flask with concentrated nitric acid (10 ml.), and concentrate the combined acid solution on the steam-bath to a volume of about 12 ml. Add water (25 ml.) to the concentrated solution and again evaporate to a volume of 12 ml. This process completes the oxidation, avoiding the need for long standing at room temperature. Cool the solution in ice, and filter off the crystalline oxalic acid at the pump. Recrystallize the solid from a small volume of hot water and air-dry on filter paper. The yield of oxalic acid dihydrate is 5 g., m.p. 101° (80% of theory).

Pinacol-Pinacolone Rearrangement

This is the acid-catalysed conversion of a 1,2-glycol into an aldehyde or ketone. The reaction is facilitated when both hydroxyl groups are tertiary, because the intermediate carbonium ions formed are then relatively stable, e.g., with pinacol (tetramethylethylene glycol):

Pinacol I
(Tetramethylethylene glycol)

II

III

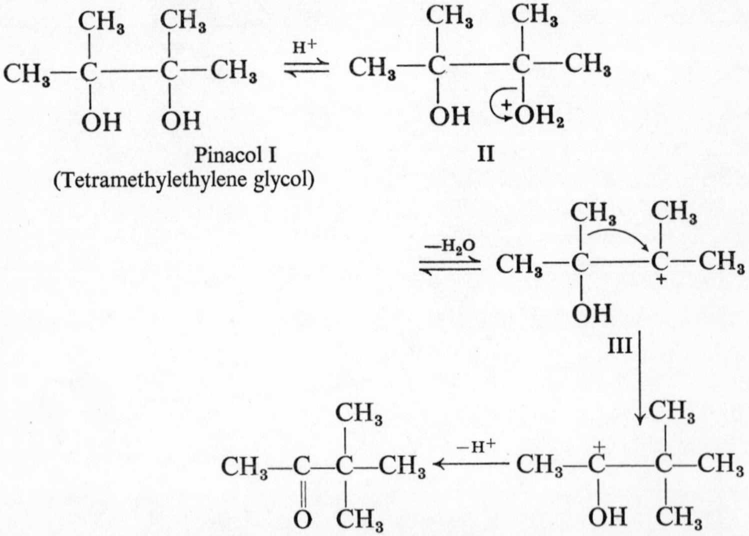

Pinacolone (tert.-Butyl methyl ketone)

The main evidence for the carbonium ion intermediates is that in dilute sulphuric acid pinacol undergoes oxygen exchange with the solvent approximately three times as rapidly as it rearranges. (I, II, III being in equilibrium). The carbonium ion may also yield an epoxide by participation of the β-hydroxyl group and, indeed, in the rearrangement of benzopinacol in acetic acid, it has been shown that approximately 80 % of the reaction goes via the intermediate epoxide.

An examination of the rearrangement of various pinacols revealed that aryl groups generally migrated more easily than methyl groups. Further p-substituted aryl groups were favoured as compared with o-substituted ones, probably due to the former being less sterically hindered. The observed order of relative ease of migration was as follows:

p-methoxyphenyl $>$ p-tolyl $>$ p-biphenyl $>$ m-tolyl $>$ p-chlorophenyl $>$ m-methoxyphenyl $>$ o-tolyl $>$ o-chlorophenyl.

Example 1. Preparation of Benzopinacolone

$$2(C_6H_5)_2CO \xrightarrow{Zn} (C_6H_5)_2C \cdot (OH) \cdot C(OH)(C_6H_5)_2 \xrightarrow{H^+}$$

Benzophenone   Benzopinacol
(Diphenyl ketone)

$$C_6H_5 \cdot CO \cdot C \cdot (C_6H_5)_3$$

Benzopinacolone

Boil a mixture of benzophenone (10 g.), glacial acetic acid (150 ml.), water (30 ml.), and zinc dust (5 g.) for 2 hours under reflux. Cool and filter off the precipitated benzopinacol. Recrystallize the crude product from glacial acetic acid, giving benzopinacol as prisms 6 g., m.p. 185–186° (with decomp.). Convert benzopinacol (4 g.) into the pinacolone as follows: Add iodine (70 mg.) and boil in glacial acetic acid (35 ml.) until complete solution is obtained, and then for a further 5 minutes. Cool, and filter off the benzopinacolone, wash the crystals with ethanol (to remove iodine) and dry. The yield is 3·5 g., m.p. 178–179° (90% of theory based on benzopinacol).

Example 2. Preparation of Pinacolone (tert.-Butyl Methyl Ketone)

(a) Pinacol hydrate
Place dry magnesium (2·5 g.) and anhydrous benzene (25 ml.) in a 150 ml. round-bottomed flask fitted with a double-surface condenser and a 25 ml. dropping funnel. Dissolve mercuric chloride (2·8 g.) (*Care: poisonous*) in pure anhydrous acetone (16 ml.) and place this solution in the dropping funnel. Run into the flask with swirling approximately one quarter of the solution; if boiling does not occur within a few minutes, warm the mixture on the water-bath.

But, if necessary, be ready to cool the flask. When the reaction has begun no heating is required. Add the remaining solution at a sufficient rate to keep the reaction proceeding briskly. Then introduce a mixture of dry acetone (8 ml.) and dry benzene (7 ml.) by means of the dropping funnel. Finally boil the mixture on the water-bath for 1 hour, the product expands and almost fills the flask. Add water (7 ml.) through the condenser with shaking which considerably reduces the volume of the solid. Heat on the steam-bath for a further half an hour with shaking from time to time. Set the mixture aside until it has cooled to 50°, and then filter with suction, retaining the filtrate. Return the solid to the flask and boil with benzene (18 ml.) for quarter of an hour to dissolve any remaining pinacol, filter, and combine the filtrates. Concentrate the filtrate to approximately half the original volume, add water (8 ml.) and cool to 0° with stirring for 1 hour. Filter off the pinacol hydrate, wash it with benzene (5 ml.), and air-dry the product. The yield is 9·5 g., m.p. 44–45° (78 % of theory).

(b) The rearrangement of pinacol hydrate to pinacolone

Place pinacol hydrate (9 g.) and 6N sulphuric acid (25 ml.) in a 100 ml. distillation flask. Attach a 25 ml. dropping funnel and condenser, and distil the mixture using an air-bath, until the upper layer of the distillate no longer increases in volume (approximately quarter of an hour). Separate the upper layer of pinacolone, dry it with anhydrous sodium sulphate, filter, and distil from a 10 ml. distillation flask. Collect pinacolone 4·8 g., b.p. 103–106° (48 % of theory).

Reduction

This is the addition of hydrogen (hydrogenation) or the removal of oxygen from an organic compound. Examples of the reagents used in the reduction of some of the more important functional groups are summarized in the equations below; these also give an indication of the scope of the various reduction procedures:

$$-CO_2H \xrightarrow{\text{LiAlH}_4}$$
$$-CO_2R \xrightarrow{\text{LiAlH}_4;\ \text{Na/EtOH}} \left.\right\} -CH_2OH$$

$$\left.\begin{array}{l} -C{\equiv}N \\ -CO{\cdot}NH_2 \end{array}\right\} \xrightarrow{\text{LiAlH}_4;\ \text{Na/EtOH};\ \text{Pt/H}_2} -CH_2{\cdot}NH_2$$

$$\overset{\diagdown}{\underset{\diagup}{C}}{=}N{\cdot}OH \xrightarrow{\text{LiAlH}_4;\ \text{Na/EtOH};\ \text{Pt/H}_2} \overset{\diagdown}{\underset{\diagup}{C}}H{\cdot}NH_2$$

$$R{-}Hal \xrightarrow{\text{LiAlH}_4;\ \text{Na/EtOH};\ \text{Pt/H}_2;\ \text{Zn/H}^+} R{\cdot}H$$

$$-CHO \xrightarrow[\substack{\text{Clemmensen reduction [ZnHg/conc. HCl]; Hot HI + Red P;} \\ \text{or Wolff–Kishner reduction (Hot N}_2\text{H}_4\text{/OH}^-)}]{\text{LiAlH}_4;\ \text{NaBH}_4;\ \text{Pt/H}_2;\ \text{M/Hg, dil. H}^+} \begin{array}{l} -CH_2OH \\ \\ -CH_3 \end{array}$$

$$R{\cdot}CO{\cdot}R' \xrightarrow[\substack{\text{Clemmensen reduction; Hot HI + Red P; or} \\ \text{Wolff–Kishner reduction (hot N}_2\text{H}_4,\ \text{OH}^-)}]{\text{LiAlH}_4;\ \text{NaBH}_4;\ \text{Pt/H}_2;\ \text{M/Hg, dil. H}^+} \begin{array}{l} R{\cdot}CHOH{\cdot}R' \\ \\ R{\cdot}CH_2{\cdot}R' \end{array}$$

$$\xrightarrow{\text{M/Hg, dil. H}^+} R{\cdot}CHOHR' + \underset{\text{(especially when M = Mg or Al)}}{RR'\overset{\overset{\displaystyle OH}{|}}{C}{-\!-}\overset{\overset{\displaystyle OH}{|}}{C}{\cdot}RR'}$$

$$R{-}NO_2 \xrightarrow[\text{SnCl}_2\text{/HCl}]{\text{LiAlH}_4;\ \text{Pt/H}_2;\ \text{Na/EtOH};\ \text{Sn or Fe/HCl}} R{\cdot}NH_2$$

199

$$Ar \cdot NO_2 \xrightarrow{\text{Pt/H}_2; \text{ Sn, Fe/H}^+; \text{ SnCl}_2/\text{HCl}} Ar \cdot NH_2$$

$$\xrightarrow{\text{LiAlH}_4; \text{ boiling Zn/NaOH, MeOH}} Ar \cdot N=N \cdot Ar \xrightarrow{\text{Na}_2\text{S}_2\text{O}_4} Ar \cdot NH—NHAr$$

$$\xrightarrow{\text{Boiling glucose/aq. alc. NaOH}} Ar \cdot \overset{+}{N}=N \cdot Ar \quad \underset{\text{Heat + Fe}}{\big\uparrow}$$
$$\underset{O^-}{}$$

$$\xrightarrow{\text{Zn dust/warm aq. NH}_4\text{Cl}} Ar \cdot NH \cdot OH$$

$$—CO \cdot Hal \begin{array}{c} \xrightarrow{\text{LiAlH}_4; \text{ Pt/H}_2} —CH_2OH \\ \xrightarrow{\text{Rosenmund reduction}} —CHO \end{array}$$

$$\underset{}{\text{C}=\text{C}} \text{ or } —C\equiv C— \xrightarrow[\text{Raney Ni/H}_2]{\text{Pt/H}_2; \text{ Pd/H}_2} \underset{}{\text{CH—CH}}$$
$$\text{or } —CH_2—CH_2—$$

$$Ar—OH \xrightarrow{\text{Heat with Zn}} Ar \cdot H$$

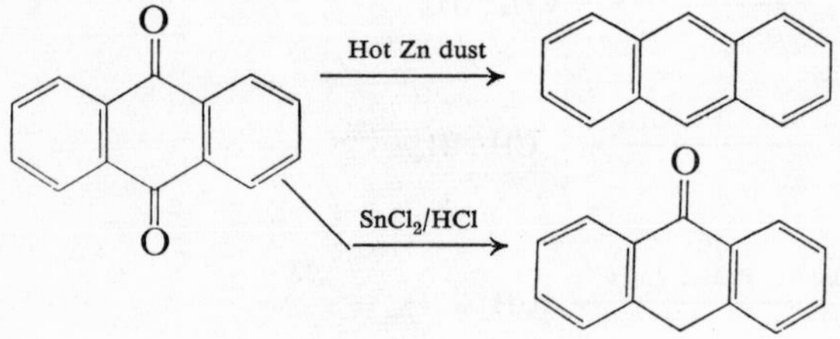

$$Ar—\overset{+}{N}_2\bar{X} \begin{array}{c} \xrightarrow{\text{SnCl}_2/\text{HCl or Na}_2\text{SO}_3} Ar—NH \cdot NH_2 \\ \xrightarrow{\text{Na}_2\text{SnO}_2, \text{ HPO}_2} Ar \cdot H \end{array}$$

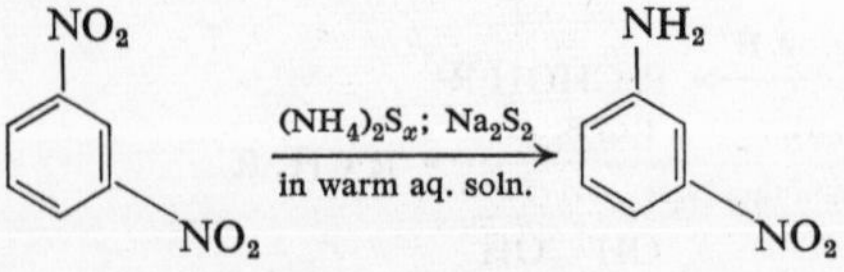

(Other reductions give the diamine)
(M = Na, Mg, or Al; R = an alkyl group)

The following experiments further illustrate the application of selected reduction methods.

Lithium Aluminium Hydride (Lithium Tetrahydroaluminate)

This is an extremely useful reagent for the reduction of many functional groups (see general introduction). It is the most important general reagent for reducing carboxylic acids, and is specially valuable for the selective reduction of functional groups in unsaturated compounds, e.g.

$$CH_3CH=CH \cdot CHO \xrightarrow{\text{LiAlH}_4} CH_3 \cdot CH=CH \cdot CH_2OH$$

Crotonaldehyde   Crotonyl alcohol

Lithium aluminium hydride is prepared by the reaction:

$$4LiH + AlCl_3 \xrightarrow[\text{Et}_2\text{O}]{\text{In dry}} LiAlH_4 + 3LiCl$$

It is a grey *spontaneously inflammable powder*, which reacts *explosively with water* and consequently must be handled cautiously. Reductions are generally performed in ethereal solution, or if a higher boiling solvent is required, tetrahydrofuran may be used. If lithium aluminium hydride inflames, *the fire can only be extinguished with dry sand*.

In the mechanism of reduction with lithium aluminium hydride, the key step is the transfer of a hydride ion to the electrophilic carbon atom of the compound being reduced. Considering the reduction of a carbonyl compound, the probable mechanism is as below:

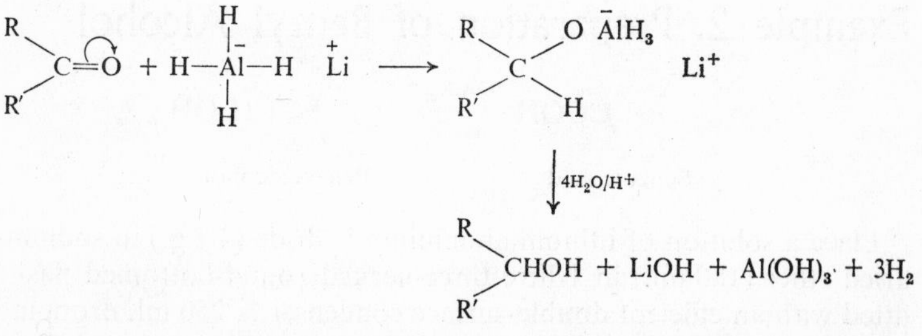

On hydrolysis, the lithium aluminium hydride complex yields the alcohol. In fact four moles of the carbonyl compound can be reduced by one mole of the reagent (i.e. all four hydrogen atoms of lithium aluminium hydride can be utilized). The closely related reagent, sodium borohydride (sodium tetrahydroborate), has the advantage that it can be used in aqueous solution but will only reduce aldehydes and ketones; accordingly it is much used in sugar chemistry.

Example 1. Preparation of Cinnamyl Alcohol (3-Phenylpropenol)

$$\langle\!\!\!\!\!\!\!\!\!\!\!\!\!\!\rangle\!-\!CH\!=\!CH\cdot CHO \xrightarrow{LiAlH_4} \langle\!\!\!\!\!\!\!\!\!\!\!\!\!\!\rangle\!-\!CH\!=\!CH\cdot CH_2OH$$

Cinnamaldehyde   Cinnamyl alcohol

Dissolve cinnamaldehyde (15·5 g.) in sodium-dried ether (40 ml.) in a 250 ml. beaker† and cool the solution to −10° by an ice-salt bath. Now add dropwise a solution of lithium aluminium hydride (1·3 g.) in sodium-dried ether (35 ml.) with stirring over a period of 15 minutes. At the end of the addition, the temperature of the reaction mixture rises to 10°. Continue stirring for a further 15 minutes to complete reaction, and then cautiously add ice-cold water (10 ml.)‡ followed by 10% aqueous sulphuric acid (40 ml.), to destroy the intermediate organo-metallic complex. Extract the mixture with ether (100 ml.); wash the ethereal solution with water, dry it over anhydrous sodium sulphate, filter, and distil off the ether from the water-bath (*care*). Finally, distil the residue under reduced pressure, collecting cinnamyl alcohol at 142–145°/14 mm.; on cooling the distillate solidifies, m.p. 33–34°. The yield is 14 g. (90% of theory).

Example 2. Preparation of Benzyl Alcohol

$$\langle\!\!\!\!\!\!\!\!\!\!\!\!\!\!\rangle\!-\!COOH \xrightarrow{LiAlH_4} \langle\!\!\!\!\!\!\!\!\!\!\!\!\!\!\rangle\!-\!CH_2OH$$

Benzoic acid   Benzyl alcohol

Place a solution of lithium aluminium hydride (4·7 g.) in sodium-dried ether (180 ml.) in 1 litre three-necked round-bottomed flask§ fitted with an efficient double-surface condenser, a 250 ml. dropping funnel and a mechanical stirrer; the apparatus is protected from atmospheric moisture by calcium chloride tubes attached to the outlets. Add from the dropping funnel a solution of benzoic acid

† All apparatus including weighing bottle and spatula must be oven-dried.
‡ Care must be taken during the addition of water to destroy the excess of lithium aluminium hydride, since the reagent reacts very vigorously with water liberating a large volume of hydrogen.
§ As previously.

(12 g.) in sodium-dried ether (150 ml.) at a sufficient rate, so as to produce gentle boiling of the reaction mixture. Continue stirring for 15 minutes after the addition has been completed. Now cautiously add ice-water to decompose the excess of hydride, followed by 10% aqueous sulphuric acid (150 ml.) (it may be necessary to cool the flask again in ice-water at this stage), giving a clear solution. Transfer the reaction mixture to a separatory funnel, and separate the upper ethereal layer. Wash it with water, dry with anhydrous sodium sulphate, filter, and distil off the ether from a water-bath (*care*). Distil the residue under reduced pressure, collecting benzyl alcohol at 92–95°/10 mm. The yield is 8·5 g. (80% of theory).

Zinc Dust and Sodium Hydroxide

Example 1. Preparation of Benzhydrol

$$\text{Benzophenone} \quad -CO- \quad \xrightarrow[2[H]]{Zn/NaOH} \quad -CH(OH)- \quad \text{Benzhydrol}$$

Place benzophenone (10 g.), ethanol (110 ml.), sodium hydroxide pellets (13 g.), and zinc dust (13 g.) in a 200 ml. round-bottomed flask fitted with a double-surface reflux condenser. Thoroughly mix the contents of the flask by swirling, and then gently boil the mixture under reflux on a water-bath for one and a half hours. Filter the hot solution with suction, and pour the filtrate into ice-water (450 ml.) containing concentrated hydrochloric acid (25 ml.). After standing, the product separates as a crystalline solid, which is filtered off at the pump. Recrystallize it from ethanol giving pure benzhydrol as colourless plates 6 g., m.p. 68° (60% of theory).

Example 2. Preparation of Hydrazobenzene

$$2 \quad -NO_2 \quad \xrightarrow{Zn/NaOH} \quad -NH-NH- \quad$$
Nitrobenzene   Hydrazobenzene

Details of this reduction are given under the benzidine rearrangement (p. 157).

Tin and Hydrochloric Acid

Example 1. Preparation of Aniline (Aminobenzene)

Nitrobenzene is reduced by treatment with tin and hydrochloric acid. The overall equation is:

$$C_6H_5 \cdot NO_2 + 6[H] \xrightarrow{\text{Sn/HCl}} C_6H_5 \cdot NH_2 + 2H_2O$$
$$\text{Nitrobenzene} \qquad\qquad \text{Aniline}$$

In the course of the reduction tin is oxidized first to the stannous and then to the stannic state; the intermediate stannous chloride being itself a powerful reducing agent. Stannic chloride combines with hydrochloric acid and aniline giving a complex salt, from which the free aniline is liberated by treatment with a large excess of sodium hydroxide. These various steps may be written as follows:

1. $Sn + 2HCl \rightarrow SnCl_2 + 2[H]$

2. $SnCl_2 + 2HCl \rightarrow SnCl_4 + 2[H]$ (i.e. $Sn \equiv 4[H]$)

3. $SnCl_4 + 2HCl \rightarrow H_2[SnCl_6] \xrightarrow{2Ph \cdot NH_2} [(PhNH_3)_2]SnCl_6$
$$\qquad\qquad\qquad \text{Chlorostannic acid} \qquad \text{Aniline chlorostannate}$$

4. $[(PhNH_3)_2]SnCl_6 + 8NaOH \rightarrow 2Ph \cdot NH_2 + Na_2SnO_3$
$$+ 6NaCl + 5H_2O$$

Place granulated tin (36 g.) and nitrobenzene (17 ml.) in a 500 ml. round-bottomed flask fitted with a reflux condenser. Gradually add concentrated hydrochloric acid (80 ml.): pour about 10 ml. of the acid down the condenser, and shake the flask; an exothermic reaction begins and the liquid in the flask starts to boil. *If the reaction becomes too vigorous moderate it by momentarily immersing the flask in cold water.* When the reaction slows down, add a further 10 ml. portion of the acid, again shaking and cooling if required.

Continue this procedure until all the acid has been introduced (approximately 30 minutes). Heat the mixture on a steam-bath until the smell of nitrobenzene can no longer be detected. (Also addition of water to a few drops of the reaction mixture should give a perfectly clear solution.) During the reduction aniline chloro-stannate may precipitate as a pale yellow solid. Cool the mixture, and slowly add a solution of sodium hydroxide (60 g.) in water (100 ml.) with slight cooling to prevent the mixture boiling. (After the addition the solution should be strongly alkaline and the initial

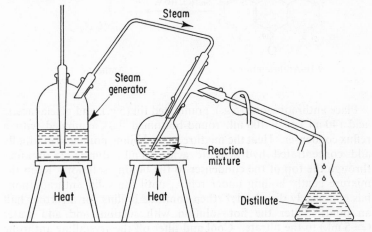

Figure 6
Steam distillation apparatus

precipitate of tin hydroxide should have redissolved while free aniline separates as an oil.) Assemble the apparatus for steam distillation, as shown above. Pass a steady stream of steam into the warm reaction mixture, until the distillate is no longer turbid and then collect a further 100 ml. of clear liquid. Measure the volume of the distillate and place it in a separatory funnel, add sodium chloride ((20 g.) for each 100 ml. of distillate). Now add ether (40 ml.) and shake well to mix the ether and the distillate. (*All flames must be extinguished during operations with ether as it is highly inflammable.*) Separate the lower aqueous layer and re-extract with a further 40 ml. of ether. Dry the combined ethereal extract over anhydrous potassium carbonate; then filter into a 100 ml. distillation flask, and distil off the ether from a warm water-bath (*care*). Finally, distil the residual liquid using an air-condenser, and collect the fraction boiling at 180–184° as a colourless liquid, which rapidly darkens on exposure to air. The yield of aniline is 13 g. (83% of theory).

Example 2. Preparation of Anthrone

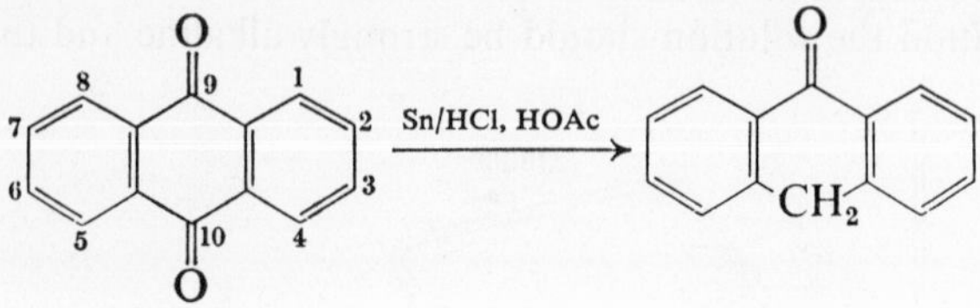

9,10-Anthraquinone   Anthrone

Place anthraquinone (5 g.), granulated tin (5 g.), and glacial acetic acid (40 ml.) in a 100 ml. round-bottomed flask equipped with a reflux condenser. Heat the mixture to the boiling point and gradually add concentrated hydrochloric acid (13 ml.) during 15 minutes through the top of the condenser to the boiling solution. Keep the mixture gently boiling under reflux, until the solid anthraquinone has completely dissolved;† then continue boiling for a further half an hour. Filter the hot solution with suction, and add water (≃ 5 ml.) to the filtrate. Cool and filter off the crystalline anthrone at the pump; wash it with water and recrystallize from a benzene-petroleum ether (b.p. 60–80°) (3:1)-mixture. The yield of pure anthrone is 3 g., m.p. 155–156° (60% of theory).

Hydrogenation

Hydrogenation of compounds containing, e.g. double or triple bonds, cyano, nitro or carbonyl groups, may be effected by shaking a solution of the compound in a suitable inert solvent with hydrogen in the presence of a finely-divided nickel, platinum, or palladium catalyst.

The reduction occurs at the surface of the catalyst, and it has been shown that nickel will combine with both hydrogen and ethylene, but not with ethane. The catalytic hydrogenation of ethylene may,

† If some solid remains undissolved at this stage, add more tin and hydrochloric acid and continue heating.

therefore, be depicted as follows:

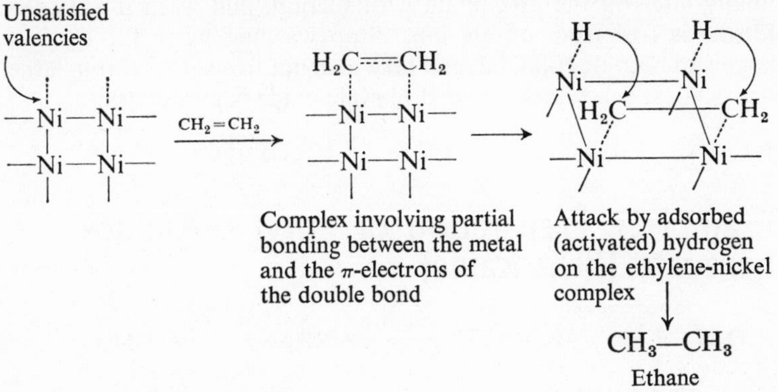

Unsatisfied
valencies

$$—Ni—Ni— \quad \xrightarrow{CH_2=CH_2} \quad \begin{array}{c} H_2C{=\!=\!=}CH_2 \\ —Ni—Ni— \\ —Ni—Ni— \end{array} \quad \longrightarrow$$

Complex involving partial
bonding between the metal
and the π-electrons of
the double bond

Attack by adsorbed
(activated) hydrogen
on the ethylene-nickel
complex

$$CH_3—CH_3$$
Ethane

The reduction proceeds, because ethane has no affinity for the nickel and so is lost, as soon as it is formed, releasing sites on the catalyst surface which are then occupied by new ethylene and hydrogen molecules. A consequence of this mechanism is that catalytic hydrogenation under the above conditions should involve *cis*-addition and experimentally this is generally true, e.g.

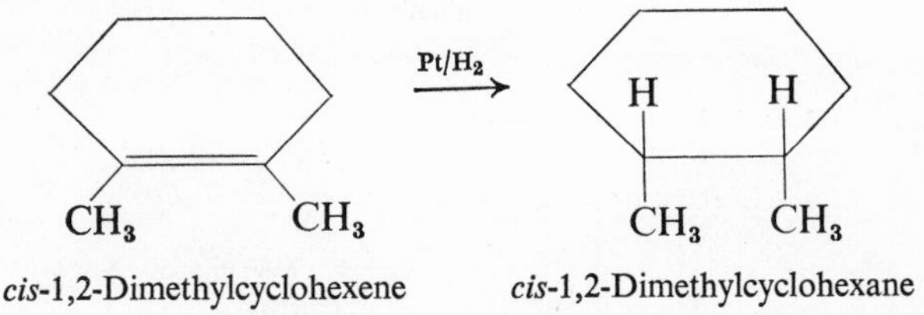

$$\xrightarrow{Pt/H_2}$$

cis-1,2-Dimethylcyclohexene   *cis*-1,2-Dimethylcyclohexane

Using highly reactive platinum or palladium catalysts the reduction often goes at room temperature and pressure; and it may be applied to determine the number of double or triple bonds in an organic molecule.

Preparation of platinic oxide (Adams Catalyst) for hydrogenation
Add sodium nitrate (35 g.) to a solution of pure chloroplatinic acid (3·5 g.) in water (10 ml.) in an evaporating basin. Evaporate the solution to dryness over a Bunsen flame with stirring. Now heat the solid mass until it is molten, when brown fumes of nitrogen dioxide are evolved. Continue heating for half an hour when the temperature should be 500–550°. Allow the melt to cool and then boil it with distilled water (50 ml.). Wash the brown precipitate of

platinic oxide three or four times with distilled water by decantation; finally filter off the precipitate with suction, and wash it until the filtrate is free from nitrate ion. Stop washing when the catalyst begins to become colloidal, and take *care* not to suck air through the dry catalyst since finely divided platinic oxide is pyrophoric.

Example 1. Preparation of Ethyl *p*-Aminobenzoate (Benzocaine)

$$O_2N\!\!-\!\!\langle\ \rangle\!\!-\!\!COOC_2H_5 \xrightarrow{\text{PtO}_2/\text{H}_2} NH_2\!\!-\!\!\langle\ \rangle\!\!-\!\!COOC_2H_5$$

Ethyl *p*-nitrobenzoate   Ethyl *p*-aminobenzoate

Place ethyl *p*-nitrobenzoate (2·4 g.) in a 50 ml. long-necked hydrogenation flask, together with absolute ethanol (25 ml.) and Adams catalyst (0·25 g.). Now shake the mixture in an atmosphere of

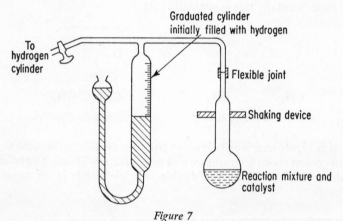

Figure 7

Apparatus for catalytic hydrogenation at atmospheric pressure

hydrogen, using the above apparatus, until the calculated volume of hydrogen ($\simeq$ 850 ml. at 25° and 760 mm.) has been absorbed (takes about half an hour). Remove the catalyst by filtration under suction, washing out the flask with a little ethanol. Distil off the ethanol from a water-bath leaving a residue which solidifies on cooling. Dissolve the crude product in boiling ethanol, add a little activated charcoal, boil it for 5 minutes, and filter. Add water dropwise to the boiling filtrate, until turbid, and then allow to cool giving ethyl *p*-aminobenzoate, 1·8 g., m.p. 90° (75% of theory).

Example 2. Preparation of Cholestanol (3-Hydroxycyclopentanoperhydro-phenanthrene)

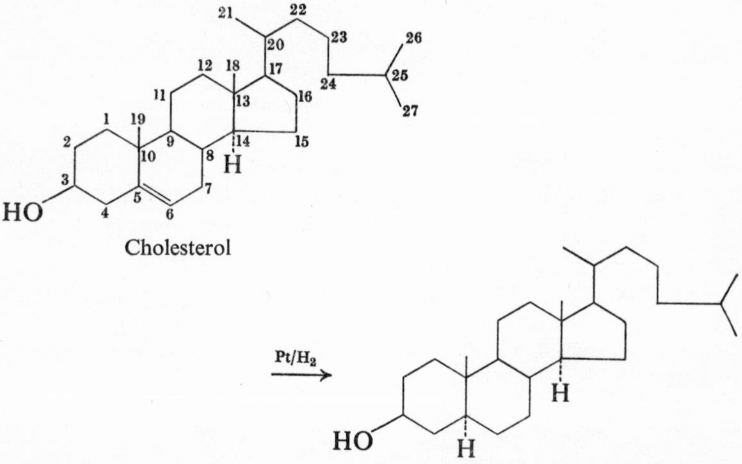

Cholesterol

Pt/H₂ →

Cholestanol

Dissolve cholesterol (12·5 g.) in tetrahydrofuran (75 ml.), then add Adams catalyst (0·25 g.) and perchloric acid (1–2 drops). Shake the suspension in an atmosphere of hydrogen until absorption ceases. The uptake of hydrogen is rapid (75% complete in a quarter of an hour) and has finished after 1 hour. Remove the catalyst by filtration with suction, and concentrate the filtrate by distillation under reduced pressure. Cool the concentrated solution and filter off the crystals at the pump, giving cholestanol 11 g., m.p. 140–142° (88% of theory).

Compound Index

Reaction Index